Henry James

D1228407

Study for a

audio response
De-emphasis

db

EM.P. Charsc
3 db/ooie

Response
Curve for
30 N   audio amp   5000 KC
1500 N

an audio system

F-M *Simplified*

BY THE SAME AUTHOR

U H F RADIO Simplified

TELEVISION Simplified — 3rd Ed.

Television and F-M Receiver Servicing — 2nd Ed.

F-M Simplified

MILTON S. KIVER

SECOND EDITION

D. VAN NOSTRAND COMPANY, INC.

TORONTO NEW YORK LONDON

NEW YORK

D. Van Nostrand Company, Inc., 250 Fourth Avenue, New York 3

TORONTO

D. Van Nostrand Company (Canada), Ltd., 228 Bloor Street, Toronto

LONDON

Macmillan & Company, Ltd., St. Martin's Street, London, W.C. 2

COPYRIGHT, 1947, 1951, BY

D. VAN NOSTRAND COMPANY, INC.

Published simultaneously in Canada by

D. VAN NOSTRAND COMPANY (Canada), LTD.

All Rights Reserved

_This book, or any part thereof, may not be
reproduced in any form without written per-
mission from the author and the publisher._

PRINTED IN THE UNITED STATES OF AMERICA

PREFACE

It is the purpose of this book to present not only the facts concerning F-M, but also to indicate and help bridge the gap between amplitude modulation and the newer frequency modulation. In this respect, the second edition is in accord with the first. However, the material and the presentation in this new edition have been completely revised. After the fundamentals of F-M have been presented in the first three chapters, a full chapter is devoted to the propagation, reception, and transmission of F-M signals. Then, in Chapters 5 through 10, F-M receivers are analyzed stage by stage and circuit by circuit, at all times adhering to simple explanations. Chapter 11 deals with circuit alignment, first with the use of nothing more than a signal generator and a vacuum-tube voltmeter, and then with the more efficient oscilloscope and sweep generator. With these circuit explanations and techniques understood, the text then turns to commercial F-M receivers (Chapter 12) and to their servicing and maintenance (Chapter 13).

The final three chapters are devoted to modern F-M transmitters. Equipment of all the major manufacturers are included, among them RCA, G.E., Western Electric, and Westinghouse. Transmitters are grouped according to the process they utilize to generate the F-M signals, i.e., whether it is by the reactance method or by the phase-shift method.

A set of questions is placed at the end of each chapter for those who wish to gauge their progress through the book and their understanding of the principles involved. With the exception of the few mathematical problems, no question can be properly answered with a single word.

The author wishes to extend his appreciation to the Stromberg-Carlson Co., the Philco Corporation, *Communications Magazine,* Dr. Robert Adler of Zenith, G. Wallin of Motorola, and the General Electric Corporation for their help in making available much of the data and material required for the book. Finally,

v

there are the author's colleagues who, through their many suggestions, helped make this a more complete book.

M. S. K.

Chicago, Illinois
January, 1951

CONTENTS

CHAPTER 1

INTRODUCTION TO FREQUENCY MODULATION

Advantages of F-M. Although many improvements had been made in radio since the days of the first radio receiver, it was not until the advent of frequency modulation that noise interference was efficiently reduced in radio reception. Noise interference, for the most part, is due to sources, either man-made or natural, that are external to the receiver. Much of the worst interference comes from natural sources, generally beyond the power of man to control. A-M receiver circuits and systems designed by engineers were of limited effectiveness in their suppression of interference. The best solution seemed to be the employment of brute-force method, using high-powered radio signals to override the disturbing interference. In A-M sets the signal-to-noise ratio had to be of the order of 100 to 1 or more to obscure the noise. With the use of frequency modulation, however, it became possible to reduce considerably the strength of the signal required to override the noise. Although the signal at the receiver input must still possess greater power than the undesired voltage, the signal-to-noise ratio in F-M receivers need be only 2 to 1.[1]

Frequency modulation, because of the ability to override interference with low signal-to-noise ratios, indirectly permits the use of many more stations within a given area than is possible with amplitude modulation. At the receiver, the desired signal must be only twice as strong as the undesired signal to hide the interference completely. Compare how much farther away an A-M broadcasting station could be and still ruin reception: with A-M a voltage only 1/100 as strong as the desired carrier will provide sufficient inter-

---

[1] In a properly designed F-M set it is possible for the signal-to-noise ratio to drop below 2 to 1 and still have the signal override any noise present. However, to be on the conservative side, the 2 to 1 ratio value will be retained.

ference to be heard in the output of the receiver. Listen some night to an A-M receiver, especially at the high frequency end of the band. Signals, not only from nearby communities but from localities hundreds and thousands of miles distant, ride in to add their voice to a complete hodgepodge of whistles and signals, an intolerable situation for intelligible listening. Bring into play a 2 to 1 signal-to-noise ratio attainable with F-M, and with one quick sweep we eliminate 99 per cent of the disturbance. Now only stations in the immediate vicinity are concerned, and F.C.C. regulations do not permit simultaneous use of similar frequencies in the same service area.

It is quite popularly supposed that F-M is capable of providing greater fidelity of reproduction than A-M. This advantage is real, but it is an indirect benefit that results from F-M's ability to eliminate more of the interference and thereby provide a signal at the receiver that adheres more closely to the original signal at the studio. But greater fidelity is not an intrinsic, direct characteristic of the process of frequency modulation itself. Fidelity is a result of the correct design of the various stages that form either system of transmission and, since the same basic components are present in each system, both have fundamentally the same potentiality of good fidelity. Indirectly, we find other limitations, aside from the circuits themselves, that contribute to provide better fidelity with F-M. For example, with A-M only audio frequencies extending to 5000 cycles are transmitted, a limitation employed to prevent each station from occupying too great a frequency range within the limited A-M broadcast band and to permit additional stations to operate. F-M, arriving on the broadcast scene later, had the advantage of operating at the higher frequencies, where spectrum space is more plentiful. Add to this the already noted intrinsic tendency of F-M completely to override an interfering signal, and it is apparent why the misconception exists concerning fidelity. With the proper care in design, amplitude modulation can provide the listener with just as much fidelity as he obtains with F-M.

A-M versus F-M. In order to understand why F-M proves so effective in reducing interference, we must first make a thorough investigation of the properties of a frequency-modulated wave.

Perhaps the easiest way of beginning is by a comparison of the effects on a carrier wave when it is amplitude-modulated and when it is frequency-modulated.

When a continuous, radio-frequency carrier wave is amplitude-modulated, the amplitude is varied in a manner determined by the audio-modulating volt-age. Refer to Fig. 1.1 in which the high-frequency carrier and the low-frequency modulating wave are shown separately. By applying the carrier to the grid of a tube, and then varying the tube's plate voltage in accordance with the modulating voltage, we obtain at the output the amplitude-modulated wave shown in Fig. 1.1C. The variations imposed onto the carrier contain the intelligence of the audio wave. Now the A-M signal can be transmitted over the high-frequency circuits, through the air and to the receiver. At the

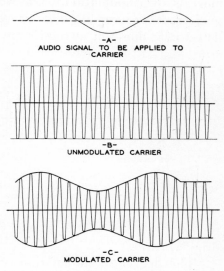

FIG. 1.1.   The components of an amplitude-modulated wave.

receiver, the 2nd detector converts the amplitude variations to their original form, in which they become intelligible at the loud-speaker.

A closer inspection of the modulated wave, Fig. 1.1C, reveals that there are certain limitations to the strength of the audio-modulating voltage. For example, it must not be too large. A small modulating voltage will affect slightly the amplitude of the carrier, and the resultant variations will be identical with those of the modulating wave. This means that no distortion, or loss of fidelity, has occurred. Increasing the strength of the modulating voltage causes correspondingly greater rises and indentations in the final signal waveform, but the essential form of the audio voltage is still preserved. However, when the applied modulating voltage becomes too great, the carrier becomes highly distorted. An example is shown in Fig. 1.2C. For the maximum modulation with no distortion the modulating voltage can only decrease the amplitude of the carrier to zero, momentarily, or raise it to twice the normal value at the peaks. We have now what is commonly known as 100 per cent modulation. Anything less is undermodulation; anything more is overmodulation. Of the two, undermodulation is to be preferred because, although it results in less power at the 2nd detector, it does not introduce any appreciable distortion. By dis-

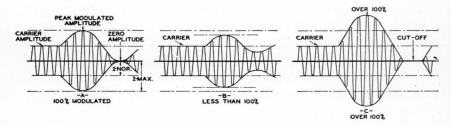

FIG. 1.2. Various degrees of amplitude modulation.

tortion, we refer to the change in the shape of a wave from its original form.

The degree of modulation of a carrier wave is generally expressed as a percentage. It is the ratio of the peak amplitude of the modulating signal to the peak amplitude of the higher frequency carrier. The word " peak " is used because each of these waves are varying sinusoidally and one reference point is necessary. Mathematically, the ratio is expressed as

$$K = \frac{i_m}{I_m}$$

where $i_m =$ peak value of the modulating signal
    $I_m =$ peak value of the carrier

When this ratio is equal to 1, we have 100 per cent modulation wherein the amplitude of the modulated wave rises to twice the normal carrier value and decreases to zero when the two voltages act in opposition (see Fig. 1.2A).

The process of varying the amplitude of a continuous carrier

wave causes the appearance of frequencies in addition to that of the
carrier.   Where a single, audio sine wave is used as the modulating
voltage, two additional frequencies are generated, each separated
from the carrier frequency by an amount equal to the audio-
modulating frequency.   As an illustration, consider the case of a
1000-kc carrier modulated by a 5-kc audio note.   If an analysis is
made of the amplitude-modulated wave at the transmitter output,
we will find that its components are the 1000-kc carrier, a frequency

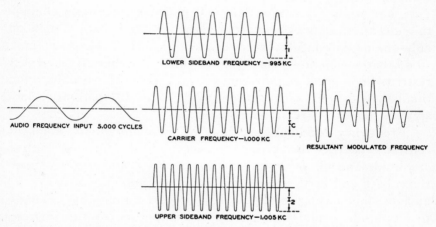

Fig. 1.3.   The sidebands generated with amplitude modulation.

of 1005 kc, and one of 995 kc.   Of the two additional frequencies
produced, one is located above the carrier whereas the other is
located the same frequency distance below the carrier.   Together,
these new frequencies are designated as sidebands.   Graphically,
they may be represented as shown in Fig. 1.3.

Now, obviously, the additional frequencies must in some way
be related to the modulating voltage (which contains the desired
intelligence), for with the removal of this voltage we find that the
sidebands are no longer present.   Without modulation only the
carrier remains.   The moment we speak into a microphone, however, a modulating voltage appears and, coincidentally, the sidebands.   A mathematical and experimental analysis reveals that all
of the extra power contained in the modulating signal goes directly

into the sidebands. The carrier itself is left untouched. Thus, although it may not be apparent from an inspection of Fig. 1.2, amplitude modulation gives rise to new frequencies, and these frequencies contain all the power and intelligence of the modulating voltage.

In all transmitting and receiving networks, provision must be made to include these sidebands. With a modulating frequency of 5000 cycles, or 5 kc, sidebands located ±5 kc from the carrier are formed, making it necessary to receive a bandwidth of 10 kc (±5 kc) wide. Anything less will partially or totally eliminate the sidebands, suppressing part or all of the intelligence. Although only one modulating frequency is mentioned, i.e., 5 kc, it is understood that any audio frequency may be used. Generally, the F.C.C. restricts the highest audio frequency to 5 kc, but this is only to limit the bandwidth of each station to 10 kc. Consequently, more stations per band are accommodated.

Frequency Modulation. In F-M we maintain the amplitude constant and alter the carrier frequency. In this instance, both the amplitude and phase of the carrier are fixed, while the frequency shifts back and forth about one central position in accordance with an audio-modulating voltage. This process is somewhat analogous to amplitude modulation, where the amplitude of the carrier is increased and decreased about the average, normal value.

The physical appearance of a wave that has been frequency-modulated by a sine wave is shown in Fig. 1.4. At each instant throughout the application of the modulating signal, the frequency of the carrier will depend *directly* upon the amplitude of the audio signal. At the start of the audio cycle, the frequency of the carrier is slightly affected because within this region the modulating voltage is small. As the audio cycle approaches its positive peak, at 90°, the frequency variation of the carrier from its mean or resting position also reaches a maximum. Between 90° and 180° of the audio cycle, the voltage is returning to zero and the modulated carrier is shifting back, in step, to its resting position. Continuing on to 270°, we see that the audio voltage is again rising, although this time in a negative direction. The carrier frequency is likewise going in a negative direction, as indicated by a lower frequency. At

270°, the carrier frequency is at its lowest point. From here it slowly follows the audio voltage back to normal. This occurs at 360°, after which a new cycle begins.

To summarize, we see that the frequency variations of the carrier are in step, at all times, with the amplitude variations of the applied modulating voltage. As the amplitude of this latter voltage rises, the frequency of the carrier likewise increases,[2] whereas,

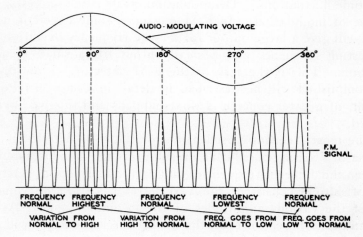

FIG. 1.4. Frequency variation in an F-M signal.

when the audio signal reverses and moves to the opposite polarity, the carrier frequency decreases correspondingly.

The variation in carrier frequency is wholly dependent upon the *amplitude* of the acting audio voltage and not at all on its frequency. This is similar to A-M where the changes in carrier amplitude are influenced only by the amplitude of the audio signal. The frequency of the audio voltage, in both forms of modulation, determines the rapidity with which the amplitude or frequency changes take place but exerts no influence on the extent of these

[2] As far as the ear is concerned, it makes no difference whether an increase in signal voltage results in an increase or decrease in carrier frequency. The important point is that a large modulating signal results in a large variation of frequency. At the receiver, the ear responds primarily to the different amplitude changes (and frequency changes) of the audio signal and not to their phase. This is due to the relative inability of the ear to respond to phase shifts.

changes. A strong audio signal, at any frequency, will cause a wide frequency deviation from the center or resting frequency; a low or weak audio signal will cause less frequency variation. The frequency of each of these signals will determine ónly the speed with which the changes occur between points.

In the receiver the detector, or demodulator, must be capable of restoring the frequency variations to their corresponding audio-amplitude fluctuations. Demodulation, as its name suggests, is the reverse of modulation. In F-M receivers, some circuit is needed which will give a large output for a large frequency deviation from the resting frequency and a small output for a small frequency variation. This is the task of the F-M detector. How this job is accomplished will be described in detail in Chap. 9. For the present, of greater concern is what happens and this we have just learned.

The most frequently used name for the F-M detector is " discriminator," arising possibly as a result of its action in discriminating between the different frequencies that arrive at its input. Actually, if we wish to be consistent, the A-M detector is also a discriminator against the various amplitudes of the incoming signal. As used here and elsewhere, however, the word " discriminator " will apply only to F-M reception.

It is simple to deduce that in F-M the signal will occupy a large bandwidth, since the primary purpose of the modulating audio signal is to vary the carrier frequency. In amplitude modulation, it will be recalled, the amplitude of the carrier was varied, and from this a frequency spread (sidebands) was created. A-M sidebands are not easily visualized and only by resort to mathematics or by direct experimentation can they be shown to exist. The maximum degree of amplitude modulation that can be applied to an A-M wave without producing distortion is limited to a value equal in amplitude to the carrier wave. This is defined as 100 per cent modulation. For the F-M system, the term " 100 per cent modulation " is much more arbitrary and the limits to which a carrier can be frequency-modulated extends far beyond those presently utilized.

It is known, from theoretical considerations, that we can alter the frequency of a carrier only to the point where we do not, so to speak, obliterate it. Consider a carrier of 90 mc which is being modulated. We can only shift the carrier frequency until it is brought to zero; anything less is obviously impossible since negative frequencies do not exist. Engineering limitations, of course, prevent us from introducing this large a shift, but even if it were possible, it would still be undesirable because of the limitation imposed on the number of commercial stations that could be licensed. Recognizing these difficulties and concerned with the problem of accommodating many stations in the available radio spectrum, the F.C.C. has decreed that the maximum deviation through which the carrier may be shifted shall be limited to ±75 kc during modulation. This may be designated arbitrarily as 100 per cent modulation, although it must be remembered upon what limitations this value is founded.

As a comparison with A-M, it is to be noted that when a carrier is completely or 100 per cent modulated, its amplitude varies periodically between zero and twice the normal carrier value. With this limitation, the modulation does not produce distortion. Any degree of modulation greater than 100 per cent would definitely produce a distorted output, as shown in Fig. 1.2C. In F-M, we could, if we wished, shift the carrier far beyond the arbitrarily defined limit of 75 kc and still introduce no distortion. Again we see that the term " 100 per cent modulation " does not apply to F-M in the same sense that it does to A-M. However, from certain considerations that will be developed later, the value of 75 kc is satisfactory. In addition, to diminish the effects of overlapping, an additional 25 kc is allotted as a means of protection between stations operating on adjacent frequencies. Each station, then, is assigned a bandwidth of 200 kc. Of this 200-kc bandwidth, 150 (±75) kc is to be employed for the modulation and the remaining 50 (±25) kc is to function as a guardband. The very definite need for the guardbands will become more apparent after a closer study of the F-M sidebands.

F-M Sidebands. Before we approach the somewhat complex subject of the sideband frequencies generated in F-M, let us pause and quickly review the situation from the A-M angle. We have noted that sideband frequencies were not present until an audio signal was applied. The carrier wave independently has no sideband frequencies. Upon the application of a modulating voltage, say of one frequency, two sidebands were formed. Their frequencies were above and below the carrier by an amount equal to the modulating frequency. Throughout this process of modulation, the carrier power remained unchanged, the sidebands deriving their power from the audio signal.

Now let us look at the F-M situation. Upon the application of a sine-wave modulating signal, the carrier frequency is shifted back and forth, from a maximum position above the carrier frequency to a minimum position below. And in the process of shifting, addi-

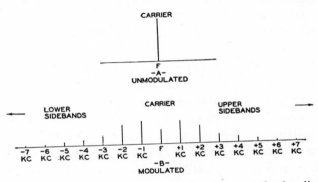

Fig. 1.5. An F-M signal with its sidebands developed as a result of audio modulation.

tional sidebands are formed, with frequencies intermediate and beyond the maximum and minimum points reached by the carrier. In fact, theoretically, the sidebands are infinite, stretching away on either side of the carrier center position in equal number.

If we attempt to illustrate the sidebands with a diagram, we obtain the result shown in Fig. 1.5B. Fig. 1.5A represents the carrier before the modulation is applied. Fig. 1.5B reveals considerable information regarding F-M and helps to answer the confusing problem arising from the statement that infinite number of sidebands are present when a carrier is modulated by an audio signal. For, you may ask, if we have an infinite number of sidebands, how is it possible to have more than one station on the air, at any one time?

Upon examination of Fig. 1.5B, we can count seven sideband

frequencies below the carrier and seven sideband frequencies above the carrier, all due, of course, to the single modulating note. Each of these frequencies, it can be mathematically shown, is separated from its neighbor by an amount equal to the frequency of the modulating signal itself. Thus, if we whistle a 1000-cycle note into a microphone, a series of sidebands appear, above and below the central resting point, each 1 kc (1000 cycles) apart. With the carrier situated at 90 mc, there would be sidebands at 90.001 mc, 90.002 mc, 90.003 mc, etc.; also sidebands at 89.999 mc, 89,998 mc, 89.997 mc, etc. It is thus clearly indicated that the frequency of the audio-modulating signal accomplishes two things:

1. Fixes the separation of the sidebands.
2. Determines the rapidity with which the sideband distribution changes.

Returning to Fig. 1.5B, we can count but fourteen sidebands in all: seven above the carrier, seven below. Apparently this is a misrepresentation, since a moment ago it was stated that there exists an infinite number of these sidebands. Actually, both statements are reconcilable; for one condition represents the theoretical condition, and the other the practical modification. With any strength of modulating voltage, we will find a certain number of sidebands generated which have sufficient power to be of value toward the reception of that signal. Beyond this, additional sidebands exist but contain *so little power* as to be of no practical importance in the formation of the signal at the receiver. Here, then, is the reason why more than one station can operate at any time. The sidebands of the other stations are so weak beyond their band limits that, as far as interference is concerned, they are without effect.

Included, too, is the answer for the establishment of guard-bands about each station. Each station is limited to 75 kc on each side of its carrier frequency, but we know from theoretical considerations that additional sidebands exist. Hence, to be absolutely certain that no interference will be caused to adjacent stations, the 25-kc guardband (at each band end) is added. In A-M no such complications arise, and consequently there is no necessity for such precautions.

Sideband Power. Let us return again to a study of Fig. 1.5B. If we compare the amplitudes of the several sidebands with each other and with the carrier, we are at once struck with two facts: first, we find that the carrier power diminishes during modulation; second, it is possible for one or more sidebands actually to contain more power than the carrier.

The power that is taken from the carrier, during modulation, is distributed among the various sidebands. The louder the modulating signal, the greater the energy that will be taken from the carrier. In fact, it is perfectly possible for the carrier, during one of these modulation sweeps, to contain no energy at all; the sidebands then possess it all. A moment's reflection should show that a transfer of some or all of the original carrier energy to the sidebands must occur, because the total frequency-modulated signal does not vary in amplitude. Thus, the only way to satisfy this condition, during modulation, is to transfer part (or all) of the carrier energy to the sidebands. This power transfer is a characteristic of frequency modulation.

The sum of the amplitudes of the sidebands plus that of the carrier gives the value of the unmodulated carrier, provided the addition is performed vectorially. This has special significance because not all the sideband amplitudes have the same polarity at one time. Counting from the carrier, in either direction, we find that all the odd-numbered sidebands have opposite polarity. The even-numbered ones have the same polarity. But, in any case, correspondingly placed sidebands (with respect to the carrier) have the same amplitude. A simple example will make this clear.

With a carrier situated at 90 mc and a modulating frequency of 1000 cycles (or 1 kc), we have sidebands at 90.001 mc, 90.002 mc, 90.003 mc, etc.; also sidebands at 89.999 mc, 89.998 mc, 89.997 mc, etc. Counting away from the carrier, in the first set of sidebands, at 90.001 mc and 89.999 mc, both frequencies would possess equal amplitudes but would be of opposite polarity. The next or second set of sidebands would be at 90.002 mc and 89.998 mc; these frequencies also would be equal in amplitude and would have the same sign. Of course, although each set would have the same amplitude, different sets would differ from one another.

This difference is mentioned because the arithmetic addition of the amplitude of the different sidebands of Fig. 1.5B, together with that of the carrier, will not give the same value as the unmodulated carrier.   If the diagram of Fig. 1.5B were drawn up with strict regard for polarity, some of the sidebands would have to be drawn below the reference line.   That they were not is due to the fact that, as far as this discussion extends, it makes no essential difference.   We are interested only in the frequencies generated by modulation and in their distribution.

Sideband Variation.   It would be instructive to see the effect upon sideband distribution when we vary the amplitude of the modulating voltage.   This is shown in Fig. 1.6.   It is apparent that, as we increase the intensity of the audio signal, the number of significant sidebands increases.   The sidebands of the low-intensity modulating voltage that were considered negligible now gain enough power to make them significant.   The energy is spreading out, creating more sidebands of appreciable power and thereby causing a greater

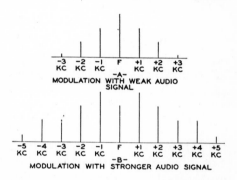

Fig. 1.6.   A comparison of the frequency spread of two F-M signals modulated by audio voltages of differing intensity.

overall frequency spread about the carrier.   This is what we mean when we say that the louder the modulating signal, the greater our carrier will deviate from its mean position.   At low modulating intensities, the important sidebands are clustered about the carrier. As we raise the volume, the energy spreads out and more sidebands must be included.

It is now possible to replace the elementary explanation regarding frequency spread given at first with the more accurate discussion given above.   We see that the shifting of the energy of an F-M wave is directly related to the intensity of the applied audio signal.   When a shift takes place, say away from the carrier, the former energy distribution is replaced by this newer arrangement, with every sideband and the carrier affected.   Thus, energy is taken by some and given up by others.   The *total* energy, however, under all conditions, remains constant.

Modulation Index.   With an appreciation of the relationships between modulating signal strength and sideband formation, we can more easily approach the problem of designing networks to receive and pass the necessary band of frequencies.   It is quite evident that if we limit the amplitude of the modulating signals we control the spread of significant sidebands and thus prevent any interference to adjacent channels.   The limit set by the F.C.C. is plus and minus 75 kc about the frequency of the carrier.   Steps must be taken, at the transmitter, to see that these limits are not exceeded.   But is the strength of the audio signal the only determining factor in bandwidth spread?   Or must we add another factor?   Let us see.

It has been noted that, whenever sidebands are formed, they are spaced by an amount equal to the frequency of the modulating audio signal.   Thus, for an audio voltage with a frequency of 100 cycles, successive sidebands are created 100 cycles apart, whereas, for a frequency of 15,000 cycles, the sidebands are spaced at intervals of 15 kc.   However, if the two signals are causing 10 important sidebands about the carrier, the 100-cycle note would result in an F-M signal with a spread of 10×100 or 1000 cycles (1 kc) and a *total* bandwidth of 2 kc.   With the 15-kc note, the total frequency spectrum would extend 300 kc.   The obvious conclusion from this illustration is that the frequency bandwidth required by a frequency-modulated carrier depends upon two factors:

1. The intensity of the applied modulating voltage.
2. The frequency of this voltage.

Recognition of the importance of both these considerations has led to the formation of the modulation index, which is defined as:

$$\frac{\text{deviation of F-M carrier}}{\text{audio frequency causing this deviation}}$$

where the deviation of the F-M carrier is a direct result of the intensity of the applied signal.

We note from this formula that, if the frequency of a signal is kept constant, the bandspread about the carrier will depend directly upon the strength of the modulating voltage; whereas if the sound amplitude is kept constant, the lower audio frequencies will produce more sidebands.   In practice, however, neither one is kept constant and both vary simultaneously.

The spread of any F-M signal will depend upon the modulation index.   At the present time, the F.C.C. has specified that the maximum shift of an F-M carrier should be limited to 75 kc.   The highest audio modulating frequency in use is 15,000 cycles.   The ratio of these two maximum quantities, according to the modulation index, is 75 kc/15 kc, or 5.   This figure, besides being known as the modulation index, is also assigned the special name of deviation ratio.   The reason for designating this one case as the deviation ratio is that any other combination of audio frequency to carrier shift less than the maximum values will always produce a narrower signal spread.   This will be seen as we progress.

Index Table.   Taken by itself, the index figure does not directly tell us anything.   But, when applied to appropriate mathematical tables derived from Bessel functions, we can obtain the number of significant sidebands that will be formed at this particular value of modulation index.

A knowledge of Bessel functions is not specifically required in order to use the tables derived from these equations.   Because of the complexity of Bessel equations, it is convenient merely to accept the tables without proof.   A modified version sufficient for our discussion is given in Table I.   Full inclusion of all possible values would fill many pages and add very little to what we can learn from the condensed version of Table I.

In Table I there is a list of the number of significant sidebands that would be obtained for some of the common values of the modulation index.   Thus, with an index of 5, there are 8 important sidebands (on either side of the carrier) formed; with an index of 10, the number of sidebands increase to 14.   For each value of index a certain number of significant sidebands are formed. In general, both vary directly.   A large index results in a large number of sidebands; a small index, a smaller number of sidebands. It is interesting to note that when the index becomes very small, of the order of 0.4 or less, only 2 sidebands are formed, similar to A-M operation when one modulating frequency is employed.

TABLE I

Modulation Index	Number of Significant Side-Bands		Bandwidth Required (f = frequency of audio signal)
	Above Carrier	Below Carrier	
0.01	1	1	$2f$
.02	1	1	$2f$
.03	1	1	$2f$
.04	1	1	$2f$
.05	1	1	$2f$
0.1	1	1	$2f$
.2	1	1	$2f$
.3	1	1	$2f$
.4	1	1	$2f$
.5	2	2	$4f$
1.0	3	3	$6f$
2.0	4	4	$8f$
3.0	6	6	$12f$
4.0	7	7	$14f$
5.0	8	8	$16f$
6.0	9	9	$18f$
7.0	10	10	$20f$
8.0	12	12	$24f$
9.0	13	13	$26f$
10.0	14	14	$28f$
11.0	16	16	$32f$
12.0	17	17	$34f$
13.0	18	18	$36f$
14.0	19	19	$38f$
15.0	20	20	$40f$

To compute the bandwidth required for each modulation index, simply multiply the frequency of the audio-modulating signal by twice the number of sidebands given for the modulation index. Thus, suppose we have a modulation index of 5 when the audio frequency is 5000 cycles, or 5 kc. From Table I, a modulation index of 5 gives us 8 important significant sidebands, each, in this case, to be situated 5 kc apart; thus, 5 kc × 8 = 40 kc on each side of the carrier, or a total bandspread of 80 kc.

It is always completely puzzling to anyone approaching F-M for the first time to learn that, although the carrier frequency in the F-M transmitter is never actually shifted beyond the ±75 kc limits specified by the F.C.C., sidebands do appear beyond these limits. As an illustration, consider the case when the modulation index is 5, obtained by shifting the carrier ±75 kc with a 15,000 cycle audio note. From Table I we see that 8 significant sidebands will be obtained. This, of course, means 8 above and 8 below the carrier position. Since each sideband is separated from its neighbor by 15,000 cycles, or 15 kc, we find that the total required bandwidth is

$$2 \times 15 \text{ kc} \times 8 = 240 \text{ kc}$$

Thus we obtain a signal extending over 240 kc (±120 kc) when the carrier frequency is shifted only ±75 kc in the transmitter during the process of modulation.

To explain this situation physically, we might use the analogy of a man moving his finger back and forth at the center of a small pool of water. We know from actual experience that, although the man may move his finger only slightly back and forth, water ripples will appear far beyond this little area. The greater the distance covered by the man's moving finger, the greater the spread of the water ripples. In F-M, the greater the carrier swing, the greater the number of sidebands obtained.

In commercial practice, it seldom happens that a 15-kc note will have sufficient volume to spread the transmitter carrier to the 75-kc limits. As the frequency of the signal is lowered, the number of sidebands that extend beyond the ±75-kc limits also decreases, until at 50 cycles a full carrier swing will just produce sidebands up to, but not beyond, the 75-kc limits. Here, then, is the reason for the additional ±25-kc guardbands. They tend to absorb any sidebands that extend outside the 75-kc limits.

Many incorrect interpretations have been placed upon the F.C.C. regulation that, during modulation, the carrier is not to be shifted more than ±75 kc. This does not mean, for example, that the end significant sideband must not extend beyond ±75 kc. It merely means that during the process of modulation, when the carrier frequency is being altered by the applied audio voltage, the maximum shift be no greater than ±75 kc. However, when the full 75-kc shift is utilized, it will generally be found that significant sidebands exist beyond the F.C.C. limits. This is perfectly permissible.

When the carrier swing is very small, 0.4 or less for the modulation index, then Table I reveals that only 2 sidebands (one above and one below the carrier) are obtained. If the audio-modulating signal is 15 kc, then a modulation index of 0.2 means that the carrier frequency is only shifted 3 kc back and forth.

$$0.2 = \frac{\Delta F}{f}$$

$$\Delta F = 15 \text{ kc} \times 0.2$$

$$\Delta F = 3 \text{ kc}$$

The frequency distribution will appear as shown in Fig. 1.7, with one carrier and two significant sidebands.

Note again that the sidebands will be spread farther from the center than the frequency shift that produced them. The sidebands are ±15 kc from the center, whereas the carrier was shifted only ±3 kc. This situation will be generally true of all F-M transmissions. However, if the reader remembers the water analogy, it may help him to understand this new idea.

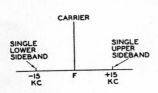

FIG. 1.7. The sideband distribution when the modulation index is small, 0.2 or less.

We have, up to this point, a fairly complete picture of F-M, both before and during modulation. Of remaining interest is phase modulation, not only because it represents a very possible method of sending intelligence but, more important from our viewpoint, because phase modulation indirectly results in F-M. The latter aspect is all the more important because interference affects an F-M signal through its phase disturbances. Moreover, Major Armstrong uses phase shifting to produce F-M in his type of F-M transmitter.   To appreciate either of these two aspects, a brief discussion of phase modulation is necessary. .   ~~Home Study~~

PROBLEMS

1. What effect does the choice of the high frequencies to transmit F-M signals have on the ability of F-M to override interference? What would be its effect if A-M was used at the same frequencies?

2. What is the significance of 100 per cent modulation when applied to A-M broadcasting? Explain its counterpart in F-M.

3. In an A-M wave, where is the intelligence contained? How does this differ from the conditions prevailing in frequency modulation?

4. What is the relationship between the sidebands produced in amplitude modulation and the audio-modulating frequency?

5. Is the carrier frequency actually shifted when a wave is frequency-modulated? What is the F.C.C. regulation in this regard?

6. What is a discriminator? What is the accepted application of this word?

7. What are guardbands and why are they required in F-M transmission?

8. Discuss the difference between the sidebands produced through amplitude modulation and those produced by frequency modulation.

9. What do we mean when we refer to a sideband as being " significant "?

10. What influence does the audio-modulating signal frequency have in the production of an F-M signal?

11. Where do the F-M sidebands obtain their power? Contrast this with the situation existing in an A-M signal.

12. Explain how the sidebands vary, both in power and number, during different portions of an audio-modulating cycle.

13. The F.C.C. specifically limits carrier shifting to ±75 kc. Can sidebands extend beyond these limits? Explain, using a numerical example.

14. Explain the importance of the modulation index.

15. With a modulation index of 3 and a modulating frequency of 5 kc, compute the complete bandwidth required when a 90-mc carrier is employed.

16. Analysis of an F-M signal revealed that the carrier frequency was 94 mc, and the upper and lower sideband limits were at ±98 kc. Further analysis indicated that the modulating frequency was 14 kc. What modulation index was being employed at the transmitter?

17. Under what conditions are the bandwidths of F-M and A-M signals exactly equal to each other?

18. The F.C.C. specifies that the modulation index, with a 15,000-cycle modulating frequency, shall not exceed 5. Assuming that the amplitude of the modulating signal remains constant, what happens to the modulation index when the audio frequency is reduced? Does the bandwidth increase or decrease as we lower the audio frequency? Illustrate your answer by computing the bandwidth required for audio-modulating frequencies of 15 kc, 9.375 kc, and 7.5 kc.

19. A sideband is considered insignificant when it contains less than 1 per cent of the total carrier power. Express this in terms of db.

20. Does a signal with a large modulation index necessarily require a wider bandwidth than a second signal having a smaller index? Explain your answer.

CHAPTER 2

F-M FROM PHASE MODULATION

Phase Modulation. It has been demonstrated that intelligence can be imposed onto a carrier by variation of its amplitude or its frequency. The only remaining electrical property is the phase of the carrier. By suitably shifting the phase of the wave in response to an applied audio-modulating voltage, we can accomplish the same transfer of intelligence as we have seen occur in the previous two methods of modulation.

A comparison is perhaps the simplest way of approaching phase modulation. Consider two carriers that are being transmitted at the same time, both of equal frequency but differing in phase by 45°. The phase difference merely indicates that when the voltage of one wave reaches its peak, at any one instant, the other carrier is 45° from its peak value. Fig. 2.1 illustrates just such a situation. In all other respects the signals are equivalent. If nothing is done to alter this phase relationship between the two carriers, nothing will be heard at the output of a phase-modulation receiver.

PHASE DIFFERENCE

Fig. 2.1. Two carrier waves differing by 45°.

But suppose the phase relationship is altered in a definite rhythm or pattern — perhaps in accordance with the amplitude and frequency of an applied sine wave. Let these audio variations be applied to the carrier that lagged by 45°. The other carrier will be kept fixed. Then the phase of the carrier to which the modulation is applied might swing, under the action of the audio signal, from 45° lag to 60° lag (see Fig. 2.2). The 60° lag would occur when the audio-modulating signal was at its positive peak. As the audio voltage decreased from this peak toward zero, the carrier would follow suit by slowly returning to 45° lag, its normal position. On the negative half cycle of the audio signal, the phase lag of the carrier shifts in the opposite direction, or towards a value less than

45°. This is opposite to its increase in phase when the audio signal was on the positive half cycle. At the negative audio peak the phase of the carrier would be brought to 30°. Note that this point

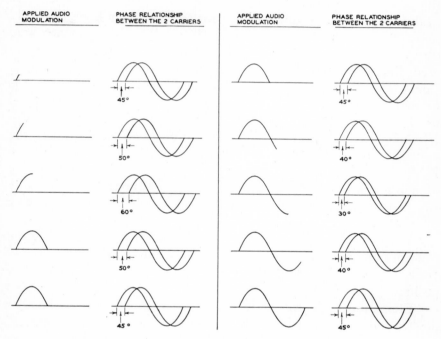

| APPLIED AUDIO MODULATION | PHASE RELATIONSHIP BETWEEN THE 2 CARRIERS | APPLIED AUDIO MODULATION | PHASE RELATIONSHIP BETWEEN THE 2 CARRIERS |

Fig. 2.2. A simplified illustration of phase modulation.

is just as far below the normal value of 45° as 60° is above. From the cycle's maximum negative peak back to zero the phase returns, in step, to 45°.

This phase shift represents one complete cycle for the audio-modulating voltage. It would occur over and over again as long as the modulating signal was active. At the proper receiver, the phase variations would be converted to the corresponding audio sound much the same way as an F-M receiver converts frequency modulation into sound. Instead of A-M or F-M we are dealing with P-M, or phase modulation.

Factors Affecting Phase Shift. The rapidity of phase shift from one value to another is determined by the modulating signal frequency. However, the number of degrees through which the carrier is shifted during modulation is dependent upon the strength of the audio signal. A weak signal, for example, might shift the phase only to 50° at its positive peak and 40° at its negative peak. A stronger signal at the microphone could, at its peak, cause a considerably larger phase shift. The receiver, working on phase differences, would note the different shifts and respond accordingly. This relation of phase shift to strength of the audio signal is entirely analogous to F-M, where a strong audio signal is needed for a wide frequency shift and a weak modulating signal produces a small frequency shift. At the F-M receiver, the discriminator is sensitive to frequency differences and derives the appropriate audio variations from the carrier. In both F-M and P-M, the total power remains fixed throughout the entire sequence of modulation. There are other points of similarity between the two systems, with the same mathematical design formula applicable to both.

The foregoing illustration is useful in introducing the basic concepts of phase modulation, but it does not clearly indicate how frequency modulation results. For this, a vector approach can be better employed.

Elementary Vectors. A vector is a shorthand method of illustrating certain facts much as numbers represent a shorthand method of expression. When we write the number 15 to designate a group of objects, we mean 15 individual pieces or parts or units. The number 15 saves us the trouble of drawing 15 squares, or circles, or other geometrical figures to indicate the total of such units.

There are certain types of physical quantities which possess not only magnitude but also direction. The magnitude may be indicated by a number, but what about the direction? For this we require an arrow. Thus a force of 100 pounds produced by a tractor pulling a block of wood, for example, in one direction could be illustrated by a number and an arrow, as shown in Fig. 2.3A.

A simpler method, however, is to have the length of the arrow indicate the magnitude of the force, and the direction in which the arrow is drawn denote the direction in which the force is acting.

If the arrow is made 1 inch long for 100 pounds of force, then an arrow 2 inches long would represent a force of 200 pounds (see Fig. 2.3B).

-A-   -B-

FIG. 2.3. Vectors represent definite forces and the directions in which they act.

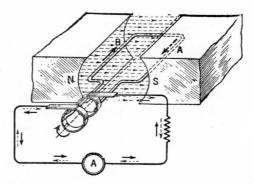

FIG. 2.4. The basic arrangement for the generation of an alternating voltage.

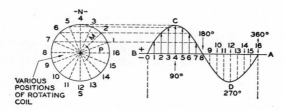

FIG. 2.5. The variation in a-c voltage with coil position.

Vectors Applied to Radio. Of specific interest is the application of vectors to radio or, more specifically, to electric waves. We know, from our first lessons in radio, that an alternating current is produced whenever a coil is rotated in the magnetic field between two magnets (see Fig. 2.4). If the field is uniform, the voltage produced across the output terminals of the coil is a sine wave. In Fig. 2.5 we see that the voltage generated depends upon the position of the coil in the magnetic field.   This may be expressed mathematically by the formula

$$e = E_{\text{max.}} \sin \theta$$

where

$e =$ instantaneous value of the voltage developed when the coil is at some angle θ

$E_{\text{max.}} =$ maximum value of the voltage

$\theta =$ angular position of the coil

Since the position of the coil determines the amount of voltage generated, suppose we replace the coil by a vector, as shown in Fig. 2.6.   The value of the voltage, at each instant, is then given by the vertical height of the vector, this vertical being proportional to the sine of the angle θ.   When the vector is placed horizontally, the angle θ is zero.   This makes sin θ equal to zero (see Fig. 2.7A).   From the formula, $e = 0$ when $\theta = 0$ and no voltage is generated.   At some other angle, say 30°, the voltage generated is

FIG. 2.6.   Substitution of vectors in place of the rotating coil. The arrowed vectors indicate the coil position at various instants.

$$e = E_{\text{max.}} \sin 30°.$$

Since sin 30° $= \frac{1}{2}$, then $e = \frac{1}{2} E_{\text{max.}}$.   This is shown with the vector placed at an angle of 30° with the horizontal (Fig. 2.7B).

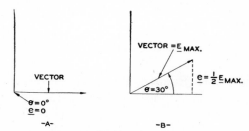

FIG. 2.7.   The value of the generated voltage depends upon sine of the angle, θ.

A vertical line dropped from the head of the arrow will then be $\frac{1}{2}$ as long as the length of the vector.   If the length of the vector is made equal to the value of E_{max}, say 100 volts, then the length of the vertical will represent 50 volts. Thus, the vector is made equal to the peak voltage of the sine wave; a vertical line dropped from the head of the arrow to the horizontal axis represents the voltage generated when the coil is in the position of the vector.

The rapidity with which the vector rotates or makes one complete revolution is the same as the frequency of the a-c wave it represents. If the frequency of the wave is 10,000 cps, then the vector will rotate 10,000 times in one second.

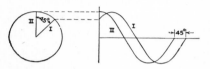

FIG. 2.8. A comparison between the vector and the conventional methods of illustrating a 45° phase difference between two waves.

Two waves acting at the same time can be represented by two vectors, as in Fig. 2.8. Any phase difference between the waves is indicated by the relative position of their vectors. Two vectors displaced by 45° represent two electrical waves 45° apart in phase. Here again we note the simpler notation made possible by the use of vectors.

Many times, when two waves are present in the same circuit, we wish to ascertain the total effect and not merely the individual

$$\underset{\text{PLUS}}{\overset{V_1}{\longrightarrow}} \quad = \quad \overset{V_1}{\longrightarrow} \overset{V_2}{\longrightarrow} \quad = \quad \overset{V_1 + V_2}{\longrightarrow}$$

FIG. 2.9.   The addition of two vectors that are in phase, i.e., point in the same direction.

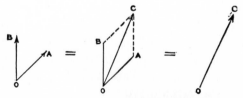

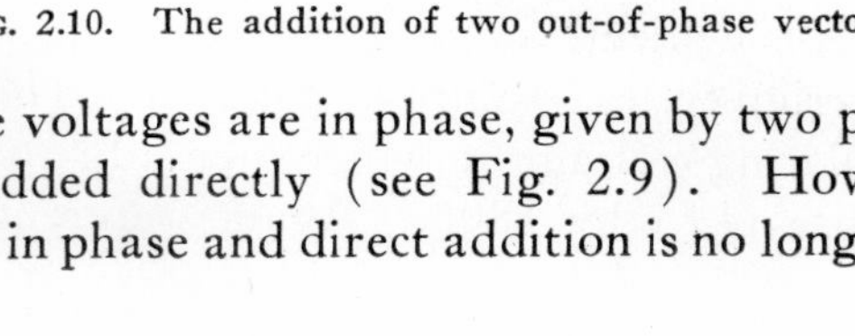

FIG. 2.10.   The addition of two out-of-phase vectors.

results.   If the voltages are in phase, given by two parallel vectors, they may be added directly (see Fig. 2.9). However, voltages generally differ in phase and direct addition is no longer possible. In

Fig. 2.10 two vectors, OA and OB, represent two voltages that differ in phase. The resultant of the two is obtained by constructing a parallelogram, $OBCA$. Line BC is parallel and equal to OA; line AC is parallel and equal to OB. The diagonal drawn between points O and C is the resultant of the vectors OA and OB.

Another interpretation of the resultant is to consider vector OA as forcing a particle to move from O to A, while vector OB forces it to move from A to C. Hence, if two forces, OA and OB, were applied simultaneously to the particle placed at point O, the particle would be forced to travel along line OC.

Vectors Applied to Modulation. The vector concept lends itself quite readily to the three types of modulation. For A-M, in Fig.

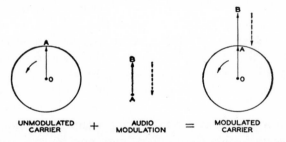

UNMODULATED CARRIER $+$ AUDIO MODULATION $=$ MODULATED CARRIER

Fig. 2.11.   Amplitude modulation demonstrated by vectors.

2.11, the carrier vector OA is rotating at a frequency determined by the oscillator in the transmitter. Let this be 1000 kc. In one second, therefore, there are 1,000,000 complete revolutions producing 1,000,000 cycles. When audio modulation is added, represented by vector AB, the length of the overall vector OB will depend on how AB varies from moment to moment. When the audio voltage is at its peak, AB attains its greatest length; for weaker modulating signals, AB becomes small.

The complete picture shows OA, the carrier vector, rotating rapidly at the radio-frequency rate while the length of $OA + AB$ varies slowly as the strength of the audio signal increases and decreases. This is evident, too, in Fig. 2.12, where one audio cycle covers many carrier cycles. Since in Fig. 2.11 AB is governed by the audio-modulating voltage it will either add to OA or be out of phase (oppose OA) by 180°. Again, reference to Fig. 2.12

will show the same thing to be true there. Note that AB can either add to OA or subtract from it, but nothing more, since this is amplitude modulation and only the amplitude of the vector OA can change.

In F-M, the length of the vector OA remains constant while the speed (frequency) at which it rotates varies from instant to instant according to a pattern set by the audio modulation. Thus, at one moment, it may be spinning around faster than normal; at the next, back to normal; a second later, slower than normal, and so on. These changes represent our frequency variation or modulation and can be detected by the proper receiver.

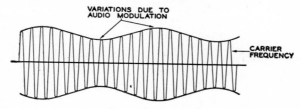

FIG. 2.12. The customary method of indicating an amplitude-modulated wave.

Now we come to phase modulation where we operate on the relative phase of a carrier, leaving the amplitude and frequency fixed. However, as we shall soon see, varying the phase of a wave results, indirectly, in frequency modulation and this can be detected by an F-M discriminator.

F-M from P-M. In the vector diagram, illustrating phase modulation as shown in Fig. 2.13, OA, as before, is the carrier to be phase modulated. It rotates at the frequency of the carrier. OB, another vector, is separated from OA by 45°. This vector is shown for reference only, and will aid in visualizing the phase changes of OA. Although it is not necessary to include OB in each diagram, it may help to understand the phase changes of OA by considering OB as always present.

The frequency and amplitude of OA are kept fixed. If now we vary the phase of OA (with respect to OB) then, as OA rotates, it will "wobble," or fluctuate back and forth, about its mean position.

Suppose that at the instant the audio modulation is applied, the vector OA is at point 1 in Fig. 2.13. Due to the acting modulation, its phase (or position) is shifted to point 2. From position 2, the audio signal brings the vector back to position 1. From position 1 to position 3, due, this time, to the opposite half cycle of the audio wave. To complete the cycle, the vector goes back to position 1, the mean point. Thus, under the force of the applied audio voltage, the phase of OA changes from position 1 to position 2,

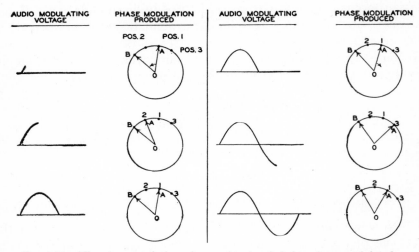

FIG. 2.13. The phase variation of a carrier that is being phase-modulated by an audio signal.

back to 1, then to position 3, and finally back to the starting point, position 1. This represents one complete cycle and recurs at the audio frequency.

Now let us see what is necessary when we shift the phase of a wave. To advance the wave to a position where it is slightly ahead of its normal position, such as shifting it from position 1 to position 2, we must momentarily cause it to speed up for if it had continued moving at its normal speed, it could never have reached the advanced position. From point 2, back to point 1, necessitates a gradual lessening in the speed of rotation. From the normal position to position 3 means a still further decrease in speed on the part of the rotating vector. Finally, to complete the cycle, the vector is brought back to its original position at 1 by a corresponding speed increase.

For the sake of simplicity, the vector OA is stopped while the various positions assumed due to phase modulation are shown. Actually OA is revolving at a tremendous rate while the phase varies, relatively, very slowly. But the overall frequency change due to these phase variations still takes place. This is the important point. Each time the carrier vector wobbles back and forth to reach the new phase positions dictated by the audio modulation, we find the frequency also changes in order to have the vector reach the new positions.

In Fig. 2.13, points 2 and 3 were the maximum phase shifts of the carrier vector OA. If the amplitude of the driving audio voltage increases, for example, then the phase shift will increase and OA will have to travel through a greater angle. Conversely, a smaller audio voltage results in a smaller shift. As we shall soon see, the size of the shift has a very direct bearing on the amount of indirect F-M generated.

The *average* frequency of the rotating vector OA, throughout the entire process, remains constant. This must be so, of course, since we are not, directly, varying the frequency of the wave. But at those instants when the phase of OA is changing, its instantaneous frequency is either increasing or decreasing. If this were not so, then how could OA ever reach the different phase positions rotating at its fixed rate? Obviously it could not. Note that what we are doing is adding sufficient change, either positive or negative, to a fixed frequency to permit the carrier to reach the desired phase position. Distinguish this from " pure " F-M where the carrier frequency itself is being directly affected and shifted in response to the modulating voltage. In the end, both may result in frequency modulation, but it is important to realize that a difference does exist.

Factors Affecting Indirect F-M. (The amount of indirect F-M that is formed by phase modulation depends upon two factors. First, there is the extent of the phase shift.) Quite naturally, the larger this phase shift, the more the carrier frequency must be altered to meet the new condition. The two are directly proportional to each other. (Second, there is the frequency of the modulating audio signal. (If the audio frequency is high, the shifting from one position to another will have to take place in less time, which means that, in any one instant, a greater carrier frequency change must occur. The result — more frequency modulation. On the other hand, if the same phase shift occurs at a lower audio frequency, the rapidity with which the carrier must change decreases. Consequently, the equivalent carrier-frequency change decreases. As with phase shift, the extent of the indirect F-M formed varies *directly* with the audio-modulating frequency.

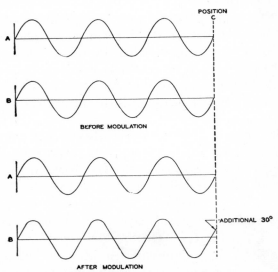

FIG. 2.14.   Prior to modulation, carriers *A* and *B* are in phase. After modulation, *B* leads *A* by 30°.

Because of the importance of the concept of forming frequency modulation from phase changes, it may prove helpful if we consider the same problem from still another angle.

When the phase of a carrier is shifted, so that it differs from another constant carrier by more than it did previously, it means that each wave must go through its cycle just a trifle faster in order to attain the necessary shift within the allotted time.   Consider the two waves, *A* and *B*, shown in Fig. 2.14.   Wave *A* is untouched by the modulating voltage and completes its cycles with unvarying regularity.   Wave *B*, however, is subjected to a modulating voltage which causes it to shift in phase, relative to wave A, by 30°. The full shift must be completed by the time position C is reached.

In order to attain this variation, each of the four cycles shown must contribute a portion of this shift, all contributions adding to the necessary 30°. But for each wave to assume an additional amount means that, besides the regular 360°, each must add a little extra. This can only be accomplished if each wave swings through its cycle of variations a trifle faster than it normally would. By the time point C is reached each cycle has added sufficient phase variation to fulfill the required 30°. Henceforth, with no further variation, wave B will reach its maximum positions (and minimum positions) 30° ahead of wave A; its frequency will continue at the same rate as that of wave A, exactly as it existed prior to the modulation. It is only *during* the shifting in phase that the frequency variations appear and, coincidentally, the indirect F-M. When the shifting ceases, indirect F-M disappears.

To demonstrate how the degree of phase shift and the rapidity with which it occurs affect the indirect F-M, consider the following two illustrations. A carrier of 90 mc (90,000,000 cps) is to be shifted ahead in phase to a maximum of 50°, this to be accomplished in 1/1000 of a second, as determined by the audio-modulating frequency. In 1/1000 of a second, 90,000 cycles of the carrier will occur. To complete a 50° shift in this interval, each carrier cycles must contribute an additional 50/90,000 degree, or approximately 0.0005°. To achieve this, the frequency of each wave must be increased slightly. This increase produces the indirect F-M. The same line of reasoning would apply if the wave were to drop 50° behind, except that now each wave loses 0.0005° from its cycle. The result — a decrease in frequency.

If we maintain the phase shift at 50°, but decrease the time in which this change must be attained, then we have the equivalent of an increase in audio-modulating frequency. Assume the completion of the phase shift is to be accomplished in 1/10,000 of a second. In this time interval, the number of carrier cycles occurring will be reduced from the previous 90,000 to 9000. For the 50° shift, we calculate that 50/9000 or approximately 0.005° are

needed from each cycle compared to the 0.0005° given above.   The
larger the shift of each wave, the greater its frequency change.

Expressed in mathematical terminology, the extent of the
indirect F-M formed through phase modulation is given by

$$\Delta F \text{ (frequency shift)} = f \times \Delta\theta \sin \omega t$$

where

$f =$ the frequency of the audio-modulating voltage (or any
other voltage) that is causing the phase shift

$\Delta\theta =$ the maximum angle through which the carrier is shifted

$\sin \omega t =$ the sinusoidal variation of the applied audio voltage

The inclusion of the term " $\sin \omega t$ " indicates, mathematically, that
the audio voltage is a sine wave and, hence, its force varies sinusoidally.   As a result, the phase shift follows suit.   Since all
complex waves can be resolved into pure sine waves, the expression is applicable to all types of electrical waves employed in
communications.

A comparison of the foregoing equation with true or direct
F-M reveals the differences between them.   In direct F-M the
value of the carrier itself swings between its maximum limits, say
75 kc, about the central or resting position.   The carrier is actually
being shifted directly by the modulation.   In indirect F-M, produced by the phase modulation, the carrier is not actually shifted
directly by the modulation.   Rather, the effect of the phase shifts
is to either add or subtract frequency variations to the fixed carrier.

In the next chapter we will use these facts to demonstrate why
F-M is so effective in reducing interference.

PROBLEMS

1. Differentiate between phase modulation, amplitude modulation, and frequency modulation.

2. Name and explain the factors which affect the phase shift of a phase-
modulated wave.

3. Why are vectors useful in describing phase modulation?   Could they be
used to illustrate amplitude and frequency modulation?

4. Illustrate vector addition.

5. How do we obtain F-M from P-M?

6. Distinguish between indirect and direct frequency modulation.

7. List the factors which affect the amount of indirect F-M produced from a
phase-modulated carrier.

8. What commercial system currently employs P-M to produce an F-M wave?

9. Two vectors are displaced from each other by an angle of 50°. One vector is 10 units long, the other is 7 units long. Draw these to scale and then determine graphically the length of the resultant vector. What angle does this resultant vector make with the 10-unit vector?

10. Two vectors are 180° out of phase. One vector is 12 units long, the other is 21 units long. Draw the resultant vector. What is the angle between the resultant vector and the longer vector?

11. A carrier is being phase-modulated by a 1000-cycle audio sine wave. At what points throughout the modulating cycle is *no* indirect F-M being produced? Why?

12. In the preceding example, at what time during the modulating cycle is the maximum amount of indirect F-M being generated? Why?

CHAPTER 3

F-M AND INTERFERENCE

Interference Suppression, F-M's Main Advantage. Frequency modulation was popularized because of its effectiveness in combating interference against which amplitude modulation operationally is seemingly ineffectual. The fact that a wider audio-frequency range may also be included without unduly increasing the bandwidth required by an F-M station is advantageous but not overly important. There is much evidence that the inclusion of audio frequencies above 5000 cycles is not greatly desired by 90 per cent of the listeners. Fidelity is another controversial issue. If fidelity is interpreted to mean the true reproduction of sound, then an A-M system is just as capable of good fidelity as any F-M network. By and large, interference suppression is the chief reason for the present popularity of F-M.

The word " interference " is applied to any voltage arriving at the input of a receiver or generated in the receiver itself which obstructs, to any noticeable degree, the satisfactory reception of the desired signal. Obviously, there are many sources that may produce interfering voltages, but only those that have been proved by practical experience to be the most important will be investigated. The others either occur too infrequently or else possess insufficient strength to warrant a separate discussion.

INTERFERENCE FROM OTHER STATIONS ON SAME FREQUENCY

One of the most prevalent annoyances in an amplitude-modulated receiver is the piercing beat-note whistle that is heard whenever two signals operating within the same channel are received simultaneously. The whistle is produced whenever the difference of two carrier frequencies is equal to a frequency in the audible range. Within the same channel, this difference seldom exceeds several hundred cycles. As they are close in frequency, the two signals pass through all the circuits together until the 2nd detector is reached. Here they are converted to their original audible form and the beat note appears. It is impossible to remove the beat note by any adjustment in the receiver because both signals are operating within the same band. A directive antenna favoring the desired signal may prove helpful but, in most cases, hardly feasible because other desired stations at other frequencies arrive from different directions. At night the interference becomes stronger because of improved propagation characteristics. In A-M, the interfering signal need be only 1/100 as strong as the desired signal to make itself heard. In other words, a noise-to-signal ratio only 1 to 100 will cause noticeable disturbance.

With F-M, a considerable improvement is possible and the desired signal need only be twice as strong as the interference to completely override it. To see why this is so, we shall examine closely the action of an F-M signal when in the presence of an interfering voltage of smaller amplitude.

Amplitude and Phase Modulation from Interference. In Fig. 3.1 we have two signals, separated slightly in frequency and differing in amplitude. Both are plotted separately to scale. Below these two waveforms is the resultant derived by combining the two waves at every point. If we examine the resultant closely and compare it with the desired signal, we note two differences. First, the amplitude of the resultant is not constant, but varies at a rate equal to the difference in frequency between the two received signals. Thus, if both voltages differ in frequency by 1000 cycles, the amplitude of the resultant will increase and decrease 1000 times per second. In an A-M receiver, this fluctuation would be " skimmed off " (detected by the 2nd detector) and heard as a beat-note whistle in the loudspeaker. What the effect is on an F-M receiver soon will become apparent.

We note, as a second effect of the mixing of two signals, that, although the *average* frequency of the resultant is the same as the larger signal, the two waves (the larger or desired signal and the resultant) do not always have the same relative position. At times the resultant will lead the desired signal in phase, at other moments there will be no phase difference, and, finally, there will be a lag.

In other words, with respect to the original desired signal, the resultant has become phase-modulated. From preceding paragraphs, we are aware that, indirectly, frequency modulation is also produced. The amount of the indirect F-M produced is directly proportional to the phase shift introduced into the resultant wave and to the frequency difference between the two carriers arriving at the receiver. This follows from the formula previously given.

The degree of phase difference caused by the two interacting waves depends wholly upon their amplitude ratio. When the ratio

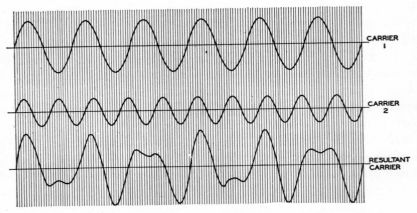

FIG. 3.1. The combination of two carriers to form a resultant which is amplitude and phase-modulated.

is 2 to 1, the maximum angle of phase shift produced is slightly under 30°. This means that the resultant wave leads and lags, alternately, the larger component by this amount. At larger ratios of desired signal to interference, the phase shift is even less. The difference in frequency between the two carriers will set the rate of variation of the phase shift.

Let us pause for a moment and consider these conclusions, for they hold the secret of F-M effectiveness in suppressing interference. Whenever two voltages are present at the input of an F-M receiver, then Fig. 3.1 demonstrates that their resultant will be amplitude- and phase-modulated. The amplitude variation is responsible for the piercing beat-note whistle that is so annoying in A-M sets; the phase modulation contributes indirect frequency modulation.

If we could eliminate both of these modulations from the resultant signal we would have the desired signal with no variations, since it is only in these two respects that the desired and resultant signals differ. Then, too, we should have effectively eliminated the disturbance of the interfering voltage, since it was this voltage that acted with the desired signal to cause these variations.

Eliminating Amplitude Variations. The simpler to remove is the amplitude modulation. This is accomplished by means of the limiter stage in the F-M receiver. Within limits, different input voltages to the limiter produce a constant output. By this device we accomplish the eradication of all amplitude modulation, leaving only the phase modulation. In this respect, then, we have made the resultant wave and the desired signal similar.

Minimizing Phase Modulation. There is no practical method currently available for removing the F-M produced by the phase variations and still receive the desired F-M signal. But, if we cannot eliminate the indirect F-M, we can, at least, reduce it to the point where it becomes negligible when compared with the regular frequency variations of the F-M signal. It is for this reason (among others) that we resort to wide-band F-M.

The degree of the indirect F-M formed from phase modulation has been shown to depend upon $f\Delta\theta$, where f is given in cycles and $\Delta\theta$ is expressed in radians. A radian is equal to $57.3°$, which means that there are 2π, or 2×3.1416, radians in $360°$. When the two reacting signals differ in amplitude by a ratio of 2 to 1, the maximum phase shift introduced in the resultant wave is approximately $30°$ or about $\frac{1}{2}$ a radian. By way of illustration, let us say that the frequency difference (f) between the two carriers is 1000 cycles, or 1 kc, and the signals differ in strength by 2 to 1. Substitution of these values in the foregoing formula indicates that a frequency shift of $1,000 \times 0.5$ or 500 cycles occurs. The shift is, periodically, above and below the average frequency of the stronger signal. In this instance, the frequency variations shift at a rate of 1000 times a second, which is the value of f.

Now compare this variation with ordinary F-M. F.C.C. regulations permit a broadcast station's carrier to be shifted from its assigned position to a maximum of 75 kc, or 75,000 cycles. The interference, in the above example, indirectly produced a frequency shift of only 500 cycles.   Certainly this is insignificant when compared to the audio intensity developed by a swing of 75,000 cycles! And, remember, for 500 cycles to be produced, the interfering voltage had to possess one half the amplitude of the desired carrier. In the more usual case, the ratio of the noise-to-signal voltage is much smaller, say 1 to 10 or 1 to 20.   Under these conditions the suppression is better still.   Thus, the use of wide-band F-M completely swamps the small F-M modulation developed indirectly from the interference.   Herein lies the power of F-M.   However, as we reduce the swing of the desired carrier, the effect of the interference becomes more and more important.   For best reproduction, wide-band F-M is required.

Frequency Separation of Interfering Signals. There is another important fact to be learned from the equation $\Delta F = f\Delta\theta$. As we bring the desired carrier and the interfering signal closer in frequency, f becomes smaller.   If the two signals are at the same frequency, their difference (f) becomes zero and no indirect F-M appears ($\Delta\theta$ times zero is zero).   In other words, the interference can have no effect.   The greater the frequency separation between the signals, the greater the indirect F-M produced.   But even this has a limit.   First, the farther the interfering signal frequency is from the center of the frequency selectivity of the tuned circuits, the more its intensity is decreased by the selectivity of the receiver circuits themselves.   Second, the frequency difference f, if greater than 15,000 cycles, becomes inaudible to most people and cannot be heard at the output.   There is still another effect tending to decrease the interference when the signals are widely separated, but this is reserved for a later section.   In summary, we see that when the interfering signal approaches the frequency of the desired signal, the $f\Delta\theta$ relation works against it whereas, when the two are widely separated, the selectivity of the circuits and our aural limitations impose other barriers.

In amplitude modulation the aural effect of bringing two frequencies together is to produce a lower beat note.   This, however, does not affect the loudness of the beat-note whistle.   From this viewpoint alone, the situation is more favorable for F-M.   Add the fact that stations can differ in amplitude by a ratio of 2 to 1 for F-M and still come through clear and free and we see the great improvement that the newer system offers. It also makes possible the closer location of broadcast stations. Aiding the latter point is the use of high frequencies for F-M operation. At the high frequencies, radio waves travel essentially in straight paths from transmitter to receiver. The ionosphere cannot be used to reflect the waves because penetration is accomplished without appreciable bending. Hence, long distance interference from other stations is avoided. Admittedly, though, this is not a property of either F-M or A-M, but of the wavelengths employed. If we operated the amplitude-modulated transmitters in this upper range, the interference from a distant station would also be decreased.

As long as the desired signal is at least twice as powerful as the interfering signal, only the desired station will be heard in the loudspeaker. As the two signals approach each other in strength, the extent to which the interfering voltage makes itself felt increases sharply. When this signal finally reaches the level where it is stronger than the desired signal, a transition occurs and it assumes full control, completely drowning out the other carrier. The worst situation is in effect when both voltages are equal, for now no clear-cut tendency exists one way or other. However, the moment one signal becomes even a trifle stronger the response changes, with the stronger signal assuming noticeable control. The process is complete when the ratio reaches the 2 to 1 point.

Domination by the Stronger Signal. The reason for the sharp transition in control when one signal becomes even slightly stronger than the other can best be appreciated by vectors. Consider two signals (Fig. 3.2), both present at the discriminator of an F-M receiver. The larger vector, 1, represents the desired signal; the smaller vector, 2, is the interfering signal; and R is their resultant. At the output of the stage it is not 1 or 2, separately, that is heard, but the resultant. Our interest is chiefly in the indirect F-M produced by the interacting of 1 and 2. Any amplitude variations will be effectively eliminated by limiters preceding the discriminator. The signal, at the discriminator, can be made wholly frequency-modulated.

In Fig. 3.2A, vector 1 is operating at our assigned frequency of 90 mc. This means that it is rotating about point O at 90,000,000 times a second. Vector 2 is also rotating but at its own rate, say 90,005,000 times a second. Their difference is 5000. Vector R will also rotate about O, but its speed will depend upon whether 1 or 2 is greater in amplitude. This will become evident as we proceed.

Since signal 2 has a slightly higher speed (frequency) than 1, it means that 2 will gradually move farther and farther away from its relative position shown in Fig. 3.2A. At one point in time, it

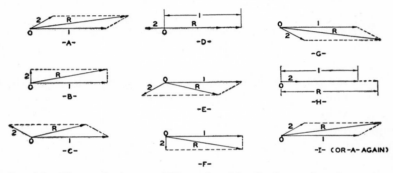

FIG. 3.2. The resultant wave (R) produced by the interaction of a strong signal (1) and a weak interfering signal (2).

may have advanced from vector 1, as shown in B; at some later instant it would be as seen in C (if we momentarily stopped the motion), then D, etc., until gradually it would work its way back to the position shown in A. The sequence is repeated for as long as the rotation is allowed to continue. If vector 2 has a lower frequency than vector 1, it would lose instead of gain a little each instant and so appear to move in the opposite direction with respect to vector 1.

The reader will note the similarity between this action and that of two cars speeding around a large oval. The speedier car will gradually increase its lead over the slower car. If this is allowed to continue long enough, then, in time, the faster car will be one full lap ahead of the slower car. At this point both cars are again racing alongside each other.

If we stop at each of the instants shown in Fig. 3.2 and draw the resultant vector, we see that it fluctuates about vector 1. At C it has shifted to its maximum position ahead of vector 1 and at E it has fallen to its maximum position behind vector 1. At other times it assumes some intermediate position. These fluctuations represent the phase modulation of vector R. As R rotates rapidly about point O, it is also wobbling back and forth about the mean positions of vector 1. In other words, vectors R and 1 possess the same average frequency, but R differs in amplitude and phase from

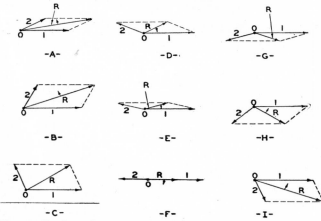

FIG. 3.3. The amplitude and phase variation of a resultant (R) carrier due to the interaction of two signals. The small arrows on R indicate whether its phase (with respect to the desired signal, 1) is going in a positive or negative direction.

1. The amplitude fluctuations are suppressed by the limiter stage (or stages), whereas the phase variations will, as already noted, cause frequency modulation. The indirect F-M depends upon the maximum angular shift between 1 and R and the speed with which R fluctuates about 1. All this, it will be recognized, has been discovered before. That it appears here is partial evidence that we are on the same track.

In this first example, vector 1 was very much larger than vector 2. This was done purposely in order to show clearly the effect of a large desired signal. In the next case, let vector 1 remain larger than 2, but only slightly so. Now let us see what happens. The action is illustrated in Fig. 3.3.

The first evident conclusion to be drawn is that here the resultant fluctuates between wider limits. But since it still fluctuates about vector 1, its frequency is that of 1. If its frequency equaled that of 2, then it would follow this vector around, with 2 as its center position. This, however, does not occur. Hence, we conclude that by bringing the two signals closer in amplitude we only succeed in causing more phase modulation in the resultant vector R. Its *average* frequency is still the same as that of the larger signal. What we hear from the output of the receiver is signal 1, but with sufficient interference to cause distortion. This, it will be recalled, is another conclusion previously discovered.

Now, if we make signal 2 greater than signal 1, what will happen? We have merely to return to Fig. 3.2 and transpose the numbers 1 and 2 (vectors) to see the result. The resultant begins to fluctuate about vector 2 and the signal heard in the loud-speaker is determined primarily by 2, with a certain percentage of indirect F-M added, due to signal 1. The transition from vector 1 to 2 is sharp and demonstrates why the predominant signal assumes control in F-M systems. Once the ratio of the two signals reaches 2 to 1, the F-M effect of the smaller on the larger, with wide-band F-M modulation, becomes negligible. This is true whether the interfering signal is another station or just plain noise of any type.

Adjacent Channel Interference

It is not at first apparent why any interference is caused by stations on the channels adjacent to the desired signal, but such interference is possible. Due to this possibility, it is the practice of the F.C.C. never to permit stations to broadcast on adjacent bands in the same community. The closest that two stations in the same region can transmit (in frequency) is on alternate channels. Thus, if the three frequencies 90.1 mc, 90.3 mc and 90.5 mc are available, only 90.1 mc and 90.5 mc would contain stations, at any one time, in any one service area. In some other region, however, it would be perfectly feasible to have a station assigned to the 90.3-mc frequency.

The interference between two stations transmitting on adjacent bands is a result of:

1. The type of selectivity curve designed for most commercial receivers.

2. The fact that sidebands of the two adjacent stations can interact to form audio frequencies at the output of the discriminator.

It was found in a previous section that F-M interference produced when two stations operate on the same band is due to the introduction of phase variations. The frequency of the audio voltage developed from the phase modulation is equal to the frequency of separation of the two carriers. Obviously, if the interacting carriers differ by more than 15 kc, no audible interference appears at the loud-speaker. When one of the carriers arriving at

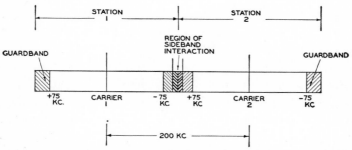

FIG. 3.4. In the darkened region between station 1 and station 2 it is possible for their sidebands to interact and produce interference.

the receiver is centered on an adjacent channel, the possibility of its creating audible interference in reception is non-existent because of the 200-kc frequency difference between the carriers. But consider the possibility of interference when the sidebands of each carrier react with each other. These would be capable of producing an audible note if both sets of sidebands extend into their respective guard bands. This can occur on strong modulation. The region that is sufficiently close to an adjacent guard band to cause audible interference is indicated in Fig. 3.4.

The selectivity characteristic of the tuning circuits of the receiver must also be a partner to the action, since a sharp cut-off at the edge of the desired channel would prevent reception of adjacent channel signals (see Fig. 3.5). In commercial receivers, the added expense necessary to include sharp cut-off resonant circuits is prohibitive.

As a compromise we find the familiar tapered response shown in Fig. 3.6.   With this form, it is quite possible to receive the sideband frequencies of adjacent channel stations.   If, during any portion of the modulation, the adjacent signal is stronger at the discriminator than the desired frequencies, the desired signal will be ruined.   On the other hand, if the desired signal has a greater intensity at the discriminator, no distortion will be present.

The solution of interchannel interference lies in good selectivity response of the receiver plus the prohibition of near-by adjacent channel stations.   The latter has been accomplished already by

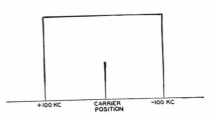

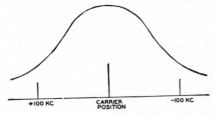

FIG. 3.5.   Perfect response characteristic for receiver tuning circuits.

FIG. 3.6.   Practical modification of Fig. 3.5.

existing F.C.C. regulations and the former is a matter of individual design.   As it is, the situation using F-M is considerably better than the corresponding situation for A-M for several reasons.

1. The use of a guardband on F-M decreases the possibility of signals on adjacent bands interfering with each other.

2. The line-of-sight transmission characteristics of the higher radio frequencies limits the interference from stations in other areas.   At the lower A-M frequencies, long distance propagation is always possible, especially at night when the attenuation is less.

3. The inherent characteristics of the F-M system where a 2 to 1 ratio causes the " practical " elimination of the weaker signal. Using A-M, this does not occur until the stronger signal is 100 times more powerful than the weaker one.

In neither system are stations in the same service area placed on adjacent channels.   However, because of reason No. 2 above, the advantage of such a condition benefits F-M more than it does A-M.

STATIC

Perhaps second in importance as a disturbing influence in radio reception is static. This is especially true during the six warmer months of the year when thunderstorms are more prevalent. During a local thunderstorm, only the very loudest programs can be heard, and even these with difficulty. The strength of the electrical waves set up is strong enough either to completely drown out radio signals or else present sufficient interference to destroy the clarity of reception. This is the existing situation with A-M and its only solution, at the time of this writing, has consisted of the following:

1. The insertion of limiters in the audio section of the set. These stages limit the maximum amplitude of all signals and prevent thundering crashes of volume accompanying a strong outburst of lightning. The limiter, however, is quite ineffective when the incoming interference is of the continuous, crackling variety. As the name suggests, these devices only limit incoming bursts. The signal, during these moments, is still ruined.

2. Designing the receiver selectivity to include no more than the necessary commercial bandwidth, 10 kc wide. It has been discovered that the energy contained in a static outburst is spread over many frequencies, with the greatest concentration at the lower frequencies. Hence, the narrower we make the bandwidth to which the receiver will respond, the less static noise we will obtain.

Beyond these two refinements of an ordinary receiver, very little can be done to overcome the effects of static. With F-M, we not only have the advantage of the 2 to 1 ratio, but also the advantage of frequency. Since most of the energy of an outburst is located at the low frequencies, very little reaches the high-frequency bands allocated to F-M. In addition disturbances due to distant thunderstorms seldom, if ever, reach the receiver because of the limited transmission range of high frequencies.

THERMAL AGITATION AND TUBE HISS

Even in the complete absence of natural disturbances and interfering stations, there remains a practical limit to the weakest signal that can be received by any set. The limit is fixed at the first or second stages of a receiver and is due to two *main* sources, thermal agitation and tube hiss.

Thermal agitation arises from the random motion of electrons in any conductor. The movement of the electrons, in both directions, constitutes a current flow. Since there are usually a few more electrons moving in one direction than in the other, a voltage is set up across the conductor which is proportional to the net current flow and the value of the conductor resistance. The polarity of the voltage due to thermal agitation changes constantly, depending on the direction in which the maximum number of electrons are moving. Because of this, there is no definite pattern to the random voltage, or, for that matter, any one frequency at which the electrons move. It has been found that the energy of the disturbance is distributed uniformly throughout the entire frequency spectrum used for communications.

The amount of voltage that is developed by thermal agitation in conductors can be computed from the following relationship:

$$E^2 \text{ (rms)} = 4KTR \times (f_2 - f_1)$$

where

$E =$ the rms value of the voltage generated across the resistance

$K =$ a constant $= 1.37 \times 10^{-23}$ watt-second/degree

$T =$ the temperature of the conductor (it is expressed in absolute degrees, Kelvin, which is equal to 273 plus the temperature in degrees centigrade)

$R =$ the value of the resistance of the conductor, in ohms

$f_2 - f_1 =$ the bandwidth of the receiver (for F-M, this would be equal to 200 kc).

To compute the voltage, merely substitute the known quantities in the equation, take the square root of the answer, and this will be the rms voltage.

An inspection of the preceding formula indicates that, with all other factors constant, the wider the bandwidth which the set is designed for, the larger the amount of thermal agitation voltage developed. Hence, so far as this one point is concerned, narrow-band F-M offers less intrinsic noise than wide-band F-M. However there are many other advantages to be gained by the use of a wide band and this is the form of present-day F-M receivers.

The other main source of internal noise is in the tubes. We obtain a series of many overlapping impulses due to the fact that the current flow from the cathode to the plate of a tube is not a continuous fluid but a moving congregation of separate particles, the electrons. This is known as the " shot effect." We obtain noise even when so-called steady current is flowing, because, at any single moment, more electrons are impinging on the plate than at some other moment. Over any time interval, the current is steady, but instantaneously it fluctuates quite rapidly because of its nonfluid nature. The instantaneous fluctuations represent the noise component. Examination has revealed that the energy of the noise is distributed evenly throughout the frequency spectrum. In this respect it resembles the noise arising from thermal agitation. For the purposes of this discussion, we can combine thermal agitation and tube hiss under the general heading of random noise as a single form of interference.

RANDOM NOISE

Random noise consists of many frequencies unrelated in phase. In the absence of a carrier, the different frequencies beat with each other to produce an audible noise when the random voltages are demodulated at the discriminator. The loud hiss received when tuning between stations is due to the random voltages. This is true of F-M and A-M sets. In fact, with F-M, the amount of interstation noise is greater because of the wider bandpass of F-M receivers. Many manufacturers eliminate interstation hiss by special silencer circuits that cut in whenever the station is tuned out. This makes for a quiet receiver.

A more important situation arises when a carrier is present. In this case we have interactions between each of the random noise voltages and the carrier plus the interactions of the random voltages among themselves. The first is by far the stronger of the two interactions, so that we can disregard the result of the action among the random voltages themselves.

The effect of the random pulses on the carrier is twofold:
1. Amplitude modulation of the carrier.
2. Phase modulation directly and, from this, frequency modulation indirectly.

If we are considering frequency modulation, then the limiter stages will remove all amplitude variations. The indirect F-M produced will depend, as before, upon the difference in frequency between the carrier and each random voltage plus the phase-angle variation of the resultant. The amount of frequency modulation is zero when the carrier frequency is the same as that of the random voltage. As the two separate, the F-M produced increases and the

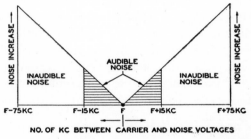

FIG. 3.7.   Noise response of an F-M receiver. The noise intensity increases directly with frequency separation between carrier and interfering signal.

output from the discriminator follows directly. The graph in Fig. 3.7 illustrates the situation. This is a graphic representation that the interference becomes stronger as the frequency difference between the carrier and the noise pulses increases.

Whereas the double triangular plot indicates the extent of the noise generated, not all of it is effective at the loud-speaker. The ends of each triangle extend to 75 kc, whereas the audio amplifiers (and our ears) cut off at about 15 kc. Hence, for practical purposes, we can discount that section of the plot extending beyond 15 kc.

Now compare this situation with the corresponding A-M case. To place A-M and F-M on a comparable basis we will assume that the full 15,000 cycles can be passed by the A-M receiving networks. Each random voltage (of different frequency) will mix with the A-M carrier to form a beat note. The amplitude of each note is the same because all random voltages have approximately the same strength. Thus, in place of the triangular response of Fig. 3.7 we obtain the rectangular response shown in Fig. 3.8. This noise extends to 15 kc on either side of the carrier and then stops abruptly because of our aural limitations.

In Fig. 3.9, half of each response curve is superimposed on the other to indicate the greater effectiveness of F-M over A-M. Only half the plots are used because both halves of each curve are identical. A rough comparison readily indicates that the F-M system gives less noise in the output. Just how much the difference actually

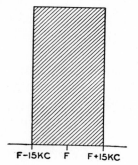

FIG. 3.8. The noise characteristic of an A-M receiver.

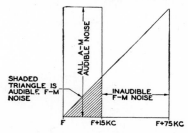

FIG. 3.9. A comparison between A-M and F-M noise characteristics. Note that all the A-M noise is audible, whereas only a small segment of the total possible F-M noise is effective.

is can be shown mathematically to be 18.75 decibels or an equivalent signal-to-noise voltage ratio of 8.65. In other words, because of intrinsic characteristics, an F-M system is more effective against the ever-present noise interferences than the A-M method of transmission. All this, of course, in the presence of a carrier. Without the carrier, it has already been noted that the F-M system is noisier.

Noise and the Deviation Ratio. The deviation ratio of an F-M system has a direct bearing on its ability to suppress noise. By deviation ratio we mean the ratio of the maximum carrier swing to the highest audio frequency. For the figures quoted previously, a deviation ratio of 5 was used; that is, a maximum carrier shift of 75 kc and an audio frequency of 15 kc.

Suppose, however, that the F-M system is designed for a maximum frequency deviation of 60 kc. The highest audio frequency will be kept at 15 kc. The foregoing set of conditions limits the shifting of the carrier, under high level audio voltages, to 60 kc. At the receiver, with the *same* degree of noise present as before, we

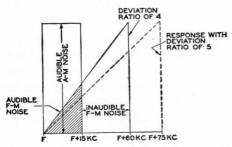

FIG. 3.10. The increase in noise in an F-M receiver with decrease in deviation ratio.

have less desired signal push-ing through to override the noise. As a consequence, the signal-to-noise ratio is lower and the effectiveness of F-M has decreased. It is the ratio of the desired F-M swing to the indirect F-M swing produced by the interference that accounts for the efficacy of the system. For a deviation ratio

of 4 (60 ÷ 15), the signal-to-noise ratio reduces to 6.92, or a decibel value of 16.75. A comparison between this F-M system and A-M is shown in Fig. 3.10. It is quite evident that the effectiveness of the F-M has diminished, as indicated by the larger proportion of the shaded triangle.

If we continue to limit the swing of the F-M carrier, the signal-to-noise improvement (over A-M) diminishes correspondingly.

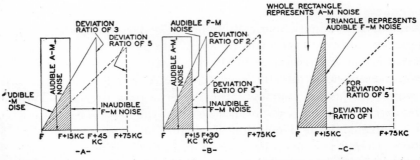

FIG. 3.11. Further comparisons between the noise in A-M and F-M systems with various F-M deviation ratios.

Comparison diagrams are shown in Fig. 3.11 for the instances where the F-M shift is reduced to 45 kc, then 30 kc, and finally 15 kc. Note that even in the worst situation, with a total frequency shift of only 15 kc, we still obtain a better signal-to-noise ratio than possible with A-M. The advantage is 4.1875 decibels.

The importance of obtaining the highest deviation ratio is thus evident. That the deviation ratio does not extend beyond 5 is due to the fact that the additional ether space required would permit less stations to be assigned operating licenses. If, for example, we permitted a deviation ratio of 7, then for a maximum audio-modulating frequency of 15 kc, we would need 105 kc on either side of the carrier. Add to this a 25-kc guardband and we have a total bandwidth of 260 kc. Since a deviation ratio of 5 has proved satisfactory, it has been established as standard.

Pre-Emphasis and De-Emphasis. In the analysis of many broadcast programs, it was found that most of the energy is contained at the lower audio frequencies. In addition, it has further been brought to light that the greatest irritating noise generated is located from 5000 cycles up. To reduce the effect of the noise, a pre-emphasis network is inserted in the audio section of the transmitter. The function of the circuit is to favor the frequencies above 1500 cycles. It accomplishes this by proportionately attenuating the lower frequencies more than the higher frequency components of the signals passing through the network.

Pre-emphasis is applied to the audio signals at the first audio amplifier. Beyond the pre-emphasis network, the audio voltages combine in the usual manner with whatever noise is present in the system. At the receiver there is a de-emphasis circuit with the reverse properties of the pre-emphasis circuit. The frequencies above 1500 cycles are reduced to their original values. At the same time a similar reduction in noise occurs. The

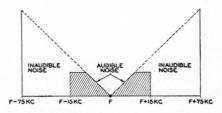

Fig. 3.12. Improvement in noise reduction due to pre-emphasis circuit in transmitter.

overall effect is a return of the signal to its proper relative proportions, but with a considerable reduction in noise.

Another beneficial effect of de-emphasis is concerned with the noise that is produced by another station or the ever-present random noise. As we have seen, the greater the difference between our carrier frequency and the interference, the greater the indirect F-M formed (see Fig. 3.7). Through the use of the de-emphasis network, the triangular response of Fig. 3.7 is modified to that of Fig. 3.12. The de-emphasis action, by reducing the level of all frequencies above 1500 cycles, slices off a considerable portion of the noise. The actual arrangement of the components of the de-emphasis circuit is shown in Chapter 9.

Impulse Noise

Impulse noise, as distinguished from random noise, consists of short, sharp bursts of energy caused by agencies, man-made or natural, external to the receiver. A very familiar example of such interference is the type of noise generated by auto-ignition systems or sparking in electrical machines. Although the average value of these bursts is quite low, the peak value may exceed the signal and hence appear noticeably in the loud-speaker. As long as the peaks exceed the signal, F-M will be unable to override them. At best, all we can do is to minimize the effect of these peaks. For this purpose, the limiter stage can be very useful if designed to respond instantaneously to the rapidly recurrent pulses. How this is accomplished will be made evident in Chapter 8.

Hum

Hum, in a receiver, may affect the desired signal at two points, in the radio-frequency stages and in the audio amplifiers. Hum, in the majority of instances, arises from insufficient filtering in the power supply, although any unshielded transformers and chokes in the power circuit may just as readily be the source, even if the final output from the unit is pure d-c.

Regarding the effect on the F-M receiver output we find that the hum introduced by way of the audio amplifiers is the most annoying. Hum effect is negligible if arising in the R.F. or I.F. stages because the resulting amplitude modulation introduced is removed at the limiter and any phase modulation is generally exceedingly minute.

We must treat hum, present in the audio amplifiers, in exactly the same manner as we do in A-M receivers. Once the F-M signal has been converted to audio variations, it no longer has the protection of F-M. Hence, anything that will affect its amplitude will be carried through to the loud-speaker. Careful by-passing of all d-c connecting points is necessary, plus adequate shielding of transformers and chokes in the power supply. Filament or heater leads must be positioned as far away as possible from grid wires, plate leads and any other links in the audio channel that would affect the audio signal. The methods are familiar to the radiomen who have encountered the same problem in A-M sets.

PROBLEMS

1. Name the most important types of interference that can affect radio reception and explain each briefly.

2. What is the cause of a beat-note whistle in an A-M receiver? How is this eliminated in F-M receivers?

3. Explain how phase and amplitude modulation arise from interference.

4. How does an F-M receiver effectively deal with the phase and amplitude modulation produced through interference?

5. Of the phase and amplitude modulation produced through interference, which is the most troublesome to an F-M receiver? Why?

6. In the expression, $\Delta F = f \times \Delta\Theta$, what does each symbol represent? Indicate the proper units for each symbol.

7. How much indirect F-M is produced when two incoming signals differ in frequency by 5000 cycles and the maximum phase modulation produced is 60°?

8. What are the advantages of wide-band F-M as compared to narrow-band F-M?

9. What effect does the frequency separation of the two interfering signals have on the amount of interference produced? Explain. For what frequency separation is the interference a minimum?

10. What is the significance of the 2 to 1 ratio in F-M reception?

11. What factors limit the effect of interference in an F-M receiver?

12. Can stations operating on adjacent channels interfere with each other? How?

13. What have the F.C.C. and the receiver manufacturers done to minimize interference arising from stations operating on near-by channels?

14. What is static? Why does it affect an F-M receiver less than an A-M receiver?

15. Under what general category can thermal agitation and tube hiss be placed? What is the frequency spectrum distribution for this type of noise?

16. "An F-M receiver is noisier than an A-M receiver." Explain under what conditions this statement is true.

17. Why is the noise characteristic of an F-M receiver triangular whereas in an A-M set it is rectangular?

18. What is the most difficult type of noise for an F-M receiver to cope with? Why?

19. What is the relationship between the deviation ratio of an F-M signal and its ability to suppress noise and interference?

20. When the deviation ratio of an F-M signal is 1, is the F-M system of modulation superior to A-M modulation?   Explain.

21. How does poor filtering in the power supply affect an F-M receiver? How does this differ from its effect in an A-M set?

22. Explain pre-emphasis and de-emphasis.

23. Why are pre-emphasis and de-emphasis beneficial to an F-M receiver? Could the same components be employed for A-M transmission?   Explain.

CHAPTER 4

PROPAGATION, RECEPTION, AND TRANSMISSION
OF F-M SIGNALS

Introduction. In this chapter we shall discuss the manner by which the generated signal at the broadcast station is radiated and the means by which this signal is intercepted at the receiver.

The present allocations established by the Federal Communications Commission set aside the frequencies extending from 88 to 108 mc for the transmission of F-M signals. Now, this band of frequencies is almost 70 times higher than the present standard A-M broadcast band, and just as differences exist between A-M and F-M receivers because of the difference in operating frequency, so differences exist between low frequency and high frequency antenna systems. In order to understand why these differences exist, a general review of radio wave propagation will be undertaken.

An antenna is simply a wire or group of wires which is placed out in the open as far as possible from surrounding objects. Energy is fed to the antenna from the transmitter with the result that currents are established in the wires, flowing first in one direction and then in the other. The currents, in turn, establish magnetic fields which expand and contract about the wires in step with the periodic rise and fall of the rapidly alternating currents. Now, if all the electromagnetic energy established by the antenna currents returned to the wires, no signal would be radiated. However, not all the energy is returned, and that portion which does not return represents the transmitted signal.

The purpose of the receiving antenna is to intercept some of this radiated energy, developing therefrom a voltage which is applied to the receiver terminals. Since the fields that the receiving antenna intercept are due to the transmitting antenna, we could quite logically state that the receiving antenna and the transmitting towers are coupled to each other. To be sure, the coupling is loose, because the two antenna systems are widely separated; but coupling exists. If we think back to our own experience with coupled coils in radio circuits, we know that maximum voltage is induced in the secondary coil when it is held in the same position as the primary coil. Minimum voltage is induced when the two are held at right angles to each other. By the same token, if the transmitter antenna wires are placed in a horizontal position, then the receiving antenna should be placed in the same relative position. Signals from antennas held in this position are said to be horizontally polarized. If desired, the antenna wires may be mounted vertically, in which case the electric component is said to be vertically polarized. Polarization of an antenna is important, as we shall see in the following discussion.

WAVE PROPAGATION

Types of Radio Waves. Radio waves radiated by an antenna system may follow one of two general paths to reach the receiver and are classified either as ground waves or sky waves, depending on the path that they travel. Ground waves are those which either travel not far above the ground or else are actually guided by the ground. Sky waves are those which travel upward away from the earth for distances sometimes as much as 250 miles before they are bent sufficiently to enable them to return to earth.

Although there is essentially only one mode for sky wave transmission, ground waves may be subclassified into surface waves, direct waves, and ground-reflected waves. Each of these subdivisions enters into the propagation picture in a different way. This will become clearer as we progress.

Surface Waves. Perhaps the best point at which to begin is the surface wave because propagation at low frequencies is accomplished principally through this medium. A surface wave is a wave which travels in contact with the ground, actually being guided by it. The wave must be vertically polarized because, to low and medium frequency voltages, the earth is a fairly good conductor, and a horizontally polarized wave would have the electric field parallel to the ground. The conducting earth would short-circuit the field, preventing its propagation for any appreciable distance.

The surface wave, as it moves over the surface of the earth, induces charges in the earth. The periodic change in wave polarity causes the charge concentration to vary from point to point. These concentrations can vary only by having electrons flow from point to point, and this, in turn, constitutes a current. Since the earth possesses resistance, forcing current to flow through it results in a power loss, the power being supplied by the transmitted wave. As the frequency of the signal increases, the amount of power that is lost rises until, at about 2 mc, the coverage obtained by means of the surface wave is confined to very short distances. However, surface propagation in this manner is extremely useful at lower frequencies. Ship-to-shore installations operating below 500 kc use enormous antennas but are capable of transmitting steady signals for distances of 1000 miles or more with unvarying regularity. At the A-M broadcast frequencies, 550 to 1600 kc, the primary and secondary service areas receive their signals almost entirely by the surface wave.

The other divisions of the ground wave, the direct ray and the earth reflected ray, do not become important until the signal frequencies rise above 30 mc. Long-distance communication between 2 mc and 30 mc is accomplished principally by the sky wave.

Sky Wave — Ionosphere. The energy radiated by an antenna which does not follow the contour of the earth travels upward through the air until it reaches a region where there exists a concentration of ions and electrons. This region is the ionosphere. For those who are unfamiliar with this terminology, ionization is the process of separating a molecule (in this instance a gas molecule) into a positive ion and one or more electrons. Molecules, of their own accord, would never separate in this manner. However, by the application of sufficient energy from some outside source, separation can be achieved. In the ionosphere ultra-violet radiations from the sun are this source of energy. These rays, penetrating the gaseous layers surrounding the earth, supply enough energy to cause the electrons to separate from their molecules, the result being a concentration of negative electrons and positively charged molecules or ions. Radio waves traveling up from the antenna enter this ionized region and, by the interaction of the wave energy and the free electrons, are bent back toward earth. This process is essentially one of refraction, similar to the effect prisms have on light rays. However, reflection from the ionosphere also occurs, although to a considerably smaller extent. Both methods are illustrated in Fig. 4.1.

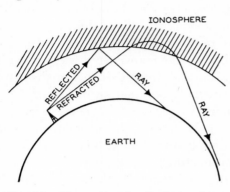

FIG. 4.1. Illustration of reflection and refraction of radio waves at the ionosphere. Reflection occurs less frequently than refraction.

The layers of ions, or ionosphere as they are collectively called, are found at distances of from 70 to 250 miles above the surface of the earth. Analysis of this region has disclosed that, although there is ionization of the gas molecules throughout the entire area, there are distinct layers in which the ion concentrations rise to a maximum. The layers are distinguishable and have been given specific designations. The lowest layer, called the E layer, is found about 70 miles above the earth, and this height is fairly constant.

The next region of maximum ion concentration occurs at a distance of about 185 miles above the earth. This layer has been labeled the F layer, but it exists as one layer only at night, after sunset. During the day it separates into two distinct groups of ions, labeled F_1 and F_2, respectively. The F_1 layer is usually found 140 miles above the ground while the F_2 layer forms at about 225 to 250 miles. At night, of course, the two regions combine again to form the single F ionized layer. The three are shown in Fig. 4.2 together with the lower E layer. The F_2 layer has the greatest degree of ionization and electron density. It is the layer that refracts the radio waves of higher frequency, the waves that other layers cannot turn back. If a wave does not receive sufficient bending in this final (F_2) layer, it continues into empty space.

Wave Bending. When a radio wave enters the ionosphere, the electric field of the wave acts on the charged ions and electrons, causing them to vibrate in accordance with the changes occurring in the electric field. The important vibrations are those of the electrons since they have a mass which is roughly 1800 times less than the ions, and therefore they are capable of executing greater vibrations than the ions. The frequency of these vibrations are the same as the frequency of the wave. Since moving electrons constitute an electrical current, we have, in effect, a large number of minute antennas, each radiating a signal having a frequency equal to the frequency of the arriving wave. At the start, when the electric field of the radio wave acts on an electron, the result is a vibratory motion which is parallel to the electric field. However, once the

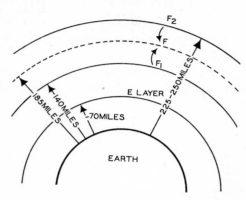

FIG. 4.2. The various layers of the ionosphere. The distances shown are only approximate values since the exact heights vary from day to day.

electron starts to move, it reacts with the earth's magnetic field, causing it to leave its straight line path and to travel a more or less spiral path. The energy that is reradiated by the electron has now changed direction. In the conditions existing in the ionosphere, this change in direction is such that the energy is reradiated partially or wholly toward the earth. We obtain the same effect as though the arriving radio wave had been bent around

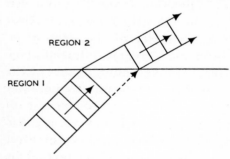

FIG. 4.3. Refraction of radio waves entering the ionosphere.

as in Fig. 4.3. The process of bending the radio wave is known as refraction.

The degree of bending that a wave receives depends primarily upon three factors: the angle at which the wave enters the ionosphere, the frequency of the wave, and the electron density of the layer. The importance of the angle may best be seen by reference to Fig. 4.4. The greater the angle ϕ, the more the wave has to be bent, or refracted, in order that it return to earth. Waves entering at very small angles require only a slight amount of bending to have their direction changed sufficiently to cause them to return to earth again.

The frequency of the wave is important because it determines the type (and length) of the path followed by the vibrating electron.

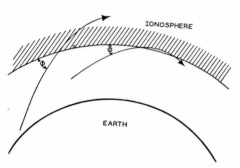

When the frequency is high, the electron direction must reverse itself so rapidly that the electron never achieves a very high velocity. Its interaction, then, with the earth's magnetic field is correspondingly slight, resulting in only a small change in electron path. Consequently, the energy reradiated by the electron does not differ appreciably in path direction from that followed by the original wave. However, as the frequency decreases, the velocity of the electron increases because the time between reversals is greater. Its path now is more truly spiral, and the electron direction is altered more by the earth's magnetic field. The reradiated energy thus shows a greater bending effect.

FIG. 4.4. As the angle ϕ which the radio wave makes with the ionosphere increases, more bending must occur before the radio wave is bent back to earth.

Finally, the density of the charged particles in the layers themselves will determine, in the final analysis, just how much the wave is bent. As the density increases, the amount of refraction increases for any one wave.

Critical Frequencies of Ionosphere. Radio waves may be sent upward at almost any desired angle, but the wave that will require the greatest amount of bending is one that is sent vertically upward or, what is the same thing, at right angles to the earth's surface. The frequency of the wave that is bent back after entering a certain layer at that vertical angle is known as the critical frequency for that particular layer. If a wave of high frequency enters this ionosphere layer at right angles, it will usually not be refracted enough to make it return to earth and will continue upward. However, this wave of higher frequency may enter the ionosphere at a smaller angle, say 50°, and have a better chance of being returned to earth. Of course, if the frequency is very high, not even a small angle of incidence will help, the wave in this case continuing out into space. At various times in the day and during the year the density of a given layer will change, whereupon its critical frequency changes. Should the density increase, the critical frequency value would rise. Should the density decrease, it would be necessary to lower the critical frequency. The critical frequency may thus be looked upon as an index of the ability of the ionosphere to return a wave to earth. All lower frequencies will be refracted to earth no matter what the angle used to transmit them upward, whereas higher frequencies may be returned only if the proper angle is used. The lowest angles achievable in practice are about 4° to 6° with the horizon. If a wave cannot be returned at this elevation, sky wave transmission cannot be used for this particular wave length.

Sporadic *E*. The discussion thus far has confined itself to what might be called normal conditions. Under these circumstances, frequencies as high as 30 to 35 mc can regularly be refracted by the F_2 layer. For frequencies beyond 35 mc, sky wave transmission becomes useless, the waves receiving insufficient bending to return to earth. However, every once in a while it is found that frequencies as high as 60 mc are refracted back to earth by the ionosphere. As this is an unusual occurrence, it is necessary to look for conditions in the ionosphere that are present only at these times and then disappear. Investigation has revealed that at these times portions of the lower *E* layer contain unusual concentrations of electrons, and it is these patches which refract the higher frequencies. The name given to these small, well-defined regions within the *E* layer is Sporadic *E* spots. These spots occur rather frequently, especially in summer, and are used to good advantage by the amateurs operating on the 56-mc band. They may last from a few minutes to many hours and may remain in one locality or travel about at high speeds.   The time of the day or night does not appear to have too great a bearing on their appearance since long-distance communications have occurred at all times.

Another phenomenon that occurs frequently is the intense magnetic " storm " that disturbs long-distance communications for periods of from 3 to 5 days.   During these storms the earth's magnetic field fluctuates widely in intensity and then gradually settles down to its normal value.   The origin of these storms appears to be in the sun where certain types of solar disturbances cause the emission of clouds of electrons and other charged particles. These particles travel from the sun to the earth, penetrating through the F layers and reaching the E layer.   The effect of these clouds of charged particles on our own ionosphere depends on their intensity and the extent of the clouds.   Under a severe invasion, the layers of the ionosphere lose their distinctiveness, varying widely in density, height, and refractive power.   The F_2 layer may even disappear for a short time.   Long-distance communication during these periods of turbulence is erratic.

The terms " reflection " and " refraction " have been previously illustrated (Fig. 4.1), and it is seen that when a wave is reflected from a surface its direction is sharply altered whereas when a wave is refracted, the change in direction occurs gradually.   Most wave-bending in the ionosphere is achieved by refraction.   However, when the frequency of the signal is sufficiently low, and the ionized layer sufficiently dense, the wave does not penetrate the layer to any appreciable extent, and change in direction occurs through reflection. The line of demarcation between reflection and refraction is not too distinct, and throughout the literature both terms are used interchangeably, especially when describing the phenomenon that occurs during periods of ionospheric disturbances.

H.F. Propagation.   The discussion, thus far, has concerned itself exclusively with radio communication using frequencies up to approximately 30 to 35 mc.   These are the highest frequencies that will be refracted by the F_2 layer under what may be termed normal conditions.   For Sporadic E refractions it is possible to go as high as 60 mc although odd conditions are encountered.   While Sporadic E refractions occur quite frequently, they cannot be depended upon for any regularly scheduled traffic. From here to the end of this chapter, frequencies in the very high region will be emphasized, extending beyond 30 mc.

Three Components of H.F. Propagation. High frequency wave propagation can be broken down into three categories, each of which is responsible for the reception of these signals by a different means. First is the so-called "line-of-sight" method which embodies both a direct ray and an earth reflected ray; second, there is refraction in the region of the troposphere; and last, there is diffraction around the curvature of the earth. These three methods are generally independent of each other. Although it may happen that all of these methods combine to lay down the same transmitted signal at the same point, it does not occur often. Usually the last two modes of propagation are responsible for signals appearing beyond the horizon, whereas the first method deals with the distances such that the receiving and transmitting antennas are in a direct line above the curvature of the earth.

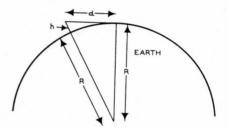

Line-of-Sight Method. In this method of wave propagation, energy from the transmitting towers travels on a direct line to the horizon. Beyond the

FIG. 4.5. How to calculate the line of sight distance.

horizon, an extension of the straight line from the transmitter shows that the energy travels into the ionosphere and on into outer space. Unless this energy is intercepted by a receiving antenna before it travels away from the earth, communication by this method becomes impossible.

The following simple derivation will indicate how to determine the distance from the transmitting tower to the horizon. To simplify the mathematics, it will be assumed that the earth is flat over that small portion of its surface. This assumption results in a right triangle. (See Fig. 4.5.) From elementary geometry it is possible to write the following equation:

$$d^2 + R^2 = (R + h)^2 = R^2 + 2Rh + h^2$$

Since h is very small compared to the radius of the earth, the h^2 term can be neglected. This gives us

$$d^2 + R^2 = R^2 + 2Rh$$

or

$$d^2 = 2Rh$$

It is possible to substitute the numerical value of the radius of the earth for R and obtain the following simplified equation:

$$d = 1.23\sqrt{h}$$

where d is in miles and h is in feet. To show the relationship between d and h for various values of h, a graph of the equation has been drawn and is shown in Fig. 4.6.

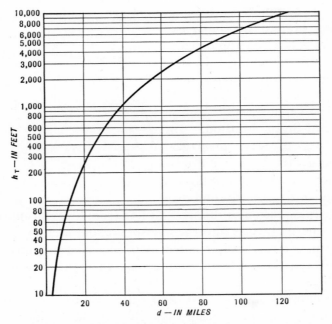

FIG. 4.6. The relationship between the height of the transmitting antenna (in feet) and the distance in miles from the antenna that the ray may be received.

It is assumed in the foregoing that the receiving point is at ground level, and the result indicates the distance from the transmitting antenna to the horizon. However, if the receiving antenna is not at ground level but is raised into the air, it should be evident that the direct-line distance between the two antennas can be made greater before the curvature of the earth again interferes with the direct line. (See Fig. 4.7.) By means of simple geometrical reasoning, the maximum distance between the two antennas is now increased to

$$d = 1.23 \left(\sqrt{h_t} + \sqrt{h_r} \right)$$

where d is the distance between antennas in miles, h_t is the transmitting antenna height in feet, and h_r is the receiving antenna height in feet. Because raising the antenna height increases the direct-line distance, transmitting antennas for F-M and television stations are

Fig. 4.7. Increasing the line-of-sight distance from the receiving antenna to the transmitter by raising both structures as high as possible.

placed atop tall buildings or on high plateaus. There may be other obstacles in the path of the direct rays which would result in absorption of the signal energy and hence tend to weaken or distort the received sound or picture. These obstacles assume great importance for television stations where the interfering influences may result in distorted images on the cathode-ray tube screen.

The signal developed at the receiving antenna is due not only to the direct ray but, in addition, to a ground reflected ray. In Fig. 4.8, the waves reaching the receiving antenna may do so by one of two paths: by going directly to the receiving antenna; or by arriving there after reflection from the surface of the earth. Whether or not a good clear signal will be received depends upon the phase relationship of the combining signals. To illustrate this point further, note what happens to the reflected wave. At the point where the reflected ray impinges on the earth, a phase reversal of 180° and, in addition, an absorption of energy in an amount dependent upon the conductivity of the earth at this point have been found to take place. The phase shift produces a wave at the receiving antenna which acts in a manner opposite to the direct ray, lowering its signal level. Fortunately, two conditions act against this decrease by the reflected ray. One is a weakening of the wave due to absorption at the point where the wave grazed the earth; the other results from an additional phase change (not the 180° just mentioned) arising from the fact that the length of the path of the reflected ray is longer than that of the direct ray. Thus, there is a total phase shift of 180° plus whatever else may have been added because of the longer path. As a result of these factors, the strength of the direct signal is not decreased as much by the reflected wave as one would at first expect. It has been found that the received signal strength increases with height of both antennas. At the same time, a decrease in noise pick-up occurs. For F-M and television signals this decrease is most important. By raising both antennas, we can increase the differ-

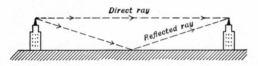

FIG. 4.8. The reflected radio wave, arriving at the receiving antenna after reflection from the earth, may lower the strength of the direct ray considerably.

ence between the lengths of the paths that the direct and earth reflected rays travel and thus bring their phase difference closer to 360°. When a phase difference of 360° occurs between the signals, they add, producing a field strength which is approximately twice that obtainable from the direct wave alone. In general, the higher the antenna, the stronger the signal received.

The combination of a direct wave and an earth reflected ray is sometimes referred to in the literature as a space wave. It is not important in A-M broadcasting because the relatively long wave lengths used make the difference in paths between the two rays negligible. The waves are then very nearly 180° out of phase because of the phase reversal in the earth reflected ray, and they effectively cancel each other completely. Hence, only the surface wave is important. However, as the signal frequency increases, and the wave length decreases, path differences between the direct and earth reflected ray become more significant.   At the same time, the effect of the surface wave diminishes.

Vertical Versus Horizontal Antennas.   The relative merits of vertical versus horizontal polarization have been intensively studied, and it has been found that for antennas located close to the earth the vertically polarized rays yield a stronger signal.   Upon raising the receiving antennas about one wave length above the ground, both types of polarization are equally good.   Further increase up to several wave lengths has shown that the horizontally polarized waves find a more favorable signal-to-noise ratio and are therefore to be desired.   Hence all F-M transmissions are done with horizontally polarized waves.

If signals were received only in accordance with the foregoing formulas and reasoning, the study of ultra-high frequency propagation would have ended there.   But signals were consistently received at points beyond the horizon, some in great quantity and evidently not due to any unusual phenomena.   Further investigation was indicated.   Finally the reasons for these added field strengths were laid to two definite causes: refraction in the lower atmospheric regions and diffraction by the surface of the earth at the horizon.

These two effects tend to increase the range of an F-M signal for some distance beyond the horizon.   A good approximation of the actual distance covered is to modify the line-of-sight equations by a factor of 1.41 instead of 1.23.   Thus the previous equation of

$$d = 1.23 \sqrt{h} \quad \text{and} \quad d = 1.23(\sqrt{h_t} + \sqrt{h_r})$$

become

$$d = 1.41 \sqrt{h} \quad \text{and} \quad d = 1.41(\sqrt{h_t} + \sqrt{h_r})$$

With this understanding of the behavior of high frequency waves in the F-M band, we are in a position to appreciate better the reasons for the choice of receiving and transmitting systems.

Receiving Antennas.   The primary purpose of an F-M receiving antenna is to develop as much voltage as possible of the desired signal.   Now, the amount of voltage which the passing field induces in an antenna wire depends essentially upon two factors: (1) the manner in which the wire is held; and (2) the length of the wire.

Technically, (1) is referred to as the polarization of the wire and (2) as its resonant frequency. The first factor, polarization, has already been considered, and it was seen that both receiving and transmitting wires should have similar polarization. In F-M reception, this means horizontal polarization.

The second factor that governs the amplitude of the induced voltage is the resonant length of the receiving antenna. Every length of wire contains resistance, inductance, and capacitance. The longer the wire, the greater the inductance. The capacitance of an antenna is the capacitance formed between the various sections of the wire itself. (See Fig. 4.9.)

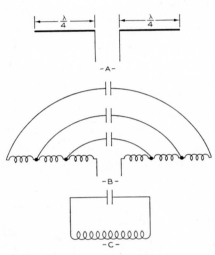

FIG. 4.9. (A) A half-wave dipole antenna. (B) The actual inductance and capacitance in the antenna wires. (C) The equivalent conventional L-C-circuit.

The resonant frequency of the antenna depends upon its inductance and capacitance just as it does in any conventional tank circuit. Since inductance (which predominates) increases with antenna length, increasing the length of the antenna decreases its resonant frequency. By the same token decreasing the antenna length increases its frequency. If the wave length of the received wave is known, it becomes a simple matter to compute the required length of the line. Thus, an antenna is similar to a resonant tank circuit, and its resonant frequency will vary with its length.

Tuned circuits are more sensitive to signals at their resonant frequency than at any other frequency. Hence, antennas designed for F-M are cut to specific lengths. The extent of the F-M band is 20 mc, and the antenna should be capable of receiving all frequencies within this band with equal response. However, whether a single frequency is to be received or a band of frequencies, a tuned antenna still provides the best results. In the case of a band of frequencies a compromise frequency is chosen generally at the center of the band and the antenna made resonant to it.

Wave Length. The distance covered by 360° of an electromagnetic wave is called one wave length and this is designated by

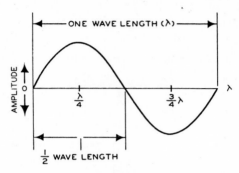

FIG. 4.10. The wave length of an electromagnetic wave.

the symbol λ(lambda). (See Fig. 4.10.) A wave length is equal to the velocity of travel of the wave divided by its frequency. Thus,

$$\lambda = \frac{V}{f}$$

where λ = the wave length in feet
  V = the velocity in feet per second
  f = the frequency of the wave in cycles per second

We can use 984,000,000 feet per second for the quantity V because the velocity of the electromagnetic wave is the same as light. Hence the foregoing formula becomes

$$\lambda = \frac{984,000,000}{f}$$

The use of the formula is illustrated by the following example:

EXAMPLE: What is the wave length of a 90-mc wave?
Answer:

$$\lambda = \frac{984,000,000}{90,000,000}$$

$$\lambda = 10.9 \text{ feet}$$

Half-wave Antennas. An ungrounded wire, cut to one-half the wave length of the signal to be received, represents the smallest length of wire that can be made to resonate at that frequency. The half-wave length antenna is most widely used because it is small, compact, and usually provides the receiver with sufficient signal. In troublesome areas it may be necessary to erect more elaborate

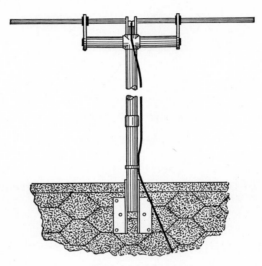

FIG. 4.11. Dipole antenna assembly used extensively for television receivers.

arrays possessing greater gain and directivity than the simple half-wave antenna. They are, however, more costly and more difficult to install.

A simple half-wave antenna is erected and supported as indicated in Fig. 4.11. Metallic rods are used for the antenna itself, mounted on the supporting structure and placed in a horizontal position (parallel to the ground). Each of the rods is one-quarter of a wave length long, both together being equal to the necessary half wave length. In this arrangement, also known as a dipole antenna, the transmission lead-in wire is connected to the rods, one wire of the line to each rod. The line then extends to the receiver. Care must be taken to tape the line at several points to the supporting mast so that it does not interfere with the operation of the antenna. Taping also prevents the line from flapping back and forth in the wind. Any such motion could weaken the connections made at the rods.

When the properties of a dipole antenna are investigated, it is found that signals are received with greatest intensity when the rods are at right angles to the direction of the signal. This is

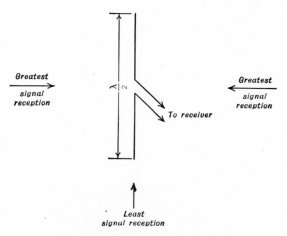

FIG. 4.12A. Dipole antenna, of the type shown, receives signals best from the directions indicated.

illustrated in Fig. 4.12A. However, signals approaching the antenna from either end are very poorly received. To show how waves at any angle are received, the graph of Fig. 4.12B is commonly drawn. It is an overall response curve for a dipole antenna.

From the diagram, with the placement of the antenna as shown, the strongest signal would be received from direction A. As the angle made with this point is increased, the strength of the signal voltage decreases, until at point B (90°) the received signal voltage is at a minimum (or zero). The reader can determine the reception for waves coming in at other angles by inspection of the graph. Notice that good signal strength is obtained from two directions and, because of this, the dipole response may be called bi-directional. Other systems can be devised that are uni-directional, non-directional, or having almost any desired properties. For each system, a response curve would quickly indicate its properties in any direction.

As stated, an antenna must be tuned in order to have the strongest signal develop along its length. Hence it becomes necessary to cut the wire (or rods) to a specific length. The length will vary with each different frequency, longer at the lower frequencies, and shorter at the higher frequencies. It might be supposed, then, that

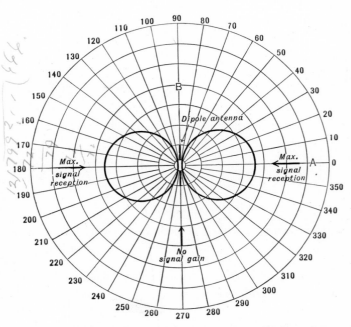

FIG. 4.12B. The directional response curve of a dipole antenna.

an F-M set, capable of receiving signals with frequencies ranging from 88 to 108 mc, would need several antennas. It is not necessary, however, to go to such extremes and, in nearly all instances, one antenna is sufficient, if tuned to a middle frequency.

Antenna Length Computations. With the F-M range of frequencies, a middle value of 98 mc might be chosen. Although an antenna cut to this frequency would not give optimum results at the extreme ends of the band, the reception would still be satisfactory.

To compute the length needed for the 98-mc frequency half-wave antenna, the following formula is used:

$$L_{feet} = \frac{468}{f_{mc}}$$

With f set equal to 98 mc, the length would be equal to 468/98, or 4.7 feet. Practically, 5 feet might be cut, with each half of the half-wave antenna 2.5 feet long. For a full-wave length antenna, approximately 10 feet is needed. In congested areas, antenna length must be as short as possible, and only half-wave antenna systems are generally found. If longer lengths are desired, the

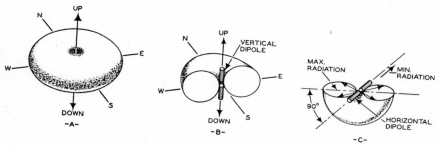

FIG. 4.13. (A) The doughnut-shaped pattern of a vertically placed dipole. (B) A cross section of the doughnut pattern. (C) A cross section when the antenna is horizontal.

equation should be modified by the proper factor. A full-wave length antenna requires a factor of 2; a wave length and a half requires a factor of 3, etc.

A little thought will show that a half-wave dipole, no matter in what position it is placed, will always radiate a maximum amount of energy at right angles to the wire axis. When the wire is held vertically, right angles to the wire is the horizontal plane and since this plane exists at all points around the wire, the radiation pattern is non-directional. However, when the wire is laid on its side or held horizontally, there are only two points in the horizontal plane that are at right angles to the wire. All other points in the horizontal plane make an angle of less than 90° with the wire, and the energy radiated in that direction varies accordingly.

If we were to illustrate the complete radiation pattern of a half-wave antenna in all directions, the radiation pattern would possess a doughnut shape.   (See Fig. 4.13.)

Connection to a half-wave dipole is made at its center terminals. The two conductors at one end of a transmission line connect here,

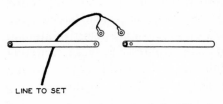

LINE TO SET

FIG. 4.14. How the transmission line is connected to the dipole antenna.

as shown in Fig. 4.14, while the other end of the transmission line is connected to the input terminals of the receiver.   The impedance which is present across the two antenna terminals is 72 ohms and, for maximum transfer of energy from the antenna to the transmission line, the impedance of the line should also be 72 ohms.   (The various types of transmission lines suitable for this purpose will be

FIG. 4.15.   The " V " antenna.

indicated presently.   At that time, the significance of impedance matching will also be covered.)

A variation of the dipole is the " V " antenna shown in Fig. 4.15.

Actually, this antenna is simply a half-wave dipole whose two arms are bent at an angle to each other. F-M transmitters emit horizontally polarized waves. However, near the receiving antenna, because of reflections from tall trees, buildings, and other obstructions, there may be a vertical component which, when combined with the horizontal component, will alter the angle of polarization above the horizontal plane. Under these conditions, dipole antennas possessing the shape shown will receive the signals better than an antenna whose elements are perfectly horizontal. In the " V " antenna, the angle between the elements is adjustable over a wide range.

In strong signal areas, where roof antennas are either prohibited or impractical, an under-the-rug antenna of the type shown in Fig. 4.16 may prove useful. The antenna is stretched out on the floor and its transmission line attached to the receiver. The unit is then moved about until a good clear signal is obtained. At this point, the antenna is placed underneath the floor rug.

Half-wave Dipole with Reflector. The simple half-wave system provides satisfactory reception in most locations within reasonable distances of the transmitter. However, the signals

FIG. 4.16. An " under-the-rug " antenna.

reaching receivers situated in outlying areas are correspondingly weaker, and noise and interference have a greater distorting effect on the sound. For these locations more elaborate arrays must be constructed — systems that can develop more voltage and provide better discrimination against interference.

A simple yet effective antenna is shown in Fig. 4.17. The two rods are mounted parallel to each other, cut to the dimensions indicated by the formula, and spaced as shown. The action of the second rod (the reflector), which is not connected to anything, is twofold. First, because of its position, it tends to concentrate signals reaching the front wire. Second, it acts to shield the front rod from waves coming from the rear. The signal voltage developed by this antenna is generally 5 db greater than that obtainable from a single half-wave antenna.

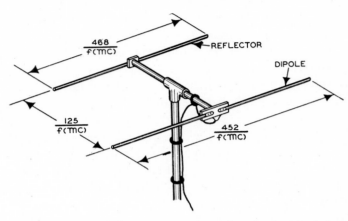

Fig. 4.17. A half-wave dipole and reflector. The length of each element and the spacing between them is given also.

The response curve of a half-wave dipole and reflector is shown in Fig. 4.18. While not all of the signals reaching the antenna from the rear are suppressed, they are diminished sufficiently to render the response of the array essentially uni-directional. This is advantageous in reducing the number of reflected rays that can affect the antenna. Finally, partial or complete discrimination is possible against interference, man-made or otherwise.

The method of erecting the antenna is similar to that of the half-wave dipole, although the adjustment of the position of the wires is more critical. A small displacement, one way or another, may alter the strength of the received signal appreciably. Many commercial antenna kits do not provide adjustment of the spacing distance between the two wires. However, if an adjustment is possible the spacing may be changed if experimentation indicates that it would result in better reception.

Gain. The gain of an array is a comparison of the signal power which this array would develop across its input terminals to the power which a standard or reference antenna would produce if placed at the same point in space as the directional array. The standard or reference antenna frequently chosen is the half-wave dipole.

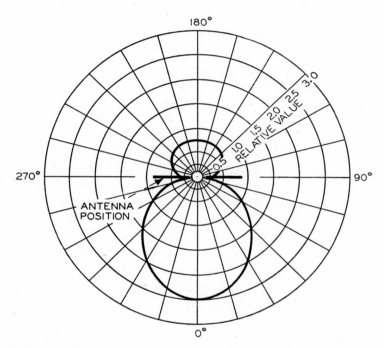

FIG. 4.18. The response characteristic of a dipole antenna with reflector. The reflector, not shown, would be placed behind the dipole, facing 180°.

Thus, when a certain array is said to possess a gain of 10, it means that this array will develop 10 times as much signal power as a half-wave dipole if it were positioned at the same point in space.

Often, the decibel is used as the unit of gain. In this case, since power is being employed, the formula is:

$$db = 10 \log_{10} \frac{P_1}{P_2}$$

A ratio of P_1 and P_2 of 100 would give the equivalent decibel rating of 20. This follows from that fact that the $\log_{10} 100 = 2$, and 2×10 equals 20 db.

Directivity. When speaking of the directivity of a directional antenna, we mean the sharpness with which the signal is confined or directed to a particular direction. It may, in a sense, be compared with the selectivity of a receiver in allowing one signal to pass through and rejecting all others. The more selective the set, the sharper and more peaked its tuning curve. In radio sets, sharp selectivity can usually be attained only when several tuning circuits are used in conjunction with each other. One coil and condenser combination, by itself, would not be adequate. It is much the same with antennas. Ordinarily several radiators must be used before a highly directive pattern is obtained. Just one or two elements, by themselves, might show definite directive effects, but these would not be as clear-cut as those obtained when a greater number of antennas are used. Again if a system of wires possesses a marked directional pattern for sending, the same antenna will show similar directivity when receiving.

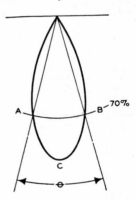

FIG. 4.19. The beam angle θ of an antenna is the angle between two points on its response curve at which the signal voltage is 70.7% of its maximum value.

When speaking of antenna directivity, the term "beam angle" is often employed. Beam angle is the angle between the two points on the radiation curve at which the signal voltage is 0.707 (or 70.7%) of its maximum value. In Fig. 4.19, the angle between points *A-B,* or the angle θ, is the beam angle for this radiation pattern. At each of these points (*A* and *B*), the signal strength is 0.707 of its value at point *C.*

Points *A* and *B* are also known as the half-power points because the radiated power here is one-half of its value at point *C.* This is an equivalent expression because power is proportional to the square of the voltage and $(0.707)^2$ is approximately equal to 0.5.

Other Receiving Antennas. The two antenna systems described are the most widely used. Other types are found, however, and the more popular of these are shown in Fig. 4.20.

1. *Folded Dipole,* Fig. 4.20A. This consists of two dipole antennas connected in parallel, each dipole being a half wave length

long. The separation between the two sections is approximately 3 inches. The folded dipole has the same bi-directional pattern as the simple dipole. Its gain, however, is somewhat greater.

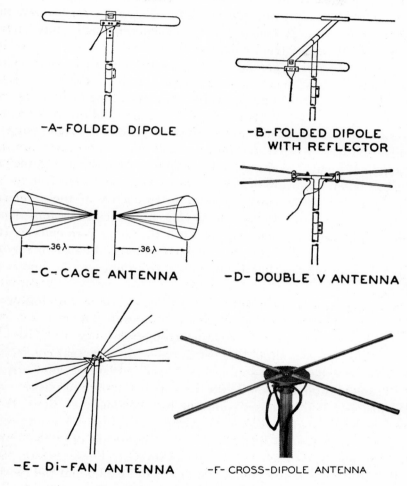

-A- FOLDED DIPOLE

-B-FOLDED DIPOLE WITH REFLECTOR

-C- CAGE ANTENNA

-D- DOUBLE V ANTENNA

-E- Di-FAN ANTENNA

-F- CROSS-DIPOLE ANTENNA

FIG. 4.20. Other popular F-M antennas.

2. *Folded Dipole with Reflector,* Fig. 4.20B. The addition of a reflector has the same effect here as with the simple dipole. Reflector spacing and length are identical with the figures previously given for the simple dipole with reflector.

3. *Cage Antenna,* Fig. 4.20C. A bi-direction characteristic with greater gain than a simple dipole. Actually, what we have here are 12 dipoles. The length of each wire, from the center to one end, is 0.36λ at the frequency for which this system is designed.

4. *Double-V Antenna,* Fig. 4.20D. There are 4 rods or wires in this antenna, each one-quarter wave length long. Signals can be received from the front and rear of this array.

5. *The Di-Fan Antenna,* Fig. 4.20E. Contains 10 wires or rods, 5 to each section of the array. Excellent broad band response. Each wire is one-quarter wave length long.

6. *The Cross-dipole Antenna,* Fig. 4.20F. All of the antennas described thus far were more or less directional. When signals come from widely separated directions, it may be desirable to have a non-directional antenna. One such unit is shown in Fig. 4.20F and consists of two dipoles set at right angles to each other. A quarter-wave section (at the operating frequency of the antenna) of a twin-lead transmission line having a characteristic impedance of 72 ohms is then connected between the input terminals of the two dipoles. To transfer the signal from the dipoles to the receiver, a transmission line is connected from one of the dipoles to the set.

After the particular antenna has been chosen, the following points should be kept in mind before installing the antenna.

1. The higher the antenna, the stronger the signal received.

2. The antenna should be set-tested with an actual connection to its receiver before the supports are fixed in place permanently.

Transmission Lines. With the antenna system in position the next problem is the transmission line that conducts the signal from the antenna to the receiver. Although many differently constructed transmission lines have been designed, only five types find any extensive use in F-M installations. These are the two parallel-wire types, the concentric or coaxial cable, and the twisted pair.

Probably the most popular transmission line is the parallel-wire transmission line shown in Fig. 4.21A. It is popular because its cost is relatively low, it is easy to work with, and it possesses a low attenuation. Physically, the two wires of this transmission line are encased in a polyethylene strip which serves to hold the wires in place and act as a protective covering. It has excellent electrical and physical characteristics, being a flexible material that is not affected by sunlight, water, cold, or alkalies. At 50 mc, the line loss is less than 0.8 db per hundred feet of line. Its characteristic impedance ranges from 75 to 300 ohms and will match a folded dipole antenna. The line is balanced, which means that both wires possess the same average potential with respect to ground. It is, however, unshielded and therefore not recommended for use in extremely noisy locations.

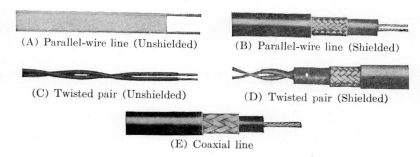

(A) Parallel-wire line (Unshielded)   (B) Parallel-wire line (Shielded)

(C) Twisted pair (Unshielded)   (D) Twisted pair (Shielded)

(E) Coaxial line

FIG. 4.21.   Various types of popular transmission lines used for F-M and television installation.

A parallel-wire transmission line that is completely shielded is shown in Fig. 4.21B. The two wires are enclosed in a dielectric, possibly polyethylene, and then the entire unit is shielded by a copper braid covering. As a protection from the elements, an outer rubber covering is used. Grounding the copper braid converts it into a shield which prevents any stray interference from reaching either conductor. Furthermore, the line is balanced against ground. It is built with impedance values ranging from 95 to 300 ohms. The line loss is greater than the unshielded parallel pair, being on the order of 2.5 db per hundred feet at 50 mc.

The twisted pair of transmission line, Fig. 4.21C, is made by twisting wires about each other in the same manner as twisted lamp cord. It is an economical line, but it has the greatest loss and becomes impractical for lengths beyond 50 feet. The characteristic impedance ranges from 50 to 150 ohms and, at 50 mc, the db loss is 4 for each hundred feet of line.   Unless this line is specially constructed, it will deteriorate in time under the ravages of the atmosphere.   A shielded twisted pair line is shown in Fig. 4.21D.   This line has more desirable characteristics than the unshielded twisted pair, but its cost is greater.

The transmission line shown in Fig. 4.21E is the coaxial or concentric cable.   It consists of insulated center wire enclosed by a concentric metallic covering, which is, generally, flexible copper braid.   The inner wire is held in position by a solid dielectric, which is chosen for its low-loss properties.   The signal carried by the line

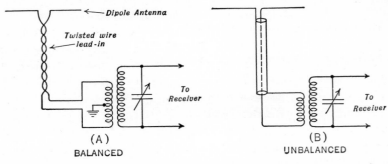

FIG. 4.22.   Methods of connecting lead-in wires to the input coil of a receiver.

is confined to the inner conductor, with the outer copper-braid conductor grounded so as to serve as a shield against stray magnetic fields.   Because of this arrangement, the line is unbalanced and the input coil of the receiver must be connected accordingly.   Coaxial cables are available in a range of impedances from 10 to 150 ohms.

At the receiver, the connections for balanced and unbalanced line differ, as shown in Fig. 4.22.   For a balanced line, the input coil is center-tapped and grounded at this tap.   Stray fields, cutting across both wires of a balanced line, induce equal voltages in each line.   The similar currents that flow because of the induced voltages are in the same direction on the two conductors of the line and they neutralize each other.   In the unbalanced line, the outer conductor of the coaxial cable is grounded, thereby shielding the inner conductor from interference.

Impedance Matching. At two points in the antenna system, connections must be made to the transmission line. One point is at the antenna, and the other is at the receiver input. For the maximum transfer of power, the antenna impedance should match the transmission line impedance, and a similar matching of impedances should occur at the receiver input.

Now, the input impedances of most F-M receivers is about 300 ohms. To match this, a 300-ohm parallel-wire previously discussed would serve nicely. At the antenna, a match to the 300-ohm line could be made by using a folded-dipole antenna. Thus there is a matching of impedances at all connecting points in the antenna system, providing assurance of a maximum transfer of power.

Now, although this situation is fairly common, it does not represent every type of installation that will be encountered. Suppose that, in the preceding example, the antenna is a dipole with an input impedance of 72 ohms. What would be the effect of connecting the 300-ohm line directly to the antenna? The answer to this question will depend upon the strength of the signals present in this particular area. If the signal intensity is of the order of 100 microvolts or more, then it is doubtful if the mismatch will have any noticeable effect upon the receiver output. True, a certain amount of the signal will be lost, but there is sufficient signal available so that the loss will not be noticed by the set listener.

However, if the signal level is appreciably below 100 microvolts it may readily happen that insufficient signal voltage will reach the set because of this mismatch. In this instance, use of a matching section between transmission line and antenna is highly desirable.

One method of achieving such a match is through the use of a " Q " section. A section of transmission line, electrically one-quarter wave length long, is inserted between the transmission line and the antenna. (See Fig. 4.23A.) The line is then connected to one end of this quarter-wave section, and the antenna is connected to the opposite end. In order to match the antenna to the line, the characteristic impedance of the " Q " section must be the geometric mean between the characteristic impedances of the antenna and the transmission line.   It can be found by the formula:

$$Z_0 = \sqrt{Z_a \times Z_t}$$

where Z_a = impedance of the antenna

Z_t = impedance of the transmission line

Z_0 = impedance of the matching section

To illustrate the use of this formula, let us apply it to the problem on hand, namely, that of matching a 72-ohm antenna to the 300-ohm line.   In this case,

$$Z_a = 72 \text{ ohms}$$

$$Z_t = 300 \text{ ohms}$$

$$Z_0 = ? \text{ (to be found)}$$

$$Z_0 = \sqrt{21,600} = 147 \text{ ohms}$$

147 ohms is an awkward value for a transmission line, but 150 ohms will do as well.   Therefore, procure a 150-ohm parallel wire trans-

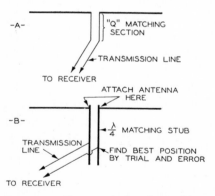

-A- "Q" MATCHING SECTION

TRANSMISSION LINE

TO RECEIVER

ATTACH ANTENNA HERE

-B-

$\frac{\lambda}{4}$ MATCHING STUB

TRANSMISSION LINE

FIND BEST POSITION BY TRIAL AND ERROR

TO RECEIVER

Fig. 4.23. Two methods of matching antennas to transmission lines.

mission line, cut it to a quarter wave length at the frequency used to design the antenna, and connect it between the line and the antenna, as shown in Fig. 4.23A.

Another solution is to use a quarter-wave matching stub.   The stub consists of two rods or wires, their length being equal to a quarter wave length at the frequency used to design the antenna. In any such quarter-wave section, the impedance varies from a low of 60 to 70-ohms at one end to several thousand ohms at the other end.   Clip the antenna terminals to one end of each cord (or wire) of the quarter-wave section, and then experimentally shift the ends of the transmission line back and forth along each rod (or wire) until maximum signal is reported at the receiver.   Since the quarter-wave matching sections have a continuously varying impedance between 70 ohms to several thousand ohms, a point will be found where the impedance of the transmission line is matched. Fig. 4.23B illustrates the arrangement of the several components. Note that with this method any type of two-wire line may be used for the matching stub. Its characteristic impedance can be of any value.

When the receiver is situated in a vicinity where the signal level is high (close to the transmitting station), the simple and economical lead-in antenna of Fig. 4.24 can be used. The twin-lead transmission line is slit down the center and suspended from two insulators to form a dipole antenna. A ring clamp is used to prevent the transmission line from tearing farther.

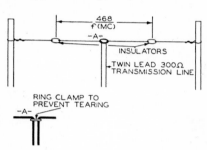

To summarize:

1. The input system should be matched at each point, i.e., the antenna to the transmission line and the line to the receiver.

FIG. 4.24. A simple antenna constructed from a twin-lead transmission line. This can be successfully used in areas of high signal intensity.

2. For strong input signals, mismatching as much as 5 to 1 is permissible.

3. For nominal strength signals, a 2 to 1 mismatch is tolerable.

4. If a choice exists as to which point in the input system is to be mismatched, it is preferable that this occur at the antenna rather than at the receiver.

In noisy locations, where the transmission line must pass through areas where the noise generated by man-made machines is high, the use of a shielded lead-in is recommended. There is available shielded twin-lead transmission lines ranging in characteristic impedance values from 95 to 300 ohms. When these are used, care should be taken to see that the metallic braid which is wound around the outside of the line, and which acts as the shield, is carefully grounded at several points along its path from the antenna to the receiver. It is also important that this shield be grounded at each end. Failure to observe these precautions will reduce the effectiveness of the shield and permit external voltages to reach the inner line.

Where the noise is only of mild intensity, its effects may be minimized if the 300-ohm unshielded line is twisted about every two feet on its way to the receiver. The purpose of this is to cause noise voltages to appear in equal strength in both conductors of the line. Since the currents developed by the noise voltages will flow in the same direction along both wires, cancellation at the receiver input will occur. (See Fig. 4.25.) Note that this will be true only when the receiver contains a balanced input, for then the two noise currents, made to flow through each half of the input in opposite directions, will effectively cancel each other. How well this cancellation is achieved will depend upon how well the input of the receiver is balanced.

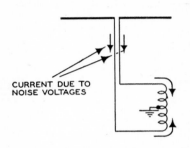

CURRENT DUE TO NOISE VOLTAGES

FIG. 4.25. With a parallel-wire transmission line, a balanced input coil is more effective in reducing the effect of noise voltages than an unbalanced coil.

There are some F-M receivers which have an unbalanced input. For these sets the input impedance is generally 75 ohms, and a 72-ohm coaxial line is recommended. At the antenna, direct connection of the inner lead of the coaxial line to one rod, and the outer shield to the other antenna rod, will provide satisfactory results if the signal level is high. Note, however, that only half the antenna is being utilized: that section which is connected to the inner coaxial cable. The other half of the antenna is grounded out by its connection to the outer conductor of the cable, which itself is grounded.

When this system is to be used in a weak signal area, better results can be obtained by a converter at the antenna which will provide a match between the unbalanced 72-ohm coaxial cable, on the one hand, and the balanced impedance of the antenna, on the other. Such units are available at most of the large radio supply houses and consist of properly wound transformers.

Antenna Installation. Once the type of antenna has been decided upon and the best position for it has been determined, the next step is the actual erection of the antenna structure itself. The structure supporting the antenna should meet the following requirements.

1. It should be easily installed. One man should be able to do the job.

2. It should be inexpensive.

3. It should be easily adjusted.

4. It should be strong enough to withstand heavy winds and support the antenna structure.

5. It should not interfere with the antenna radiation pattern.

6. It should not mar the appearance of the building upon which it is placed.

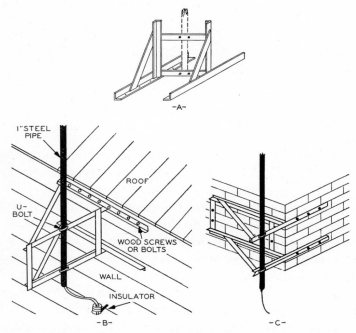

Fig. 4.26. (A) A universal mounting bracket and several ways in which it may be mounted.

Supporting Brackets. There are various types of supporting brackets on the market, a few of the more common ones being shown in Fig. 4.26 and 4.27. In Fig. 4.26A is a universal support-ing bracket which can be mounted in a variety of positions. It can be mounted flat on the roof, attached to the side of a building (Fig. 4.26B), or used as a corner mounting (Fig. 4.26C). Other types of brackets are shown in Fig. 4.27. In Fig. 4.27A is a vertical wall bracket, usually made of heavy gauge galvanized steel. In Fig. 4.27B is a vent-pipe bracket, designed to fit snugly around vent pipes. In Fig. 4.27C, there is an adjustable, all-angle bracket, adaptable with index positions from horizontal to the vertical plane. With this type of bracket, the antenna may be

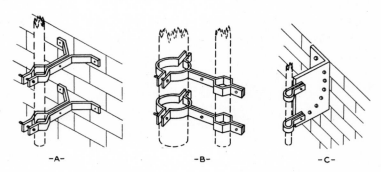

FIG. 4.27. Several other types of mounting brackets. (A) Vertical wall bracket. (B) Vent pipe bracket. (C) An adjustable, all-angle bracket.

set at the most suitable angle for maximum reception. Chimney brackets, Fig. 4.28, have been widely used because of the ease with which they are installed.

For slant roofs, the bracket shown in Fig. 4.29 is often used. The angle which the bracket makes with the antenna pipe can be set to almost any point, permitting its use on all types of slant roofs. Where necessary, guy wires can be used to steady the antenna structure itself.

Window mounting of antennas may be necessary where roof installations are prohibited or the set is located in a high building and the length of transmission line needed to bring a signal to the set from a roof antenna would be several hundred feet long. Several suggested window mounting methods are shown in Fig. 4.30.

The transmission line lead-in from the antenna should not be permitted to hang loosely so that it flaps in the wind since it will, in short time, break its connection to the antenna rods. To prevent any unwanted movement of the line, it should be securely taped to the antenna supporting rod. After it leaves the antenna, the

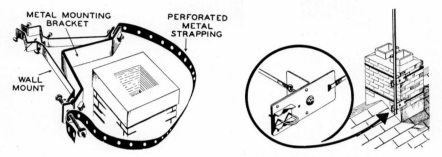

FIG. 4.28. Several chimney brackets.

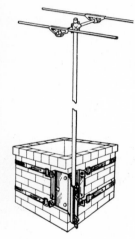

line should be supported every three or four feet by stand-off insulators. (See Fig. 4.31.)

A question that is generally asked concerns the use of lightning arrestors. Experience indicated that if the antenna is the highest point within a hundred feet of the installation, then a lightning arrestor should be installed. However, if there are taller objects in the immediate neighborhood, then the arrestor need not be used. When using these units, mount them as close as possible to the point where the transmission line enters the house. The grounding wire from the lightning arrestor should be connected to a metallic stake driven well into the earth. A poor ground connection renders the arrestor useless.

Guy Wires. When the mast is high or the array is heavy, guy wires may be required for support. The need for guy wires depends upon:

1. The weight of the array.
2. The wind-catching area of the array.
3. The height of the array.
4. Rigidity of the anchor.
5. Strength of the mast.

A simple dipole generally requires no guy wire supports.   For any mast over 10 feet high, guy wires should be used.   This is a good

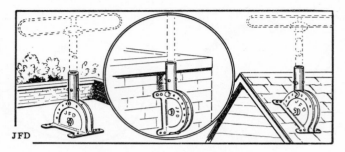

FIG. 4.29.   A bracket suitable for slant roofs.

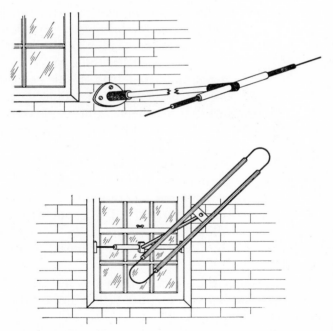

FIG. 4.30.   Two methods of mounting antennas near windows.

general rule to follow.   When the mast is less than 10 feet high, the serviceman will have to decide whether or not to use them. If a mast swings appreciably, with slight or nominal pressure, guy wires should be used. In fact, if there exists any doubt at all about the mechanical strength of the antenna, guy wires should be used. The guy wires are broken by insulators at various intervals

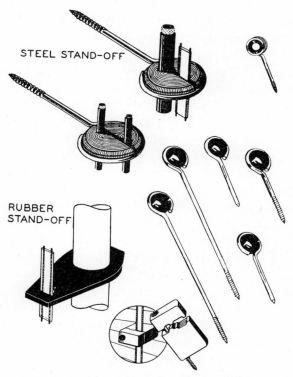

STEEL STAND-OFF

RUBBER STAND-OFF

FIG. 4.31. Various types of stand-off insulators.

to prevent them from becoming resonant and altering the response characteristics of the antenna.

F-M TRANSMITTING ANTENNAS

The design and shape of F-M transmitting antennas are governed (and, in the same sense, limited) by the following major considerations:

1. Horizontal polarization.
2. Location at center of service area.
3. Frequency allocations from 88 to 108 mc.

The F.C.C. established horizontal polarization as standard for all F-M broadcast signals, which requires, in general, that the radiating elements themselves be horizontally placed.

Antenna location at the center of the station service area is usually dictated by convenience, both with regard to studio placement and the relatively high expense of incorporating phasing networks to produce non-symmetrical radiational patterns. By placing the antenna at the center of its service area, a non-directional pattern is required.

Finally, there is the allocation of the F-M broadcasting services to the frequency band extending from 88 mc to 108 mc. As noted previously in the discussion of wave propagation, signals with frequencies extending above 35 mc are limited to the line-of-sight distance from the transmitting antenna to the horizon. This means that the extent of the area served by any one station depends upon the height of the antenna structure above the ground. The higher the antenna, the greater the area over which its signals can be received. Now, one of the simplest methods of achieving height is obtained by erecting the antenna atop a high building. To do this effectively, however, requires that the antenna structure be light in weight and fairly compact. Furthermore, precautions must be taken to prevent the antenna structure from becoming an obstruction to aircraft, from accumulating too much ice, from becoming targets for static discharges and lightning, and from buckling under the strain of high wind velocities.

While the height of the antenna determines the line-of-sight distance to the horizon, full use of that area is not possible unless sufficient power is radiated by the antenna. High frequency operation imposes certain limitations on the amount of power that can be economically generated in the transmitter. To overcome this limitation to some extent, it has become general practice to design antennas which can concentrate whatever power they are given only in the desired plane, thereby reducing to a minimum the amount of power which is radiated in undesired directions. In the latter category would fall any power which is radiated vertically upward, since energy transmitted in this direction does not, at the present F-M frequencies, return to earth. To achieve this concentration of energy in the horizontal plane requires the vertical mounting (or stacking) of a number of units.

In the following pages, commercial F-M antennas will be analyzed to determine how the foregoing specifications are attained. Fortunately, in the range from 88 to 108 mc, such designs can be achieved with structures of moderate dimensions.

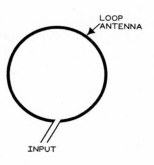

FIG. 4.32. A loop antenna.

The Cloverleaf Antenna. A very simple type of antenna which is capable of radiating a horizontally polarized wave to all points about the antenna in the horizontal plane is the loop antenna. (See Fig. 4.32.) The radiated field will be uniform if the current flowing around the loop is uniform, both in amplitude and phase. To achieve this uniformity, the length of the loop (around its circumference) should not be greater than ⅛ λ long. At the A-M standard broadcast frequencies this restriction can be observed quite readily, even when the loop contains more than one turn. To remain within this restriction at the F-M frequencies, however, requires that the loop diameter be extremely small, causing its input impedance to become quite low, and thereby making it difficult to feed power to the loop efficiently. Fortunately, the desirable radiation and polarization characteristics of the loop can be obtained without actually using a continuous loop. Instead,

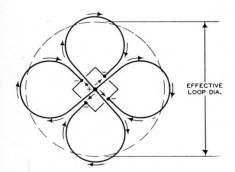

FIG. 4.33. Arrangement of four radiating elements constituting a radiating unit of the Cloverleaf antenna. Arrows indicate assumed instantaneous directions of current. (Courtesy I.R.E.)

it is possible to employ a group of radiators which, when electrically combined, present the same electrical equivalent circuit as a loop. One such construction is the Cloverleaf antenna, shown in Fig. 4.33.

The Cloverleaf antenna consists of four half-wave curved radiating elements. One end of each of the radiating elements is connected to a common central conductor of a coaxial line, while the other end of each of the four radiating elements is attached to a separate post of the tower structure which serves as the return conductor. With this arrangement, the currents coming up through the center conductor will, at point X, divide equally between the four radiating elements in the manner shown in Fig. 4.33. If we consider only outer portions of each curved radiator,

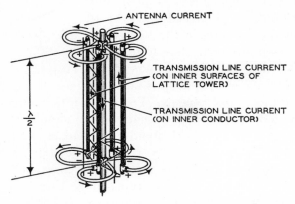

ANTENNA CURRENT

TRANSMISSION LINE CURRENT
(ON INNER SURFACES OF
LATTICE TOWER)

TRANSMISSION LINE CURRENT
(ON INNER CONDUCTOR)

$\dfrac{\lambda}{2}$

FIG. 4.34.   A section of a Cloverleaf antenna showing two sections.   Usually a commercial structure contains four or five sections.

we note that the current flows in the same direction in each one, producing effectively a circular flow of current. Points on each radiator which extend in toward the center of the Cloverleaf have currents flowing in them which are in opposition to the currents flowing in the adjacent radiator, with the result that the fields due to this portion of the antenna current flow cancel each other. Thus, only the currents flowing in phase at the outermost portions of each half-wave antenna are effective in developing the radiational pattern for this array.

To minimize the vertical radiation of the Cloverleaf, a series of four or five similar units are stacked one above the other, separated by distances of approximately one-half wave length. Two such units are shown in Fig. 4.34. Since there is a voltage phase reversal at half-wave intervals along a transmission line, the direction in which the individual radiating elements comprising each unit are curved is reversed.   In this way the current flowing in all units all along the array do so in the same direction, and the field radiated by all sections is everywhere in phase.

Direct connection of the ends of the radiating elements to the supporting structure simplifies the mechanical construction of the antenna.   Furthermore, this direct connection places the entire antenna assembly at d-c ground potential, affording protection against static discharges and light-ning.   To prevent ice from forming on the antenna, electrically operated heating elements are inserted into the grounded ends of the loops. The power connections are brought up through a conduit which is fas-tened to the tower structure.   The power gain of the Cloverleaf an-tenna is given by

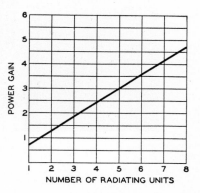

$$G = 0.565n + 0.18$$

where n = number of radiating sections of the antenna.   The fore-going equation is plotted in Fig. 4.35.

FIG. 4.35. A graph showing how the power gain of the Cloverleaf an-tenna increases with the number of radiating units.

The G. E. Circular F-M Antenna.   Another approach to a loop antenna is the General Electric circular antenna shown in Fig. 4.36.   This unit may, in a sense, be considered as a circular folded dipole.   In a folded dipole, shown in Fig. 4.37A, the cur-rent is maximum at the center, diminishing gradually to zero at the two ends of the dipole. (In contrast, the voltage is minimum at the center, increasing gradually toward the ends).   If, now, we place conducting plates at either end of the folded dipole, we accomplish two things.   First, the overall length of the dipole decreases due to the capacitive effect of the end plates.   Second, the current variation from the center of the folded dipole to either end is not as great as it is in the unloaded folded dipole.   (See Fig. 4.37B.)

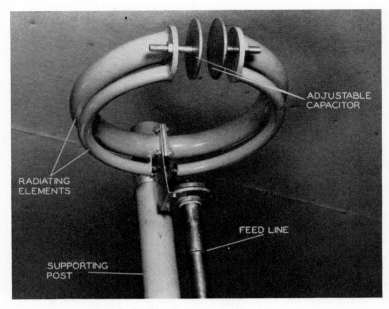

FIG. 4.36.   A close-up view of the General Electric circular F-M antenna.
(Courtesy G.E.)

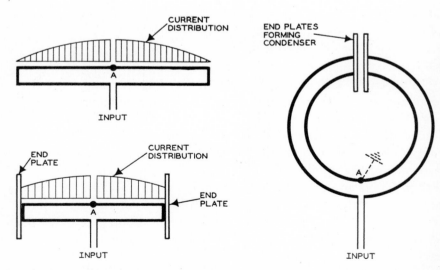

FIG. 4.37.   Development of the G.E. circular F-M antenna from a folded dipole.

Finally, by bending the dipole rods into circular form, a loop antenna is produced. The current distribution around the loop is now fairly uniform, producing a uniform field at all points around the antenna.

By adjusting the separation between the two end plates, which form a condenser, the resonant frequency of the antenna can be varied over the frequency range for which the unit is designed. This can be done without any change in the main physical structure of the antenna loop.

Since the voltage at the center of the folded dipole (*point A* of Fig. 4.37B) is very low, connection of a ground here will not noticeably affect the operation of the unit. Such connection is made in actual installations, with point *A* attached directly to the supporting pole. A transmission line then brings the transmitter power to the input terminals.

To minimize vertical radiation from the array, four to six circular antennas are stacked vertically.

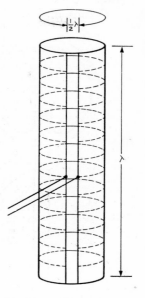

FIG. 4.38. The Pylon antenna may be considered as being made up of a large number of circular elements, each of which radiates.

The Pylon Antenna. The Pylon or slotted tubular antenna also bases its operation on the loop. In appearance this antenna is a cylinder, each section of which is approximately 13 feet high and 19 inches in diameter with a narrow slot cut from top to bottom. The cylinder is fed by a single transmission line running up the inside of the cylinder to the midpoint of the slot.

To understand the operation of the Pylon, consider it to be composed of a large number of circular elements, each of which functions as a loop antenna. (See Fig. 4.38.) When power is fed to the slot, it functions as an open wire transmission line, establishing a voltage distribution along the length of the slot as shown in Fig. 4.39, and causing currents to flow around the surface of the cylinder. Since these circumferential currents are very nearly in phase throughout the length of the cylinder, a field is radiated which is very nearly the same at all points in the horizontal plane. (See Fig. 4.40.)

Pylons may be stacked in one, two, four, or eight sections, the gain increasing with the number of sections. Furthermore, as the number of sections increase, the power radiated in the vertical direction decreases. It is important that each Pylon section is fed in phase, and this is accomplished by using suitable lengths of transmission lines.

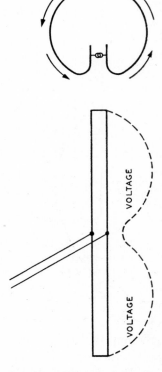

Mechanically the pylon cylinder is rolled from a single sheet of metal. It is capped on each end with a cast base to give the unit greater mechanical stability.

The Square-Loop Antenna. The circular radiation pattern of the loop can be obtained even when the shape of the loop is not circular or the cross section of the radiator is not round. In fact, the loop elements can be square, rectangular, or even triangular, without modifying the essential electrical behavior of the loop. Advantage of this was taken by the Federal Telephone & Radio Corporation to develop what they refer to as a square loop antenna. (See Fig. 4.41.)

Fig. 4.39. Power is fed to the slot which functions as a transmission line. Currents flow around the circular path as shown. (Courtesy R.C.A.)

To understand the electrical and physical construction of the square loop antenna, consider the two half-wave radiators, A-B, and C-D, in Fig. 4.42A. Each radiator is fed from a common point, E, and since the distance, E-A, is equal to the distance, E-C, the instantaneous voltage polarity at points A and C will always be the same. Hence, the currents flowing in A-B and C-D will, at any instant, be flowing in the same direction as indicated by the arrows, producing the equivalent of an in-phase current all around the circular path.

If the feeder line *AEC* is exposed, it, too, will radiate, tending to destroy the desired circular radiation pattern of the loop sections, *A-B* and *C-D*. To prevent this, the arrangement shown in Fig.

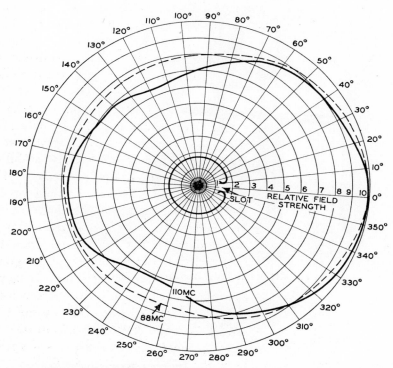

FIG. 4.40. The horizontal field pattern of the Pylon for frequencies at either end of the F-M band.

4.42B is employed. A coaxial transmission line is used for the feeder, and sections *A-B* and *C-D* are made rectangular in shape, with their center hollow. To feed section *A-B*, the inner conductor from point *E* goes to point *G*, where it enters at the center of section *C-D* and travels through the interior of this section until it reaches point *A*. At this point it makes electrical contact with section *A-B*.

To feed section *C-D,* another inner conductor extends from point *E* to point *H,* enters at the mid-point of section *A-B,* travels

FIG. 4.41.   The Federal square-loop antenna.

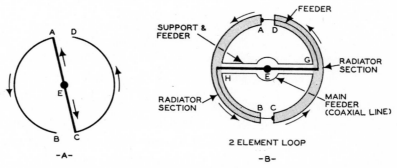

FIG. 4.42.   Two steps in the development of the square-loop antenna.

through the interior of *A-B* until point *C* is reached where electrical connection is made to section *C-D.* Thus, both feed lines from E are shielded until they actually reach the rectangular radiating sections, A-B and C-D.

The current distribution from end to end of each section (A-B or C-D) is maximum in the center, diminishing to a minimum at either end. By making the length of each section somewhat less

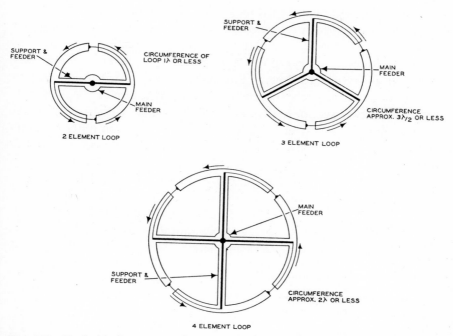

Fig. 4.43. Evolution from a two element to a four element loop. For ease in understanding, the loops are shown as circular, although in the Federal F-M antenna, the loop is rectangular.

than a half wave length and utilizing the end effect of each section, the difference between maximum and minimum current is only 12 per cent. This results in a radiation pattern which is very nearly circular.

While the current at the center of each section is a maximum, the voltage here is very low, and actually grounding this point to the supporting structure does not noticeably affect the operation of the antenna. The outer conductor of the feeder coaxial cable also connects to the radiating section at this mid-point, while the inner conductor extends into the center of the radiating section.

In the Federal F-M antenna, the number of sections is not two but four, permitting the circumference to be increased to approximately two wave lengths. The electrical transition from the two sections discussed above to four sections is shown in Fig. 4.43. As seen, the instantaneous current along the radiating members are always in the clockwise or counterclockwise direction.

To achieve a power gain, a number of square-loop units are mounted above each other. The gain varies with the number of square-loop units, each section increasing the power gain by 1.1. Thus, with two sections, the power gain is 2.2, with four sections the power gain is 4.4, etc. The separation between units is somewhat less than one wave length at the operating frequency of the antenna.

The Turnstile Antenna. An F-M antenna which has been widely used is the turnstile antenna shown in Fig. 4.44. Essentially this antenna consists of two half-wave dipole antennas, positioned at right angles to each other, and fed 90° out of phase. The radiation pattern from each dipole is the familiar figure-8 pattern. However, by positioning the two half-wave dipoles at right angles to each other and then feeding them as indicated, we obtain an overall pattern which is closely circular. Furthermore, the energy radiated by this system is horizontally polarized, which makes it suitable for F-M broadcasting. Finally, to minimize radiation in the vertical plane, a series of 3 to 5 turnstile units are mounted above each other, spaced by distances of approximately one-half wave length.

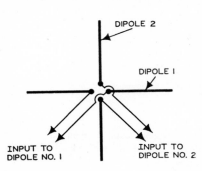

Fig. 4.44. The turnstile antenna. The input voltages to the two dipoles differ in phase from each other by 90°.

The turnstile, as originally designed, contained simple dipoles as the radiating elements. However, folded dipoles may be used as well and, in fact, have so been used. (See Fig. 4.45.) The folded dipole possesses a higher input impedance than the simple dipole and for this reason is more desirable from the standpoint of impedance matching and power transfer from the transmitter to the antenna system. Furthermore, the transmission line feeding system for the folded-dipole turnstile array can be designed so that the center of the folded dipole may be grounded to the supporting mast, affording protection against lightning and static discharges. The radiation pattern of a folded dipole is the same as that of a plain dipole.

The super-turnstile antenna represents a further improvement in turnstile antenna design. In place of the simple dipole arms, solid radiating sheets approximately one-half wave length high are used. (See Fig. 4.46A.) In actual construction, the solid sheets are replaced by an open framework as shown in Fig. 4.46A and 4.46C because it was found that essentially the same results could be obtained.

The operation of the super-turnstile antenna and the reason for its peculiar shape may be understood by considering that a pair of super-turnstile radiators form a large plane surface containing a slot. In Fig. 4.47 such a slot is shown, the length of the slot being one-half wave length long, with the ends of the slot grounded. If, now, we connect a

FIG. 4.45. A turnstile antenna array using folded dipoles.

generator across the center of the slot, the voltage potential which will be established along the slot is indicated by the distance of the dotted lines from the sides of the slot. It is evident that the voltage potential will be greatest at the center of the rectangular slot, gradually diminishing to zero at the ends of the slot. Currents will flow in the plane surface with a magnitude and instantaneous direc-

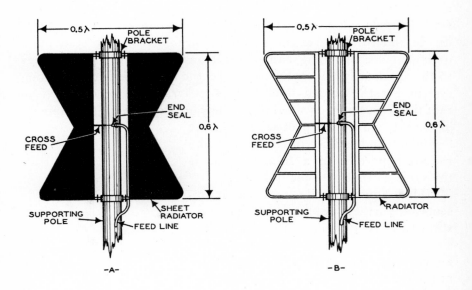

-A-   -B-

-C-

FIG. 4.46. (A) The original form of the super-turnstile antenna using solid sheet radiations. (B) The present commercial appearance of the super-turnstile using an open framework. (C) An actual photograph of a super-turnstile antenna. (Courtesy R.C.A.)

tion as shown by the arrows. This same distribution of voltage and current will be obtained whether a solid metallic sheet is used for the plane surface or an open framework.

The radiators are attached to the supporting pole at the top and bottom. The R.F. currents in the side rods will radiate proportionately to the length of each rod and to the current in that rod. Hence, to obtain uniform radiation from each rod, the length is made inversely proportional to the amount of current flowing in the rod. Thus, at the center, where the current distribution is high, the rod length is made small; to obtain the same amount of radiation near the ends of the slot, where the current is small, the length of the radiators is increased. In this way, a very close approximation to the radiation pattern of two simple dipoles, spaced one-half wave length apart, is obtained.

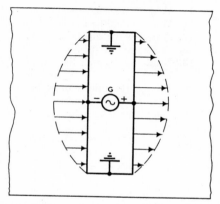

FIG. 4.47. Currents and voltages in the region of the half-wave slot in a large conducting surface.

To obtain a circular radiation pattern, each super-turnstile bay contains a pair of radiators facing north and south and a pair facing east and west. Energy concentration in the horizontal plane is achieved, as in previous arrays, by mounting several bays above each other. Feeding of each pair of radiators is done at the center of the unit.

PROBLEMS

1. Name the various categories into which radio waves can be divided.

2. What is the ionosphere and of what use is it?

3. Describe the convention regarding the polarization of radio waves.

4. Name the three general layers in the ionosphere? At what average heights can they be found?

5. Why is the ionosphere useful for long-distance communication? Which layer is responsible for the bending of 35-mc waves? Why?

6. What is the difference between reflection and refraction?

7. Name three conditions upon which ionospheric refraction depends.

8. What is meant by the critical frequency of an ionospheric layer?

9. What is the Sporadic E layer? What is its significance?

10. Does U.H.F. propagation differ from low-frequency radio wave travel? Explain.

11. Name the three methods whereby U.H.F. waves are propagated.

12. What is the range of frequencies that can be normally refracted by the ionosphere?

13. Discuss the line-of-sight method of propagating U.H.F. waves, deriving the equations applicable to this method.

14. What primary factors determine the amount of voltage developed in a receiving antenna?

15. What is the wave length of a 100-mc wave?

16. What would be the length of a half-wave dipole tuned to 106 mc?

17. A half-wave dipole antenna designed for 108 mc is to be used at 88 mc. By how much should its length be altered?

18. Name and sketch five different types of antennas that could be employed to receive F-M signals.

19. What precautions must be observed in choosing and installing a transmission line?

20. Define antenna gain and antenna directivity.

21. Illustrate a balanced and unbalanced input system.

22. Name and describe four types of transmission lines.

23. Discuss briefly the effects of impedance mismatch in the antenna system.

24. Describe two methods of matching impedances between the antenna and the transmission line.

25. What general factors determine the design and shape of F-M transmitting antennas? Discuss each item briefly.

26. Sketch the Cloverleaf antenna and describe its operation.

27. How is the amount of energy radiated vertically by an antenna minimized?

28. Explain the operation of the G.E. antenna.

29. Compare the operation of the Pylon and square-loop antennas.

30. Explain the operation of the turnstile and super-turnstile antennas.

CHAPTER 5

R.F. TUNERS FOR F-M RECEIVERS

Introduction. In conventional, sound-broadcasting receivers, it is current practice to tune the set by means of variable air condensers, or by changing the position of iron cores within certain inductances. These units are ganged together, enabling the use of one dial to tune several stages simultaneously. At the standard broadcast frequencies, 550 to 1700 kc, and even at the higher short-wave frequencies, the coils and condensers used are quite substantial in appearance. As we increase the operating frequency of the receiver, however, the units decrease in size until, at the F-M band, 88 to 108 mc, the coils contain fewer than 10 turns and the condensers have 3 or 4 small plates. Furthermore, extreme care must be taken in parts placement and in circuit wiring. Consider the latter, for example. Any length of wire, regardless of shape, contains a certain amount of inductance. This inductance is present at the lower frequencies just as concretely as it is at the higher frequencies. That it is important in one instance and not the other is merely due to its relationship to the rest of the circuit, particularly the tuning networks. At the low frequencies, the inductance introduced by the wiring is negligible when compared to the tuning coil's actual inductance. Hence, it may be (and is) disregarded. At the higher frequencies, however, this same inductance of the wiring forms a substantial percentage of the tuned-circuit inductance and, as such, cannot be ignored. It is here that the difficulty arises. Not only must the connections be made as short as possible, but we find that there is considerable inductance present in the condenser structure itself. Microphonic howls and inductive coupling between the various sections of the condenser structure (and hence between the stages controlled by these sections) are two of the undesirable results that occur.

In present-day F-M receivers, tuning by means of suitable variable condensers and fixed inductances is still widely used and, when properly constructed, will yield good results. However, there has been developed a whole new group of tuners which are designed to meet the altered conditions imposed by the higher frequencies with greater efficiency and more gain. It is the purpose of this chapter to investigate these newer types of tuners so that the serviceman, when working with F-M receivers, will be able to service them intelligently. We are entering an era where service ability is more closely linked to circuit understanding than it has been previously.

Inductuner. Although this book is concerned primarily with F-M, cognizance must be taken of the fact that the F-M and television frequencies are closely adjacent. It would be highly

FIG. 5.1.   The Mallory Inductuner.

desirable if some tuner could be used to tune over both bands. Not only would this make for compactness, but it would also increase the usefulness of the set since the listener would be able to receive all F-M and television stations within his community. A tuner possessing these characteristics is shown in Fig. 5.1. It was designed by Paul Ware, manufactured by the P. R. Mallory Company, and is commonly known as the Inductuner.

As can be seen from Fig. 5.1, the Inductuner consists of three separate variable inductance units on a common shaft. The coils are wound on ceramic forms, with movable trolley sliders for making contact at each point on the coil. At the coil end, an internal stop mechanism limits rotation to ten turns. Each coil is tunable continuously for ten turns which permits an inductance variation from approximately 0.02 to 1.0 microhenry. Note that this represents an inductance ratio of 1 : 50 and accounts for the

extremely wide band coverage of 44 to 216 mc.   The range covers
all the present television and F-M channels.

The movable trolley contact divides each coil into a used and
unused section.   As the trolley moves along, the low frequency end
of the coil is shorted to the contact.   When the entire unit is
shorted out by the contact arm (position of minimum inductance),
it still contains enough inductance to resonate at approximately 355
mc, which is well beyond television channel 13.

The advantage of using a variable coil instead of a variable air
condenser lies in the wider frequency coverage that is possible.   A
length of wire and its inductance can be reduced to a smaller value
than the minimum capacitance of a variable condenser.   Furthermore, as the inductance decreases, the losses
reduce proportionately.   In fact, it is even
possible for the losses to decrease faster
than the inductance, giving a rising Q with
frequency.   This, in turn, produces a desirable rise in gain at the high frequency
end of the band.

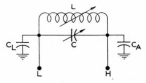

FIG. 5.2. The equivalent
electrical circuit of the Inductuner.

The electrical diagram of each winding
of the Inductuner is shown in Fig. 5.2. C_A
and C_L are stray capacitances from the high and low frequency ends
of the coil to the case.   In shunt with the inductance is a third
capacitance, C, which consists of two parts:

1. A fixed portion representing interelement stray capacitance.

2. A variable portion which is the distributed capacitance of the
winding itself.   As turns are progressively shorted out, the distributed capacitance of the coil changes.

Each Inductuner contains three windings, which permits three
circuits to be controlled at one time.   These would be the R.F.
amplifier, the oscillator, and the mixer input circuits.

The Inductuner does not necessarily have to be used over its
entire range.   The internal stop mechanism can be set so as to
restrict the movement of the trolley to only the desired portion of
the unit.   Other possible combinations are shown in Fig. 5.3A and
Fig. 5.3B.   In Fig. 5.3A, the addition of a fixed end coil, L_1, permits us to obtain a better Q characteristic than if the variable coil

were run out to the limit in order to reach the highest frequency. With the addition of the end coil, the trolley on the variable coil is turned to the end, and the separate end inductance, L_1, provides the highest frequency.   Properly designed, it is possible to produce a rising Q with frequency, which is highly desirable in view of the

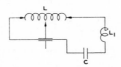

FIG. 5.3A. The addition of a fixed end coil, L_1, is often employed to obtain a better high frequency response.

FIG. 5.3B. The connection of a shunt coil, L_s, across the Inductuner provides a simple method of bandspreading a desired section of the dial.

poorer overall performance of receivers at the high frequency end of the band.   For the circuit in Fig. 5.3A, the tuning ratio is given by

$$\frac{f_2}{f_1} = \sqrt{\frac{L(\max) + L_1}{L_1}}$$

where $f_2 =$ the highest frequency it is desired to reach
     $f_1 =$ the lowest frequency

When one section of the Inductuner is used for the oscillator and one section for the mixer, a shunt coil is placed across the Inductuner oscillator unit in order that its frequency be higher than that of the other unit.   In television receivers, for example, the oscillator is above the signal frequency by an amount equal to the intermediate frequency.   The same is true in some F-M receivers.   Hence, the circuit for the oscillator would be as shown in Fig. 5.5, whereas the Inductuner section serving the mixer would be simply as shown in Fig. 5.3A.   To adjust the circuit of Fig. 5.5, we adjust the condenser trimmer at the low frequency end and adjust the end inductor until the highest frequency of the band is obtained.

Recently another version of the Inductuner has appeared using a spiral type of winding (See Fig. 5.6) in place of the solenoid type shown in Fig. 5.1. Operation of this new unit is identical with that of the older Inductuner, except that now the contact arm moves

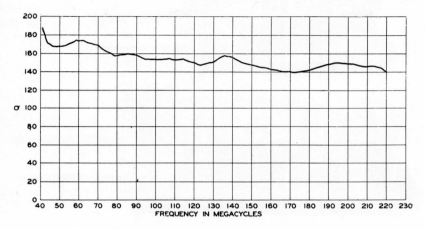

FIG. 5.4.   The variation in Q with frequency of the Inductuner.

along the spiral instead of along the solenoid. When the contact arm is on the innermost turn, the inductance is .025 microhenry. When the contact arm is on the outer turn, the inductance is .985 microhenry.

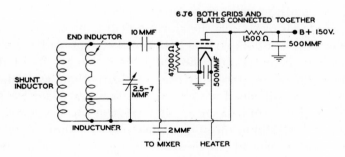

FIG. 5.5.   A high frequency oscillator circuit using the Inductuner.

The advantages gained by the use of a spiral winding are greater compactness, lower cost, and increased mechanical stability. The smaller size permits the addition of a fourth winding which

FIG. 5.6.   The spiral Inductuner, successor to the unit shown in Fig. 5.1.   It is available with either 3 or 4 windings.

can be used at the input to an R.F. amplifier.   In the three-winding Inductuner, the front end of the R.F. amplifier is untuned, leaving the set susceptible to spurious responses.

Permeability Tuning.[1]   There are several methods by which the inductance of the coils can be varied in order to tune the receiver. We can use brass or copper slugs or a powdered-iron, permeability-tuning element.   A comparison between the slugs and the permeability element indicates that the inductance change, for a definite decrease in Q, is greater with the iron core than with the slug. Furthermore, a coil tuned with a slug possesses a wider bandwidth than one which has an iron core.   The reason for this is due to the eddy current loss within the slug, which acts as a shorted turn.

In the design of a H.F. permeability tuner, cognizance must be taken of the stray or circuit capacitance which is present across the coil.   With careful design, the lowest value of the capacitance is close to 15 mmf.   The small value, in conjunction with the rela-

---

[1] Z. Bevin, " A Permeability-Tuned 100 Mc Amplifier." A paper presented at the National Electronics Conference, Chicago.

tively high value of inductance, presents a high L/C ratio. Since gain is directly proportional to the impedance presented by the resonant circuit and this, in turn, is governed by the L/C ratio of the network, we find that a high gain is available with the foregoing arrangement. However, when this thought is put to practical use in the receiver, it will be found that the R.F. selectivity is poor. The result, as shown in Chapter 7, is a large number of spurious responses.

The reason for poor R.F. selectivity at high frequencies is due to the damping or shunting effect of the R.F. tube input. A nominal value for the tube input loading at 100 mc is approximately 3500 ohms. This impedance is across the permeability-tuned coil and the stray 15-mmf shunting capacitance. At resonance, the impedance of the tuned circuit is given by

$$\frac{Q}{\omega C}$$

where $Q =$ the Q of the coil
       $C = 15$ mmf

The coil Q is determined by the dimensions of the coil and is approximately 90. At 100 mc, the value of the foregoing expression, after substituting the figures listed, is 10,000 ohms. Since the tube shunts the tuned circuit, the total impedance of the two is 2600 ohms. Practically, then, the impedance of the tuned circuit, which is what the incoming signal " sees," is 2600 ohms. Hence, we can set

$$\frac{Q}{\omega C} = 2600 \text{ ohms}$$

Since ω and C have not changed, the lowered value (from 10,000 to 2600 ohms) must be due to the lowering of the effective Q of the network. Solving, we obtain an effective value of 23 for Q.

Now, let us increase the total capacitance from 15 mmf to 30 mmf by the addition of more capacitance. The Q of the coil remains approximately at 90 in spite of a decrease in the number of turns due to the added capacitance. Solving for $Q/\omega C$ now, we obtain a value of 5000 ohms. This value, in parallel with the tube

(3500 ohms), produces a total input impedance of 2100 ohms. The effect on the overall Q is to bring it to an effective value of 38. Thus, although raising the shunt capacitance decreased the impedance (from 2600 to 2100 ohms), it did raise the effective Q of the circuit, in this instance by 65 per cent. The result is a slight loss in gain but a substantial increase in selectivity. Hence, in the receiver, a small capacitance is shunted across each coil.

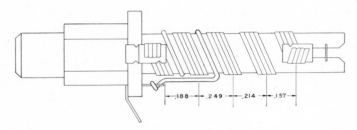

FIG. 5.7.   A four-wire permeability-tuned coil.   The variable pitch produces a linear characteristic.

In the particular permeability-tuned coils shown in Fig. 5.7, four-strand tinsel wire was used to retain wire flexibility in winding. The use of four parallel wires is due to the difficulty of obtaining the necessary inductance change with the small number of turns on the coil.   It was just pointed out that, for better selectivity, the shunt capacitance is increased and the coil inductance is lowered.   Hence, the ratio of inductance change for a certain core travel decreases, and the frequency band is not covered by a complete travel of the core within the distance allotted to it on the dial.   To overcome this difficulty, the width of each turn is increased.   As the wire width increases, the tuning range is increased.   A similar result may be had by winding the coil with parallel wires.   This accounts for the four conductors shown in Fig. 5.7.

Coil Spacing: A serviceman, called upon to repair one of these coils, would be completely unable to return the set to its proper operating condition unless he wound the coils correctly.   If the coils are closely inspected, it will be found that the winding is not uniform in pitch.   Fig. 5.8 illustrates the shape of the tuning curve for a permeability unit if the winding is made uniform in pitch.   The

nonlinear slope at each end occurs because the incremental inductance variation is maximum when the leading edge of the core is in
the center of the coil and minimum at the start or finish of the
core travel.

To straighten out the curvature at the ends of the characteristic,
the coil turns are bunched at the ends and spread out in the center.

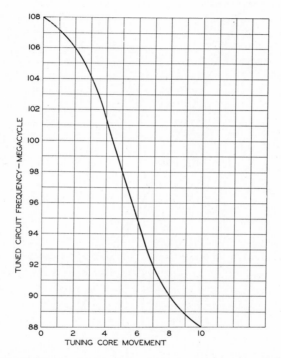

FIG. 5.8.   The nonlinear shape of the tuning curve when the winding of the
permeability-tuned coil is uniform in pitch.

This increases the inductance variation (with core movement) at
each end and decreases it in the middle.   To insure further that an
almost linear characteristic response is obtained, only part of the
complete tuning curve is used.   The coil and core lengths are made
larger than necessary, and the core, over the band desired, is never
out of the coil.   The curve of Fig. 5.9 is the result.

In the mass production of permeability-tuned coils, it must be

expected that a certain variation between units will occur.   Since
the R.F., mixer, and oscillator coils are tuned simultaneously by one
mechanism, some method must be available which will permit a
preliminary adjustment in order that all the coils track.   The idea
of using a variable trimmer condenser is possible, but a variable con-

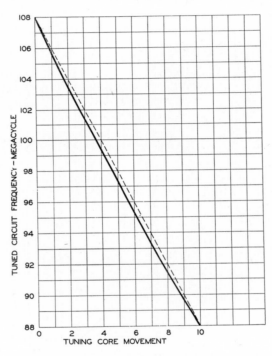

FIG. 5.9.   The improved tuning curve (solid line) when the turn spacing is made
logarithmic.   The dotted line, which is exactly linear, is used for comparison.

denser is highly susceptible to change with temperature and would
be highly detrimental to receiver stability.   It was discovered, however, that, by means of a single adjustment of the initial core position
with respect to the coil winding, it would be possible to compensate
for small differences.   Thus, when the coils are mounted and tested,
any difference in tracking is compensated for by a single initial
advancing or retarding of the iron core of each coil.
    Photographs of the entire tuning assembly are shown in Fig.

5.10.   The antenna, mixer, and oscillator coils are mounted on a bracket fastened to the side of a conventional variable condenser. The latter is used, in this receiver, to tune the A-M broadcast and short-wave bands.   A cam is mounted on the shaft of the variable condenser and operates a rocker arm which moves the iron tuning cores in the three high frequency coils.   The unit is very compact, reducing all stray capacitance and inductance to a minimum.

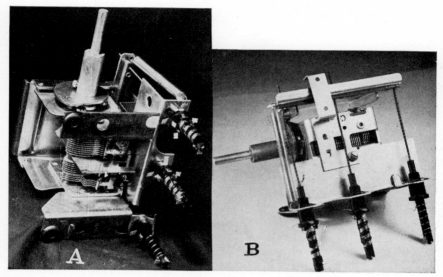

FIG. 5.10.   (A) Receiver tuning assembly showing the mounting of the permeability coils.   (B) Underside view.

The Guillotine Tuner.   In the preceding section, tuning over the F-M band (88–108 mc) was accomplished with permeability tuning.   However, a definite knack is required in winding the coils to obtain the proper pitch in production so that satisfactory calibration and tracking may be maintained.   The coils have few turns, and a small displacement from the desired position is sufficient to throw off the calibration noticeably.   Another solution to this method of tuning has been developed by the General Electric Company.   It uses a modified form of variable inductance tuner which, it is claimed, is more easily adaptable to production methods.

The tuner, shown in Fig. 5.11, consists of two identical brass frames which form a two-turn inductance when connected at their open ends.   To vary the inductance of these two turns, a brass blade is inserted between frames.   The effect of the brass blade is to reduce the inductance of each turn or frame as the blade is moved down in the slot between the frames.   To obtain the desired tuning curve, slots are cut in the blade.   Once the form of the slot has been determined, the entire unit can be mechanically assembled, reducing

FIG. 5.11.   The guillotine tuner assembly.   (Courtesy of G.E.)

the possibility of error.   After the unit has been combined, the two terminals of the tuner project through the receiver chassis.   This, in addition to providing a rugged tie point for soldered connections, makes possible short leads to the unit.

The various sections of the tuner are shown separately in Fig. 5.12.   Because of the physical appearance of the unit it has been nicknamed the " guillotine tuner."   In G.E. receivers, it is used to tune the F-M bands and two or more short-wave bands.   The low frequency ranges are tuned by adding shunt capacitance and by

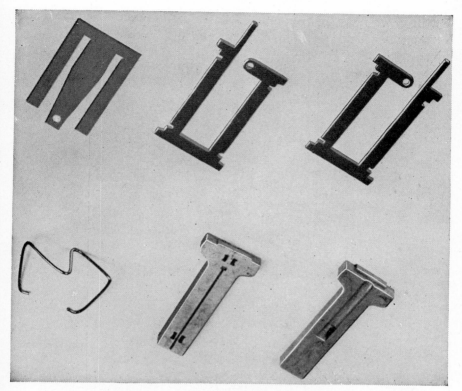

FIG. 5.12. The several components of the guillotine tuner. Note the relatively simple construction permitting easy fabrication.

inserting series inductances in the guillotine circuit. Fig. 5.13 shows inductance and Q characteristics of the unit over the tuning range of 88 to 108 mc.

A photograph of an assembly using the guillotine tuner is shown in Fig. 5.14. The blades of the tuner are raised and lowered by a plastic elevator which, in turn, is attached to a windlass. At the right-hand side of the assembly there can be seen the broadcast-band coils. These are permeability-tuned, with the iron core raised and lowered by the same assembly.

The entire tuner in final form is enclosed in a metal box which shields the unit and keeps out dust. To date, no trouble has been encountered from microphonic howl. Furthermore, since the blade of the tuner is ungrounded, there are no sliding contacts to produce noise.

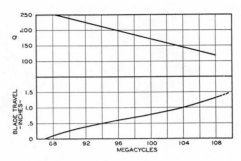

Fig. 5.13.   Inductance and Q characteristics of the guillotine tuner.

Fig. 5.14.   The guillotine tuner used in a G.E. receiver.

Coaxial Tuners.[2]   One of the prime reasons for using a high intermediate frequency is that a receiver becomes less sensitive to image signals.   Image signals (see p. 153) are separated from the

[2] From a paper presented by G. Wallin and C. W. Dymond at the National Electronics Conference, Chicago.

desired signal by twice the I.F. value. In equation form,

$$\text{Image frequency} = \text{Desired signal} \pm 2(\text{I.F.})$$

The plus or minus depends upon whether the mixing oscillator frequency is above or below the signal frequency. As the I.F. value decreases, the frequency separation between the image and desired signals becomes less. This narrowing of frequency separation requires, consequently, that the R.F. tuned circuits of the receiver possess a higher Q (or selectivity) in order to reject image signals. It has been proved in practice that a 60-db attenuation by the input tuning circuits on undesired signals will eliminate any possibility of interference from even the strongest undesired signals found normally. It can be shown, when the I.F. value is 10.7 mc, that each tuned circuit must possess a Q of 75, whereas when the I.F. is 4.3 mc the effective Q per circuit rises to 200.

The advantage of a lower I.F. lies in the greater stage gain. An I.F. amplifier designed for 4.3 mc is capable of 1.57 times more gain than an I.F. amplifier functioning at 10.7 mc. More gain means less stages and a resulting greater economy.

The problem of tube loading at 100 mc was previously treated in the section on **Permeability Tuning.** Covered, too, was the effect of increasing the capacitance across the circuit. Since neither of these is capable of producing the desired high Q of 200 (if an I.F. of 4.3 mc is to be employed), some other method of approach is necessary.

When the input signal from the antenna is fed directly into an R.F. amplifier, the input or grid impedance is nominally in the neighborhood of 3000 to 3500 ohms. However, if the signal is fed directly into the grid of a converter tube, the input impedance may be of the order of 7000 to 12,000 ohms. To obtain the desired effective Q, it becomes necessary to feed the signal directly into the converter instead of an R.F. amplifier, to use a high value of tuning capacitance, and to use high Q elements. For the last component, a high Q tuner, transmission lines are employed. Before we actually analyze the application of these lines to tuners, let us briefly review transmission lines.

Transmission Lines: Every radio man is familiar with the

conventional inductances, capacitances, and resistances, the types of which can be purchased in any radio shop. These units are said to be lumped because each is complete and distinct from the other.

Now, if two wires are mounted close together, using one to conduct the current away from the source of voltage and the other to bring the current back, it would be found that the source of voltage " sees " not just two wires with some resistance in them, but rather a complex impedance which, when broken down, will reveal inductance and capacitance, too. The last two components are not visible upon a physical inspection of the wires, yet electrically they exist.

Of the two quantities, the presence of the capacitance can perhaps be more readily understood since, by definition, a capacitance is formed whenever two conductors are separated by a dielectric. In this instance the dielectric is air, although it may be any nonconductor. Since the dielectric is never a perfect nonconductor, it is represented schematically by placing a large resistance across the condenser, this denoting leakage.

The presence of the inductive reactance is much more difficult to explain. It is best to go back to the concept of magnetic lines of force and attack the problem from that angle. Inductance may be considered proportional to the number of magnetic lines of force per unit ampere that encircles a wire carrying the current. By starting with this idea, the inductance per unit length of any wire or system of wires can be developed.

To represent the foregoing inductance, capacitance, and resistance in schematic form for analytical purposes, a diagram such as shown in Fig. 5.15 is often used in engineering books on transmission lines. Although the various components are shown separate and distinct from each other, they are actually distributed evenly along the line. It is only because of our inability to show these components as they really are that we resort to this method.

Since the transmission line contains exactly the same three components as any ordinary resonant circuit, it is reasonable to expect that the same results can be obtained from these as from a resonant circuit. Hence, the length of the transmission line determines the frequency at which it will operate.

In common use today are three types of transmission lines: the twisted-wire, the parallel-wire, and the coaxial transmission line. In the twisted-wire form, the two wires forming the line are twisted

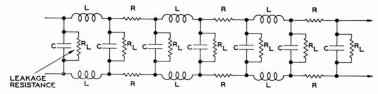

FIG. 5.15.   The electrical components of a transmission line.

about each other, in the same manner as a lamp cord.   In the next type, parallel-wire lines, the two wires are kept parallel and equidistant to each other, usually by means of spacers or by imbedding both wires in the dielectric material. The latter is true of the recently developed polyethylene transmission line used as lead-in cables for F-M and television antennas.   Finally, there is the coaxial cable, shown in Fig. 5.16, in which one conductor is placed inside and at the center of

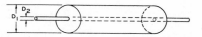

FIG. 5.16.   A coaxial cable, D_1 is the inside diameter of the outer conductor; D_2 is the outside diameter of the inside conductor.

an outer conductor.   It is this final type which is used as a tuner in the F-M receivers manufactured by Motorola.

Transmission Line Tuners.   In choosing a transmission line, there were two factors to consider.   First, the length of the line, in order to obtain the proper impedance at the operating frequencies, and, second, the best possible Q.   It has been determined that the maximum impedance results when the outer to inner conductor ratio is 9.2 to 1.   Actually, a 10 to 1 ratio is used with very little decrease in impedance.   For this particular line the expressions governing the length of the line in order to give the required inductance and the Q are as follows:

$$L = 0.0117l \text{ microhenries}$$

$$Q = 0.802D_1\sqrt{F}$$

where L = the inductance presented by the length of line used
   l = length of coaxial line
   D_1 = diameter of inner conductor
   F = frequency at which the line is to be used

In common with conventional tuning circuits, one of the circuit components must be made variable in order that a definite range or band of frequencies be covered.   It would be possible to resonate the inductance of the transmission line with a variable condenser placed across the end of the line.   However, since the magnitude of the inductance is low, the use of a gang condenser — one section for each transmission line tuner — would introduce too much additional inductance to prove useful.   We can, however, resonate the

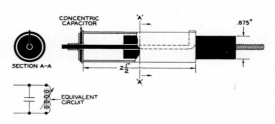

Fig. 5.17.   The construction of the coaxial tuner.   The equivalent coil and condenser is also shown.

inductance of the transmission line with a fixed condenser, and then vary the inductance of the line by means of a powdered-iron core. In other words, we would have permeability-tuning, but in a form which is substantially different from any of the previous units.

The coaxial line, with an iron core, is shown in Fig. 5.17.   The iron core is mounted on a threaded rod and its position in the coaxial line is adjusted by turning the head or top of the threaded rod. The Q of the tuner, with the iron core, at 100 mc is 335.   The tube load reduces the effective Q of the circuit to 195 and this is approximately its final value, although the antenna loading lowers the Q somewhat.   In the same diagram is the equivalent conventional circuit.

An inexpensive, high-quality, concentric condenser was developed for this particular unit.   This is also shown in Fig. 5.17.   The condenser is of silver on mica construction.   A highly desirable feature of the tuner is that the unit can be constructed as a mechanical assembly, without the necessity of electrical checking.   With materials that are commercially available, the variation in inductance as calculated by the expressions previously given, is only ±0.5 per cent. The coaxial line and condenser type of construction forms a very compact unit. This reduces considerably the importance of the inductance present in leads connecting the tuned lines in the circuit. At 100 mc, the problem of confining the desired signal pick-up to the antenna terminals of the receiver is quite difficult. Chassis pick-up, for example, tends to degrade the image and adjacent channel attenuation. However, when the entire unit is confined within the coaxial cable, the undesired pick-up becomes negligible. Removing the antenna, in the presence of a strong signal, completely kills the receiver output.

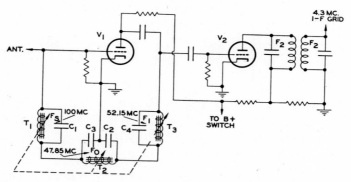

FIG. 5.18.   Coaxial tuners employed in a superheterodyne circuit. The three ganged coaxial units are: T_1 and C_1; T_2, C_3 and C_z; C_4 and T_3.

Transmission Tuner Application.   One application of the tuner to a superheterodyne F-M receiver is shown in Fig. 5.18.[3]   The circuit is novel in that it employs one oscillator in a double super- heterodyne network. C_1 and T_1 (the coaxial tuner) tune over the range of 88 to 108 mc, and the input signal is applied to the grid of V_1.   At the same time V_1, using C_3, C_2, and T_2, is functioning as a Colpitts oscillator and generating a voltage which mixes with the incoming signal.   For a station signal of 100 mc, the frequency of the Colpitts oscillator is 47.85 mc.   The difference between these

[3] This tuner may be used in a conventional circuit arrangement producing a 10.7 mc I.F. and, in fact, some of Motorola's F-M sets are so designed. However, the double superheterodyne approach used in other models is novel and is explained here in detail.

two frequencies is 52.15 mc, and this is the frequency at which C_4 and T_3 are resonant. This frequency now mixes with the oscillator voltage again, 47.85 mc, this time in V_2, and the resulting difference frequency of 4.3 mc is obtained and fed to the intermediate frequency amplifiers. Here, then, one Colpitts oscillator feeds two circuits. The incoming signal is lowered twice to reach the final 4.3-mc I.F. The movable iron cores of each coaxial cable are ganged together in a mechanical arrangement and moved up and down in unison.

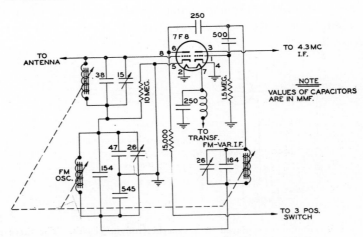

Fig. 5.19.   The commercial application of Fig. 5.18.

F_s, the signal frequency, F_o, the oscillator frequency, and F_1, the frequency of C_4 and T_3, are related according to the following expressions:

$$F_s - F_o = F_1 \qquad (1)$$

(The difference frequency, F_1, is obtained by mixing the signal and the oscillator voltage.)

$$F_1 - F_o = \text{I.F.} \quad (4.3 \text{ mc})$$

Then F_1 is mixed with the oscillator to step down the signal to 4.3 mc.

The final circuit used in the F-M receiver is shown in Fig. 5.19. A duo-triode, 7F8, replaces the two previously separate tubes.

In the receiver using this system for tuning, only one I.F. stage is used. The output of the amplifier then feeds into a ratio detector. Fig. 5.20 shows the entire receiver with the coaxial tuners.

Parallel-Wire Transmission Line Tuners. Another approach to transmission-line tuners, this time using parallel-wire lines, is shown in Fig. 5.21. The R.F. section consists of three sets of parallel-wire lines, each set having movable shorting bars which determine how much of the line is active. The shorting contacts are mounted on plastic bars and then attached to a common shaft. As the shaft is rotated counterclockwise, the bars progressively short out more and more of the

F-M COAXIAL
TUNERS

FIG. 5.20. Transmission line tuners mounted in receiver. (Courtesy Motorola)

FIG. 5.21. A parallel resonant line tuning assembly. (Courtesy Approved Electronic Instrument Corp.)

lines, raising their resonant frequency from 88 to 108 mc. (See Fig. 5.22.) To permit the three lines to track with each other, each line contains small end inductances and semi-fixed, temperature-compensated silver ceramic condensers. At the high frequency end of the F-M band, the series condensers are adjusted for maximum output. At the low end of the F-M band, 88 mc, the end inductance coil turns are either spread apart or squeezed together to achieve tracking here. The whole unit is rubber-mounted to give freedom from microphonics. Miniature tubes are used to provide excellent frequency stability and sensitivity. A 6AG5 is the R.F. amplifier, and a 6J6 double triode functions as a combination mixer-oscillator. Injection of the oscillator voltage into the mixer is accomplished with a 2-mmf coupling condenser. The unit, mounted on the receiver chassis, is shown in Fig. 5.23.

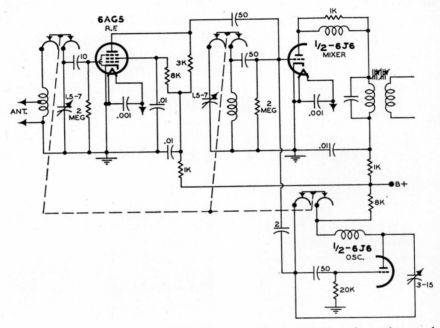

FIG. 5.22. Schematic diagram of the front-end section of an F-M receiver using parallel wire transmission line tuners.

Schematically, R.F. amplifiers used in F-M receivers do not differ from comparable R.F. amplifiers used in standard A-M broadcast receivers. (See Fig. 5.24.) Structurally, of course, these amplifiers use smaller tubes and components as previously indicated.

Grounded-grid Amplifiers. In standard-broadcast A-M receivers, pentodes are used exclusively in the R.F. amplifier. Triodes have been ruled out because of their tendency to oscillate owing to the relatively large capacitance existing within the tube between plate and grid. Recently, however, an arrangement known as the grounded-grid amplifier has permitted the use of triode R.F. amplifiers with good results. The grounded-grid amplifier is contrasted with the conventional amplifier in Fig. 5.25.

Note that the grid of the tube is at R.F. ground potential and that the signal is fed to the cathode. The tube still functions as an amplifier because the flow of the plate current is controlled by the grid-to-cathode potential. Instead of varying the grid potential and maintaining the cathode fixed, the grid is fixed and the cathode potential is varied. The net result is still the same. However, the grid, being grounded, acts as a shield between the input and output

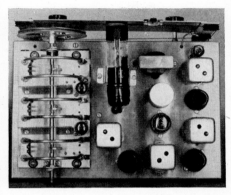

FIG. 5.23. The tuning assembly mounted on the receiver chassis. (Courtesy Approved Electronic Instrument Corp.)

circuits, thereby preventing the feedback of energy which is so essential to the development of oscillations.

The desirability of using triodes in the R.F. stage of the high-frequency receiver is due to their low internal noise level. Tubes generate a small amount of noise voltage because the electrons moving from cathode to plate do so as separate units and not in a continuous stream. The amount of such noise voltage is seldom more than 10 to 15 microvolts and is ordinarily of no importance. However, at the front end of a receiver, the

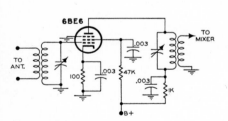

FIG. 5.24. Schematic diagram of an F-M, R.F. amplifier.

signal level may approach this figure and, consequently, it is important that the tubes chosen generate as little noise voltage as possible. In this respect, the triode is considerably superior to the pentode. As a general rule, the greater the number of positive grids in a tube, the greater the internal noise generated.

In standard broadcast receivers, the signal reaching the set is seldom so weak that internal tube noise becomes an important factor.   However, in high frequency reception, the ability of a set

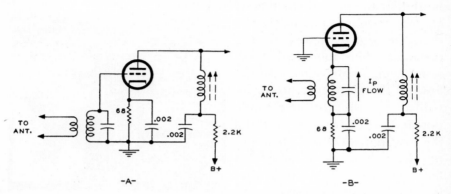

Fig. 5.25.   (A) A conventional amplifier.   (B) A grounded-grid amplifier.

to receive weak signals is important and the minimum usable signal is determined by the amount of noise voltage which the set itself develops — hence the use of triodes in R.F. amplifiers.

PROBLEMS

1. Why do conventional-type tuning circuits prove less suitable for high-frequency operation than for low-frequency use?

2. What general characteristics should high frequency tuners possess?

3. How does the Mallory Inductuner operate?

4. Draw the circuit schematic of a high frequency oscillator circuit using the Inductuner.   Explain how this circuit is aligned.

5. Explain why inductance tuning is better suited for high frequency circuits than condenser tuning.

6. What ordinarily happens to the Q of a tuning circuit as its frequency is raised?   Why?

7. How does permeability tuning differ from the method employed in the Inductuner?   What is slug tuning?

8. Why is a high L to C ratio desirable in a tuning circuit?   When is it purposely lowered?

9. Why do we find four parallel wires used on some permeability-tuned coils? How could a single wire be made to produce the same effect?

10. What is the reason for the uneven turn spacing found on some coils?

11. How does the " guillotine tuner " differ from the Inductuner and the permeability tuner?

12. Describe the structure and operation of the G.E. " guillotine tuner."

13. What properties of a transmission line enable it to be used for tuning?

14. What advantages are offered by the use of a low intermediate frequency? What disadvantages?

15. Why does the choice of a coaxial transmission line tuner permit us to use a low intermediate frequency?

16. What is the double superheterodyne principle?

17. Draw the schematic diagram of a coaxial tuned circuit employed in a double superheterodyne receiver.

18. Draw the circuit of a grounded-grid amplifier. What advantages does this amplifier offer over the conventional amplifier for high-frequency operation?

CHAPTER 6

HIGH FREQUENCY OSCILLATORS

Converters and Mixers. In order to take advantage of the benefits of the superheterodyne it is necessary to convert the incoming signal to the lower I.F. If no R.F. stage precedes the converter, then the incoming signal is fed directly to the converter (or mixer) input and reduced to the I.F. immediately. Otherwise, it is fed first through a stage of R.F. amplification and then applied to the converter.

The terms " frequency converter " and " frequency mixer " are used interchangeably by many writers, although a distinction does

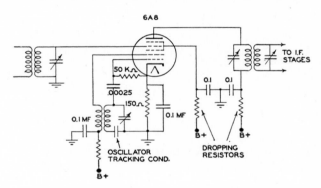

Fig. 6.1. A typical pentagrid converter circuit.

exist between them. A converter is a tube which produces the oscillator voltage and mixes this voltage with the incoming signal, all within the same tube. A mixer tube, on the other hand, is more limited in scope. It merely mixes or beats together a separately generated oscillator voltage with the incoming signal. Its function is purely one of mixing. Whichever arrangement is employed depends to a great extent upon the frequencies involved. At the standard broadcast frequencies, a converter tube is more common because it gives satisfactory results and permits an economical arrangement where only an additional coil is needed to generate the oscillations. Fig. 6.1 is an example of a typical frequency converter.

As the signal frequency is raised above 50 mc, the operation of the oscillator becomes more critical. Instability in output voltage and interaction between the oscillator and the signal are more likely to occur with converters. To minimize these effects, the oscillator

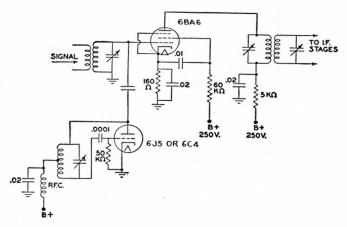

FIG. 6.2. A mixer (6BA6) with a separate oscillator.

is separated from the mixing action, as shown in Fig. 6.2. A separate tube (usually a triode) is employed as the oscillator.

The use of a separate oscillator increases the space and cost requirements of the set, but the stability is superior to the frequency converter circuit.[1]

Oscillator Stability. Stability in the oscillator is one of the most important engineering aspects of high frequency receivers. Frequency conversion is based upon the fact that a fixed oscillator frequency, beating against an incoming signal, will result in a certain I.F. Little need be said about the constancy of the frequency of the incoming signal. Transmitter channel accuracy is held to within

---

[1] This does not exclude the possibility of using a converter for F-M receivers in their present band. In fact, many manufacturers do incorporate such circuits using specially designed tubes. However, where good stability and low noise level are desired, separate oscillators are used.

0.002 per cent — safeguarded by many elaborate electronic devices that report instantly any appreciable frequency deviation. At the receiver, the major limiting factor toward stability and the production of a constant I.F. is the stability of the oscillator.

When the oscillator drifts in frequency during receiver operation, the difference, or intermediate, frequency, produced as a result of the oscillator frequency mixing with the signal, changes. A relatively small oscillator drift shifts the signal partially or completely outside the range of the tuned I.F. stages. The receiver output then becomes distorted.

The desired stability in an oscillator has been found to be ±0.01 per cent of the carrier or ±10 kc at 100 mc. With ordinary precautions, such as the use of low-loss sockets, well-placed components permitting free circulation of air, and air-dielectric trimmer condensers, the principal drift is due to the capacitance changes within the oscillator tube during the warm-up period. Of consequence, too, but not quite as important, are the frequency changes due to the variations in oscillator tuning coil and condenser. The total drift usually amounts to 0.03 per cent, or 30 kc at 100 mc. The drift is never completely developed the instant the set is placed in operation but is attained gradually, perhaps over a period of one-half hour to an hour. After the initial warm-up period, the oscillator frequency levels off to a fixed value unless a sudden change occurs in receiver operation. A typical drift curve is shown in Fig. 6.3. Note that the oscillator always drifts to a lower frequency, a result of the increase in inductance and capacitance due to the increase in temperature.

In an inductance, increase in temperature — due to surrounding heat generated by the tubes, resistors, and transformers in the receiver — expands the copper wire of each turn. Consequently, the length of each winding increases, and with it the effective radius of the coil. Examination of the design formulas governing single layer coils reveals that increasing the length of a coil decreases the inductance by the first power. However, an increase in the winding diameter raises the inductance by the squared power. The net result, then, is an overall increase in inductance. With condensers, the increase in capacitance is due to the linear expansion of the condenser plates. The capacitance of a condenser plate varies directly with its surface area.

Countermeasures. A simple countermeasure against the positive increase in inductance and capacitance is the use of a small, fixed mica condenser having a negative temperature coefficient. Available in many sizes, the proper condenser can be selected to counter-

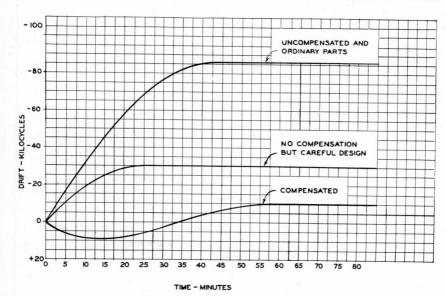

FIG. 6.3. The effect of careful design and compensation on oscillator frequency drift.

balance most positive temperature increases to the point where good stability is obtained. It is simple to install and is extensively used by many manufacturers. Other precautionary measures include regulation of the voltage applied to the oscillator plate, adequate electrical shielding of the oscillator plate, and the use of tubes with high mutual conductances and low input and output capacitances. A tube with a high g_m provides a strong output. Low input and output capacitances minimize the effect of the oscillator tube on the tuning coil and condensers in the circuit. During the heating-up period, the internal capacitance of a tube changes. This occurs, also, with changes in current through the tube. Hence, to minimize the effect of these changes on the output frequency of the oscillator, it is necessary that the internal capacitances form a negligible part of the total capacitance present across the tuning circuit.

Another method used by some manufacturers is to operate the oscillator at some low frequency and utilize the second harmonic for mixing. The lower fundamental frequency permits the use of a high lump-circuit capacitance which, in effect, minimizes the stray and tube capacitances.

Harmonic operation is not feasible unless the oscillator voltage can be fed into the mixer tube by way of a separate grid. The

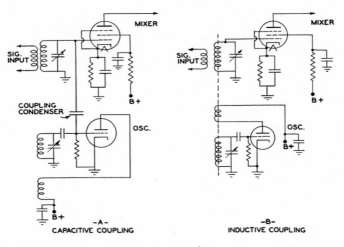

Fig. 6.4. Two widely used methods of coupling between the oscillator and mixer.

capacitive and inductive injection methods shown in Fig. 6.4 (A and B) require a considerable oscillator voltage to be effective. The oscillator, in each instance, must transfer its voltage to the mixer grid tuned circuit. Since this network is resonant to the higher incoming signal (higher by the I.F. value), the impedance presented to the oscillator voltage will be low. Hence, considerably more oscillator voltage must be available because of the mismatch. (In any mismatch there is inherently a large waste or loss of power and consequently a greater amount of power must be expended to develop the required smaller value.) Since the second harmonic output is lower than the fundamental, it means pushing this unit more.   When the mixing voltage can be applied directly to a separate grid, with only a resistor as the impedance, then a closer match may be made with a resultant rise in efficiency.

Conventional Converter Instability.   The inability of conventional pentagrid converters to function satisfactorily at higher fre-

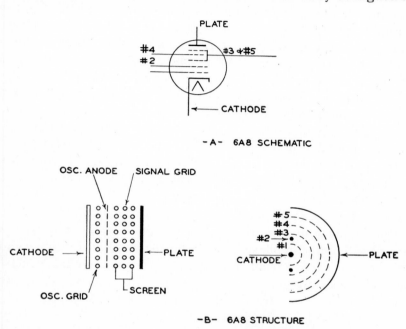

FIG. 6.5.   The conventional schematic (A) and actual electrode placement (B) of a 6A8 converter tube.

quencies can perhaps best be understood by an examination of the action within such tubes.   The 6A8 is typical of these converters and will serve to illustrate the points.   The conventional schematic and the actual element placement are shown in Fig. 6.5   It is current practice to identify each grid by number, commencing with the grid nearest the cathode.   The use of each grid is also indicated.

When the circuit is in operation, electrons leave the cathode area in pulses, controlled by the voltage variations on the oscillator grid, G_1.   As part of the oscillator, G_1 is negative during most of its cycles, becoming sufficiently positive (or less negative) for only a small portion of the time.   It is during these short intervals that the electrons flow past G_1, attracted by the positive potential on G_2 and G_3.   It is to be noted that G_2, the oscillator anode, is not truly a grid, but only two posts or vertical rods without any of the usual grid turns of wire.

Some of the electrons that flow past the screen grid, G_3, come to a halt in the region between G_3 and G_4 because of the negative potential on the signal grid, G_4.   This cloud of electrons constitutes a virtual cathode.   The number of electrons reaching the plate of the tube is controlled by the variations of the potential on G_4 set up by the incoming signal.   The overall action then is the control or modulation of the tube's electron flow by two sources, the oscillator grid variations and the input signal changes.   The I.F. beat note is produced as a consequence of this interaction.

It is seen from the above that the number of electrons in the space charge between G_3 and G_4 will vary in accordance with the voltage variations on the oscillator grid, G_1.   Because of the closeness of the space charge to G_4, a voltage at the oscillator frequency will be induced into the circuit of the signal grid.   The resultant current will not be in phase with the normal oscillator voltage and it will therefore act to buck or cancel out part of the effectiveness of the oscillator voltage.   A reduction in gain results, or, in other words, the conversion transconductance is low.

A second and more serious reaction within the tube is the change produced in oscillator frequency by the signal grid.   It is the signal grid, G_4, that determines the number of electrons taken from the virtual cathode as constituted by the space charge and passed on to the plate.   This, in turn, has been found to react on the oscillator grid, altering its capacitance with respect to the rest of its circuit and thereby forcing a change in frequency.   With a separate oscillator, this latter effect cannot occur and the stability of the oscillator frequency from a separate source is not affected.

The use of a single tube to function as an oscillator and mixer is attractive economically and, under the pressure of this advantage, the tube companies have developed pentagrid converters which perform satisfactorily at the F-M frequencies.   Examples of such tubes are the 6SB7Y, the 6BE6, and the 6BA7.

An indication of the altered construction of these tubes can be seen from an examination of the internal structure of the 6SB7Y. (See Fig. 6.6.)   At the center of the tube is the cathode, closely surrounded by G_1 which serves as the oscillator grid.   Beyond G_1 is a second grid, G_2, which functions as the oscillator plate and also

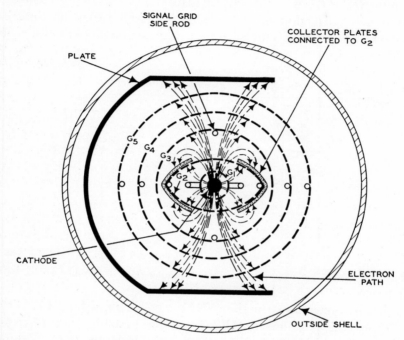

FIG. 6.6.   The internal construction of the 6SB7Y tube.

serves to accelerate the electrons emitted by the cathode.   Internally G_2 is connected to G_4, and both elements are properly by-passed so that essentially only a d-c potential is present here. G_2 also has connected to it two side plates whose function it is to shield G_1 by intercepting any electrons that might be repelled by the nega-tively charged G_3.   In this way, interaction between the signal and the oscillator circuits is materially reduced. G_3 is located between G_2 and G_4 and receives the signal voltage.   The two supporting rods of G_3 are placed in the center of the electron stream traveling from the cathode to the plate.   Since the average potential of G_3

is negative, the effect of this rod placement is to split the electron stream into two diverging beams, as shown. Because of the particular structure of the elements and the distribution of the electric fields within this structure, electrons repelled back by G_3 are forced to strike the side plates of G_2, effectively preventing them from reaching G_1. G_5 is a suppressor grid and is externally connected to ground. Insertion of this suppressor grid raises the internal resistance of the tube and permits a higher conversion gain to be achieved.

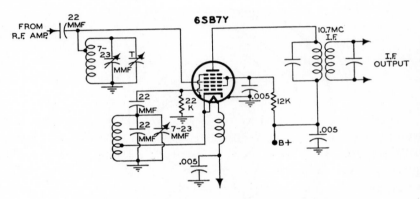

FIG. 6.7. A typical circuit application of the 6SB7Y tube.

Circuit connections for the 6SB7Y are shown in Fig. 6.7. The oscillator coil is connected between the cathode and G_1. G_3 receives the signal voltage either from an antenna or an R.F. amplifier. The plate of the tube attaches to the primary of the first I.F. transformer.

In the choice between a frequency converter and a separate oscillator and mixer, there is one additional factor to consider — tube noise. As the number of grids or controlling elements within a tube increases, the amount of tube noise generated likewise increases. In fact, the amount of noise generated in a pentagrid converter, as compared with a straight R.F. amplifier, is in the ratio of approximately 4 to 1. The minimum signal reaching the grid of a pentagrid converter must be this much stronger in order to override tube noise. The noise will also limit the minimum signal that the receiver can amplify successfully without interference from the amplified tube noise.

Before we leave the subject of pentagrid converters, mention should be made of the gain that is obtained when the signal passes through the stage. Converter gain is defined as

$$\text{gain} = \frac{S_c r_p R_L}{r_p + R_L}$$

where

S_c = conversion transconductance, i.e., the effect a signal voltage has in producing a current in the plate circuit at the I.F. value

r_p = plate resistance of the tube

R_L = resistance of tuned plate circuit to the intermediate frequencies

In the equation, S_c, the conversion transconductance, is the controlling factor. S_c, in turn, depends upon the oscillator voltage. Increasing the gain of a converter lowers the minimum value of signal voltage needed at its grid to override the noise generated in the tube. Of triodes, pentodes, and pentagrid converters, the last possesses the smallest S_c. However, pentodes have a much higher internal plate resistance (r_p in the foregoing formula), and the overall gain, using the pentode, is higher.

When a separate oscillator is used, its voltage may be injected at the control grid, cathode, screen or suppressor grids of a pentode tube, or at the control grid or cathode if a triode is used as the mixer. The cathode is most convenient, since control over the grid and plate circuits may thereby be effected simultaneously. Control grid injection is more critical than cathode injection because of the increased possibility of interaction between the signal and oscillator circuits. The screen and suppressor grids are seldom used for injection because a greater amount of oscillator driving voltage is needed to obtain a satisfactory degree of mixing.

Oscillator Coupling. Coupling to the control grid may be accomplished either inductively or capacitively. Both methods are shown in Fig. 6.4. For cathode coupling, either method of energy transfer can also be employed. Loose coupling is necessary at the oscillator in order that the tuning circuit shall not be loaded down to any appreciable degree. With loose coupling, the oscillator is least affected by any undesirable feedback and the stability is much better.

Another reason for loose coupling is to keep the amount of oscillator energy that is fed to the mixer at the lowest point consistent with good operation. Every oscillator output contains a large number of harmonics. These harmonics may react with certain undesirable incoming voltages to produce a difference frequency equal to the I.F. The result is known as a spurious response and, if sufficiently strong, may easily interfere with the desired signal. By keeping the oscillator voltage fed to the mixer as low as possible — consistent with good operation — we decrease the ability of these oscillator harmonics to produce spurious responses. It is well to keep this in mind when either building or repairing a receiver.

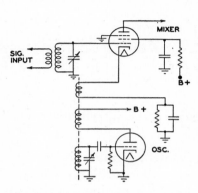

FIG. 6.8. Coupling oscillator voltage to the cathode of the mixer.

Previously the most important reason for not extensively using a triode for a mixer, despite its excellent signal-to-noise ratio and high conversion transconductance, was its relatively large grid-to-plate capacitance. A large C_{gp} permits a high percentage of feedback. Since the signal frequency is higher than the I.F., the I.F. tuning circuit in the plate circuit appears to be wholly capacitive to the signal. All frequencies higher than the resonant frequency of a tuned circuit find it much easier to pass through the condenser than the coil. When this energy feeds back through C_{gp}, the Q of the input tuned-grid circuit is decreased. In a pentode feedback is negligible because of the extremely small grid-to-plate interelectrode capacitance.

Recently high frequency triodes have been developed in which the coupling between plate and grid is minimized so that undesirable feedback is not too serious. Some receiver manufacturers are using these tubes and the results appear satisfactory.

Types of Oscillators. Three oscillator circuits have been widely used in the majority of sets. These are the conventional Hartley (A), the modified Hartley (B), and the ultraudion oscillator (C), the latter being a modification of the familiar Colpitts oscillator. (See Fig. 6.9.) Each unit, if properly constructed,

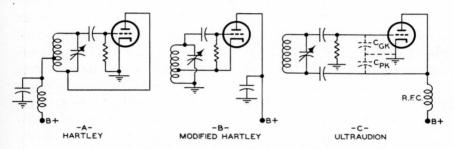

FIG. 6.9. Three popular oscillator circuits.

oscillates readily and possesses good stability. Triode tubes are usually preferred because they require but one regulated voltage; pentodes need two. Popular triodes are the 6J5 and 6C4, although, of late, other triodes have been made available. These have:

1. Low internal shunting capacitances.

2. Special construction enabling the tube to function readily at higher frequencies.

3. A high value of mutual conductance to provide a strong output voltage.

Crystal Oscillators. Great stress has been given to oscillator stability because of the commanding position that the oscillator holds in the superheterodyne circuit. This feature is especially important in F-M mobile receivers (used commercially) where the circuit must be designed to operate under conditions which are considerably less favorable to stability than is ever encountered in home receivers. Furthermore, most commercial operation is restricted to certain specific channels which have been allocated by the Federal Communications Commission for that purpose. Under these circumstances, preset circuits actuated by pressing a push button greatly simplifies receiver tuning and assures the user of a properly tuned receiver each time. Ordinary preset circuits, such as we find in standard-broadcast A-M home receivers are unsuitable for commercial usage because of their tendency to drift after a short period of operation. Preset circuits, to have any commercial value, must be able to retain their calibration under the rugged conditions encountered in such operations.

In order to obtain better frequency stability, quartz crystal oscillators are used. Crystals, on a production basis, can be obtained with a stability of ±0.005 per cent, which represents 5 kc at 100 mc. Included in this figure are variations due to temperature and humidity. Desirable stability has been previously stated as ±0.01 per cent, which is a lower degree of stability than the 0.005 per cent obtainable with a crystal. The need for specially constructed temperature-compensating components in crystal oscillators is also less. This does not mean that the crystal oscillator section need not be carefully constructed, but it does mean that greater leeway is possible in choosing components. Through the use of crystals, push-button tuning becomes perfectly feasible because consistent operation is achieved over long periods of time. For the layman user of an F-M receiver, this form of selecting stations assures optimum results without much effort and eliminates entirely the need for any form of tuning indicator.

When crystal oscillators are used, however, reception is restricted only to those stations for which crystals are provided. In other words, each separate frequency to be received requires another crystal in the oscillator in order to develop the proper mixing frequency for the signal. Generally the number seldom runs beyond three or four, although the actual space required is small and a larger number of crystals could be accommodated without increasing the physical dimensions of the receiver appreciably.

Crystal Oscillator Circuits. In choosing a crystal oscillator circuit, we desire a circuit that will require nothing more than the insertion of the crystal to make it oscillate. For this reason, the tuned-grid, tuned-plate circuit using the crystal would be unsatisfactory. Here, besides the insertion of the crystal, we must tune the plate tank condenser. A suitable circuit is the grid-plate crystal

oscillator shown in Fig. 6.10.   The crystal is connected between the grid and ground.   In the cathode tuned circuit, the radio frequency choke and the fixed condenser, 0.0001 mf, tune to a frequency that is lower than the crystal frequency.   Good output is ob-
tained on the fundamental and on harmonics.   Good output on the harmonics is especially desirable because, as we shall soon see, it is not the fundamental frequency that is used for mixing but a harmonic.   In order to accentuate the desired harmonic,

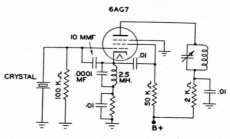

FIG. 6.10.   A grid-plate crystal oscillator.

the plate tank circuit is tuned to that harmonic.   The setting of the plate tank has no effect upon the functioning of the oscillator but is inserted to insure that sufficient voltage is generated at the harmonic frequency.

For crystal control, the mixing oscillator frequency is generally below the signal input by the I.F. value, say 10.7 mc.   If the set is tuned to 152 mc (one of the frequencies allocated to taxicabs), then the mixing oscillator must generate a signal which is 10.7 mc lower than this, or 141.3 mc.   With a strong fundamental crystal frequency near 11.8 mc, multiplication by a factor of 12 is required to reach 141.3 mc.   (The actual crystal frequency would be 11.775 mc.)   This means that we must use the 12th harmonic of the fundamental crystal frequency.   A well-designed crystal oscillator will develop an output which is rich in harmonics and possess sufficient voltage at the 12th harmonic to permit use of the simple oscillator circuit shown in Fig. 6.11.   For each frequency a sepa-
rate crystal and two trimmer condensers are brought in by a push button or a rotary switch.   The trimmer condenser C_1 across L_1 is peaked at the factory to resonate L_1 to the proper harmonic frequency. L_1 and its trimmer do not in any way influence the oscil-
lations of the crystal unit.   They merely serve to produce a strong output at the harmonic mixing frequency.   The other trimmer condenser, C_2, tunes the antenna input coil, L_2, to the signal frequency.

The addition of an R.F. stage would add one more trimmer condenser.

Instead of operating the crystal oscillator at the 12th harmonic of the crystal, many manufacturers prefer to use a crystal with a low fundamental frequency and then use two quadrupler stages. The advantage of using a low fundamental frequency crystal lies in the fact that it is thicker than a higher frequency crystal. Thicker crystals are more easily manufactured and they can with-

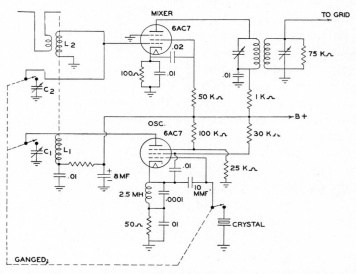

FIG. 6.11. The input stages of a crystal-controlled F-M receiver. The suppressor grid of the oscillator is made slightly positive to produce a strong output.

stand greater current surges without cracking. The thinner a crystal is, the more easily it may break, either from jarring or excessive current flow in its circuit. Outweighing the advantage of a thicker crystal is the fact that a higher order harmonic must be used in order to obtain the proper mixing frequency. The higher the order of the harmonic, the lower the voltage developed in the oscillator. Too low a mixing voltage will not permit full advantage to be taken of the conversion transconductance of the mixer. The output on weak signals may drop so low as to make good reception impossible.

Where to Place Oscillator Frequency. The oscillator frequency, we know, must be separated from the incoming signal frequency by an amount equal to the intermediate frequency. The question then arises as to where this oscillator frequency is to be placed, whether above or below the signal. As far as the outcome is concerned, it makes absolutely no difference which point is chosen, as long as the difference between the point chosen and the signal results in the proper I.F. It is usual in many F-M high frequency sets to place the oscillator below the signal frequency.[2] This is quite contrary to the present practice at the standard broadcast frequencies, where the oscillator always operates above the signal. The reasons for the placement of each, however, are simply explained. At the lower frequencies, the signal frequency range extends from 550 kc to 1700 kc. The usual I.F. is 455 kc. Suppose we designed the mixing oscillator so that it functioned 455 kc below the signal. Then it would have to cover a range from 95 kc to 1235 kc — or a range where the highest and lowest frequencies were in the ratio of 13 to 1. For a single coil and condenser to cover a range this wide would present a practical problem that would be most difficult to solve. Most tuning combinations possess a tuning ratio of 2 or 3 to 1. Here we need 13 to 1. For this reason the oscillator frequency is made higher than the signal. Now let us see what happens. Being above the signal, the oscillator must generate frequencies from 1005 to 2155 kc — or a range with approximately a 2 to 1 ratio. This is easily obtained in practice with one condenser and coil.

Now let us look at the higher F-M band, 88 to 108 mc. We will assume an I.F. of 15 mc. If the oscillator is placed above the carrier frequencies, its range will be from 103 to 123 mc. If placed below the carrier frequencies, its range will be from 73 to 93 mc. Design of tuning circuits does not enter into this discussion because both ranges are perfectly possible with one set of

[2] While the reasons outlined stress placement of the oscillator on the low frequency side of the signal, there are sets manufactured in which the oscillator frequency is above the signal. In this position any radiated oscillator power will not cause interference in near-by television receivers which do receive signals in the 76–82 mc and 82–88 mc video channels. Interference may arise when the oscillator frequency is below the F-M (88–108 mc) signal frequency.

components. But in choosing the lower frequencies, we gain the advantages of greater ease in construction, more easily obtained stability, and the use of less critical components. The advantages of lower frequency oscillators become even greater when crystal control is desired because here we are using a fairly high harmonic of the crystal and the strength of the harmonic voltages decreases rapidly. The lower the crystal harmonic used, the simpler the receiver design becomes. Hence, the oscillators in many F-M receivers will be in the range from 77.3 to 97.3 mc, this being 10.7 mc below the signal range, 88 to 108 mc.

PROBLEMS

1. Why are the I.F. amplifiers important in a superheterodyne receiver?

2. What is the difference between the terms " frequency converter " and " frequency mixer"? Which is found most frequently in standard broadcast A-M receivers? In F-M receivers?

3. Draw the circuit of a mixer with a triode Hartley oscillator.

4. Why is oscillator stability so important in a high-frequency receiver?

5. Discuss the various factors which govern oscillator stability.

6. What are some of the countermeasures employed to stabilize the oscillator frequency?

7. From the standpoint of noise and efficiency, what type of tube is most desirable? Why?

8. Draw representative circuits illustrating how the output of a separate oscillator is coupled capacitively to the mixer. Illustrate, too, inductive coupling. Is there any other method of coupling possible between the oscillator and mixer? Explain.

9. Why is the frequency drift in an uncompensated oscillator always toward the lower frequencies?

10. In Fig. 6.3, the initial frequency drift of the oscillator frequency is positive. Explain why this differs from the situation in an uncompensated oscillator.

11. Are frequency converters ever used in F-M receivers? Illustrate your answer using the circuits in Chapter 12.

12. Which three oscillator circuits are commonly employed in F-M receivers? Draw one and couple its output capacitively to a mixer.

13. Is it desirable for an oscillator to produce harmonics? What effect do these harmonics have on the receiver operation?

14. What desirable properties should an oscillator tube possess?

15. Why would a crystal oscillator be advantageous in an F-M receiver? What disadvantages would it introduce?

16. Are there any limitations on the placement of the oscillator frequency? Explain.

17. Draw the circuit diagram of a crystal-controlled oscillator and the associated mixer.

18. What type of crystal oscillator circuits are used?

19. What considerations govern the choice of a crystal?

20. Explain the operation of a mixer.

21. Define conversion transconductance. Contrast this with mutual conductance of a tube.

22. Why is loose coupling employed between an oscillator and a mixer?

23. Explain why the placement of the oscillator frequency in a standard broadcast receiver is restricted more than it is in a high-frequency F-M set.

CHAPTER 7

I.F. AMPLIFIERS

Design Factors of I.F. Amplifiers. The superiority of the superheterodyne lies in its I.F. amplifiers. The incoming signal frequency is purposely lowered to a level where a large degree of amplification is more readily, and efficiently, achieved, using conventional radio components. In addition, it permits the designing of fixed tuned circuits with a bandspread sufficiently wide to include all the sideband frequencies arising from modulation. An engineer,

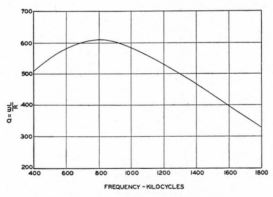

Fig. 7.1. The variation of Q (of a coil) with frequency.

designing a tuned circuit for use at one frequency only, can better obtain the maximum amplification than if he were faced with the prospect of having to adapt the circuit for uniform operation over a range of frequencies. A coil designed to function over many frequencies, such as is necessary in the input stages of a receiver, generally produces uneven amplification over the entire band. In Fig. 7.1 is shown a curve illustrating the variation in the Q of a coil ($\omega L/R$) with frequency over the standard broadcast band. Note that the Q has a high value at the beginning and then drops fairly rapidly at the higher frequencies. This latter decrease is due to the fact that R increases more rapidly than ωL with the rise in frequency. R represents a combination of:

1. Losses in the form on which the coil is wound.
2. Skin effect, which confines the current to a narrow layer near the surface of the wire.
3. Eddy current losses in near-by metallic objects.

Through the use of a circuit tuned to one fixed frequency, the amplification and selectivity may be held constant — adding to the stability of the receiver.

In the design of an I.F. amplifier, or an I.F. system containing several stages, three basic factors must be considered:

1. Frequency of the I.F. stages.
2. Gain.
3. Selectivity.

These quantities are certainly interrelated, but the general procedure is to choose first the operating frequency and then to consider the problems of gain and selectivity together.

Choosing the Intermediate Frequency. The choice of an intermediate frequency may appear, at first, to be quite simple since we know that at the lower frequencies it is easier to arrange and design circuit components to obtain high gain. However, there is a limit to the low frequencies that can be used because of the stability of the oscillator and other circuit components located ahead of the I.F. stages in the receiver. When a set is first put into operation, it may require as much as an hour or so before the oscillator frequency becomes stable. When ordinary parts are used in the construction of a receiver, the oscillator may drift as much as 0.2 per cent in frequency. At 95 mc, this means a drift of 190 kc With a low value of I.F., the station would soon drift outside of the I.F. range. Through compensation of an oscillator, such as the use of low-loss tube sockets, careful wiring, condensers with negative temperature coefficients, etc., the amount of drift can be lowered to a figure of 0.05 per cent of the carrier frequency or 48 kc. This is a considerable improvement over the previous uncompensated figure. Further improvement can be achieved only at much greater cost, perhaps involving specially constructed components or the use of crystal-controlled oscillators.

A second limitation on the use of a low I.F. is the tendency of most oscillators (excepting, possibly, crystal oscillators) to lock-in with other more stable oscillators when they are quite close in frequency. With a low I.F., a strong signal could readily pull the oscillator out of its desired position into the same frequency as the signal. As might be expected, under these conditions, no difference or intermediate frequency will be produced.

Still another consideration governing the choice of an I.F. value is the spread of the incoming signal. An F-M broadcast, fully modulated, occupies a frequency bandwidth of 200 kc. Obviously, it would be ridiculous to use any I.F. below this figure, for then how would it be possible to vary an I.F. of say 125 kc plus and minus 200 kc? There are no negative frequencies. Hence, an I.F. higher than 200 kc is necessary. But how much higher? 400 kc? 800 kc? 1 mc? or still higher? Before we definitely answer this question, let us investigate the different types of spurious responses capable of affecting a receiver and their influence on the choice of an intermediate frequency.

Spurious Responses. A spurious response is defined as the reception of a signal at a point other than desired on the dial. For example, a station may be received at more than one point on the dial, or two or more stations obtained at the same time when only one should be present. In using the phrase " spurious response," we refer only to interference caused by stations appearing at undesired points of the dial. Atmospheric and man-made noises are not included.

The most important spurious responses to which an F-M set is subjected are:

1. Image response.

2. Response of two stations separated in frequency by the I.F. value.

3. Direct I.F. response.

4. Combination of harmonics from oscillator and signal.

We may pause here and note that the appearance of any of these spurious responses is in no way connected with the noise-reducing qualities of frequency modulation discussed in Chapter 1. Any interfering signal, either arising from one of the sources listed above or from another station on the same channel, will be completely suppressed if the desired signal is at least twice as strong as the interference. However, the danger lies in the fact that this relationship may not exist. In fact, the undesired signal may be many more times stronger than our desired signal. In such an event, the desired signal could be either badly distorted or else completely obliterated. The choice of an I.F., coupled with proper design, will do much to minimize the interference from the four main sources listed above.

Image Response. Image response is due to the mixing of an undesired signal with the oscillator voltage in the converter stage to produce a voltage at the intermediate frequency. Since a frequency equal to the intermediate frequency is produced, this signal will be accepted and passed by the I.F. amplifiers. To understand how this may occur, suppose that a receiver is tuned to a station at 95.3 mc. With the oscillator set at 99.3 mc, the difference (4.0 mc) which is also the intermediate frequency will be produced in the frequency converter or mixer plate circuit and fed into the I.F. stages. Modulation would swing the carrier ± 75 kc about the center value.

Now suppose — and this may readily happen — there is another powerful station in the vicinity operating on a frequency of 103.3 mc. If sufficient selectivity is not provided ahead of the converter stage — or an R.F. stage of amplification is not included in the set — then an appreciable amount of the signal voltage from the 103.3-mc station may appear at the converter grid. Subsequent mixing with the 99.3-mc voltage from the oscillator will produce a difference frequency of 4.0 mc which is also equal to the I.F. This second interfering signal is referred to as an image station.

It makes little difference — so far as the production of image response is concerned — whether the oscillator frequency is higher or lower than the desired station. In the preceding example, the oscillator was operating above the desired signal. It may also be located lower in frequency by an amount equal to the I.F. In fact, most manufacturers prefer the lower oscillator frequency because of the increased stability of oscillators at lower frequencies.

Using the last example, but with the oscillator below the desired signal, say at 91.3 mc, an image response will be obtained if the signal is below the oscillator by an amount equal to 4.0 mc. In this instance, this would mean a station at 87.3 mc. Under present allocations, the F-M band starts at 88 mc and no F-M station is located at 87.3 mc. However, if we tuned the receiver to another station, say at 97.3 mc, then with the oscillator at 93.3 mc and the image station at 89.3 mc we create a possibility for an image response. It will be noted that whenever the oscillator frequency is higher than that of the desired station, the image is above the oscillator by an amount equal to the I.F. On the other hand, the image station is lower in frequency than the desired station when

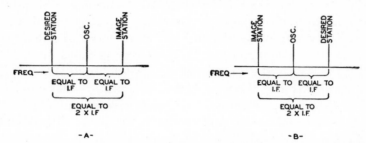

FIG. 7.2. The relationship between the desired and image stations when the oscillator frequency is above (A) and below (B) the signal frequency.

the oscillator is also lower. The image station and the desired signal are always separated from each other by an amount equal to twice the I.F. value. This is shown in Fig. 7.2.

One solution for minimizing interference due to images is increasing the selectivity of the tuned circuits preceding the converter stage. Not only is the number of tuned circuits important but also the attenuation they impose on any signal extending beyond the ±100-kc limits of the desired station. It is generally operationally difficult and most times economically impractical to develop in these high frequency input circuits a high degree of selectivity. At the low frequencies, one megacycle separation between signals represents a considerable percentage of the carrier frequency. Thus, for example, two stations separated by one megacycle at 15 mc could be resolved readily, without interference, by a circuit possessing a much lower Q (and, hence, selectivity) than if the carrier frequency is raised to 90 mc. It is not the numerical frequency difference between stations that is important but the percentage difference. In the first case, the percentage separation is approximately 6.7 per cent; at 90 mc, a 1-mc separation represents a percentage separation of approximately 1.1 per cent. Two tuned circuits possessing the same selectivity could be more economically manufactured at the low frequencies than at the high frequencies.

The foregoing illustration is one reason why superheterodynes have proved so popular. In a superheterodyne, the signal on reaching the receiver is converted or " stepped-down " to a lower frequency which is known as the intermediate frequency. Once the frequency is lowered, we can better apply selectivity and gain to the signal than if it had remained at 90 or 100 mc, its incoming value. No lowering occurs in tuned radio-frequency receivers — receivers which are practically out of production except in very cheap sets built to receive the standard broadcasting frequencies. Despite additions of R.F. amplifier stages to a receiver and despite any sharp selectivity of the input resonant circuits, it is still the I.F. amplifiers which are chiefly responsible for the selectivity or sensitivity obtainable from a superheterodyne.

The choice of an I.F. has a direct bearing on the amount of image response to which a set is subjected. If the I.F. is too low, say 1, 2, or 3 mc in value, then the possibility of interference from image stations is correspondingly increased because of the small percentage difference between the desired signal and an image signal. Raising the I.F. provides a greater separation between these signals and makes it easier for the preliminary or input circuits to weaken the interfering signal — weaken it probably to the point where the desired signal could normally override it. In practice, it is common to make the I.F. slightly greater than half the width of the entire F-M band. Thus, since the band extends for 20 mc — from 88 mc to 108 mc — an I.F. of 10.7 mc would eliminate interference from image stations entirely. The reason is quite simple. We have just noted that the desired station and the image station are always separated by 2 × I.F. value (see Fig. 7.2). But, if 2 × I.F. value is greater than the width of the entire broadcast band, then it is obvious that the reception of image signals, within that particular band, is impossible.

Of course, we must not overlook the possibility of stations on adjacent bands causing trouble. Thus, for instance, adjacent to the F-M band, 88–108 mc, at the lower side is the television band, 82–88 mc. However, sufficient discrimination is provided by the input resonant circuits to make this possibility small.

Stations Separated by the Intermediate Frequency. The second source of spurious response listed is interference arising when two signals mix, both separated in frequency by an amount equal to the I.F. of the receiver. In this situation, one incoming signal acts as the mixing oscillator for the other signal, their difference frequency appearing at the output of the mixer or converter stage as the intermediate frequency. As an illustration of this type of spurious response, consider a receiver where the input selectivity is such that two signals, say 90.3 mc and 99.4 mc, are present at the converter grid in appreciable strength. When these mix with each other, in the converter circuit itself, a difference frequency of 9.1 mc (the I.F., say) will appear. The oscillator of the set itself does not enter into this action, and with poor input selectivity these two stations will be present no matter where the set is actually tuned. Hence, they will be heard all over the dial.

There are two solutions to the problem. One is to provide sufficient discrimination in the circuits preceding the mixer that they will reject two signals so widely separated in frequency. The other is to provide a high I.F., preferably an I.F. slightly greater than the entire bandwidth. In present-day operation, this would mean an I.F. above 20 mc. By so doing, we make it impossible for any two stations within the band to mix with each other at the converter (providing they reach this stage) to produce a difference frequency equal to the receiver I.F.

Direct I.F. Response. The third type of spurious response that may arise is due to direct reception of a frequency equal to the receiver I.F. itself. If some station or service is transmitting at the I.F. value used in the receiver, this signal could easily reach the I.F. amplifiers either through the usual input channel or else directly by the development of the signal voltage on the grid of the first I.F. amplifier when adequately shielding is not provided. That this can be a serious source of trouble has been demonstrated by many tests.

To forego the need of incorporating special filters, wave traps and shielding to prevent interference from the latter source, an I.F. is chosen whose frequency is seldom that of any commercial transmission. This accounts for such seemingly odd figures as 4.3 or 10.7 mc for the value of an I.F. On many frequencies, the only traffic is ship-to-shore messages or perhaps traffic between mobile experimental equipment, etc. These frequencies have been set aside by the government for the particular services. Since the stations operating at these frequencies are not very powerful, the possibility of their interfering with our home receivers is fairly remote. Hence, these frequencies are chosen for the I.F. in the receiver.

Harmonic Spurious Responses. The fourth and final item on the list of spurious responses is the production of interference from harmonic relationships occurring between signal and oscillator voltages that could produce a voltage at the I.F. value. Perhaps the best way of demonstrating this source of spurious response is by an actual example. Suppose the oscillator is at 95.1 mc. Its second harmonic would be at 190.2 mc. If a strong signal of 90.5 mc overloads the input of the receiver, a very good chance exists that its second harmonic would be formed, the frequency being 2 × 90.5 mc, or 181.1 mc. The difference between 190.2 mc and 181.1 mc is 9.1 mc. This would reach the plate circuit of the converter stage and be accepted by an I.F. amplifier designed for 9.1 mc.

The probability of the foregoing situation occurring in a receiver depends to a great extent upon the care taken in the receiver design. Since the appearance of this form of spurious response depends upon the generation of second harmonics of both a signal and the oscillator, the obvious solution is to minimize the possibility of such harmonics. In the oscillator, it is almost impossible to prevent the appearance of harmonics because of the nonlinear operation of the circuit itself. In general, though, the strength of the harmonics decreases with the order of the harmonic. Thus, the fundamental frequency component is strongest, the second harmonic not quite as strong, the third harmonic weaker still, etc. The rapidity with which the strength of the harmonics decreases is a function of the Q of the tank circuit. The higher the Q, the greater the harmonic attenuation.

At the converter, best results are achieved at some value of oscillator voltage. This means that if the oscillator injection voltage is kept at or slightly below the optimum figure, the largest amount of I.F. voltage will be obtained at the converter output. Increasing the oscillator voltage does not improve the amount of desired I.F. produced, but it does strengthen the effectiveness of the harmonics of the oscillator in the conversion process. Hence, one way to minimize the effect of the oscillator harmonics at the converter is not to overload the converter with oscillator voltage.

To minimize the formation of any second harmonic components of signals appearing across the receiver input, the circuits should possess adequate selectivity. All R.F. tubes should be of the variable mu type, preferably controlled by some small amount of AVC. Although a sharp cut-off tube generally has a greater g_m (mutual conductance) and hence capable of greater gain, it is, at the same time, more easily overloaded, a condition that readily leads to the production of harmonics. By forfeiting a little gain and using a variable mu tube with a small amount of controlling AVC, we can also reduce the production of harmonics. The AVC voltage is obtained from the limiter, or, if necessary, from the discriminator.

The foregoing discussion has, by no means, exhausted the subject of spurious responses. However, the important sources have been covered and sufficient information obtained to understand their effect on receiver design and operation. It is quite evident that a high I.F. is desirable, and to a certain point, the higher the better. This not only is advantageous in reducing the probability of spurious responses, but also in permitting a lower oscillator frequency to be used. When the I.F. is high, the oscillator can be operated that much lower than the signal. An oscillator operating at a lower frequency can be more easily designed for greater stability and efficiency than an oscillator functioning at the much higher frequencies. Against the use of a high I.F. are the disadvantages of reduced gain, necessity for greater care in choosing components to prevent excess losses, additional shielding and increased tendency toward feedback through the tubes and adjacent circuits. Also, we have the ever-present requirement of selectivity which rears its head at every turn and is certainly one of the most important factors in any consideration of operating frequency. All these factors must be weighed against each other and the trend of late is to use high intermediate frequencies. For the F-M band, the choice of 10.7 mc has been recommended. It would not be at all surprising to see it rise — and settle — at some higher frequency, possibly between 20 and 30 mc.

Gain and Selectivity. After the frequency of the I.F. system is chosen, we are faced next with the problems of gain and selectivity. So far as the latter is concerned, the response should be uniform up to the sideband limits on either side of the carrier. A desired shape for the response curve is shown in Fig. 7.3. In general, though, the expense involved in attempting to construct a circuit possessing anywhere near such a response characteristic is prohibitive. The more readily achieved curve, shown in Fig. 7.4, is one practical compromise. At the plus and minus 75-kc points from the carrier, the response is down about 4 db. In terms of voltage attenuation, this represents a decrease in the ratio of 1.25 to 1. At 100 kc the attenuation has risen to 10 db (3.2 to 1) and at 200 kc from the carrier, it has reached 30 db (14 to 1). These represent figures which can be achieved in practice and which tend to provide the necessary discrimination against unwanted signals in adjacent channels. It must be understood that when we assign a figure such as a 30-db loss at 200 kc, we are referring to the total attenuation of the I.F. system and not to any single stage. Thus, suppose there are four tuned circuits in the I.F. system. Then each circuit contributes $\frac{1}{4}$ of 30 db or 7.5 db. The overall curve, though, would introduce this much loss to the particular frequency attempting to pass through the amplifiers.

When we speak of the selectivity of a tuned circuit, we refer actually to its Q. Q is defined as the ratio of the inductive reactance of the coil in the tuned circuit to the a-c resistance of that coil. When the Q is high, the impedance presented to any frequency (or narrow band of frequencies) is high, resulting in a large voltage being developed across the coil (at that frequency). When circuits are inductively coupled this results in a large transfer of energy between them. At other frequencies, the opposition offered is not as high, and the transfer of energy is reduced. Here is where the loss, or attenuation, arises at these other frequencies.

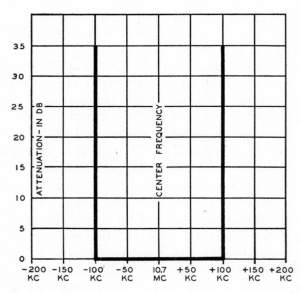

FIG. 7.3. An ideal selectivity response curve. All frequencies having values above 10.7 mc + 100 kc and below 10.7 mc — 100 kc are rejected by the circuit.

The overall selectivity curve (Fig. 7.4) is the product of the Q of each tuned circuit in the system. Each set of coils must be properly wound, correctly spaced and, at the high frequencies, loaded down to produce the proper characteristics. Not only must the engineer determine the effect of Q on attenuation but also its effect on the gain of a stage, because the stage amplification is governed by the formula

$$A = g_m \frac{\omega L Q}{2}$$

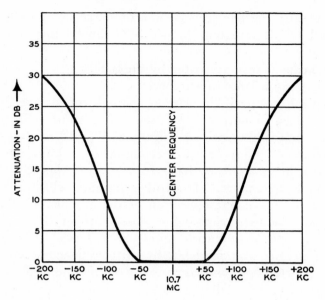

FIG. 7.4. The practical selectivity curve of an F-M receiver.

where g_m = mutual conductance of the tube and ωL = inductive reactance of the coil. This formula is based on a double tuned arrangement (Fig. 7.5) where $L_1 = L_2$ and $Q_1 = Q_2$. This is customary as it simplifies mass production.

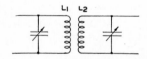

FIG. 7.5. A double tuned transformer. For ease in production, $L_1 = L_2$ and $Q_1 = Q_2$.

The special importance of gain in its relationship to limiter operation is discussed at a later point. In the tuned circuit, a high Q means a high L to C ratio. The higher L is, the more inductive reactance (ωL) is presented to the tube and the greater the output voltage. But from the formula

$$f = \frac{1}{2\pi \sqrt{LC}}$$

where L = inductance in circuit
C = capacitance across coil
f = resonant frequency at which circuit functions

we see that, for any one frequency, large L requires a correspondingly small C. The extent to which C can be lowered depends upon:

1. The capacitance presented by the tube.
2. The stray wiring capacitance.

For a typical case, 6BA6, with a mutual conductance of 4400 micromhos, has an output capacitance of 5 mmf. Stray wiring capacitance may amount to an additional 5 to 10 mmf, depending upon how well the layout was accomplished. Thus, from these extraneous sources alone we have 15 mmf, and this will represent the minimum capacitance. If a coil is designed which utilizes only the stray capacitance, the operation of the amplifiers may become unstable because of the changes that occur in this capacitance with heat, length of operation, moisture and other factors. The I.F. tuned circuits would repeatedly shift frequency each time the set was operated. Good reception would be difficult. Experience has demonstrated that a physically inserted condenser of at least 35 mmf should be included for stable operation. However, this limits the highest value of inductance for any one frequency and consequently places a ceiling on the gain possible for any stage.

The gain of a stage also varies directly with the mutual conductance of the tube, and a high g_m value is desirable. The particular usefulness of a high g_m is the large change in current flow caused by a relatively small change in grid voltage. In any plate load circuit, whether it be resistive or inductive, a large current variation gives rise to a large voltage drop and a consequent increased transfer of energy. After all, amplification within any circuit is merely a measure of the effect a small incoming voltage has in producing a large output. The greater this ratio, the higher the amplification factor. A high g_m is one way of achieving this goal.

To obtain greater values of mutual conductance, it is necessary that the grid exercise greater control over the electron current flow within the tube. Increased cathode emission, by an increase in the cathode area, would result in a greater transconductance. The interelectrode capacitance, however, would also increase by as great a factor, further limiting the L/C ratio of the tank circuit. One solution employed in the design of many miniature tubes is based upon the fact that by bringing the grid closer to the cathode, g_m would increase inversely as the square of the spacing, whereas C_{gk} would only rise inversely as the spacing. In other words, the g_m would rise more rapidly than the interelectrode capacitance. To a certain point this procedure is advisable but its limits — both in the nearness to which the grid can approach the cathode and the amount of interelectrode capacitance that can be tolerated — are quite evident.

Due to the importance of the interelectrode capacities and the mutual conductance of a tube in determining the gain and stability of an amplifier, a " Figure of Merit " has been assigned to tubes on the basis of their ratio. Expressed mathematically,

$$\text{Figure of merit} = \frac{g_m}{C_{\text{in}} + C_{\text{out}} + C_{gp}(A + 1)}$$

where $C_{\text{in}} = $ the input capacitance of the tube
$C_{\text{out}} = $ the output capacitance of the tube
$C_{gp} = $ capacitance between grid and plate electrodes
$g_m = $ mutual conductance of tube
$A = $ amplification of the stage

The values for the three capacitances can be obtained from any tube manual. The same is true for G_m. The value of the stage amplification, however, must be computed. The amplification is given by the equation

$$A = Z_L \times g_m$$

where Z_L is the load impedance expressed in ohms and G_m in mhos. For the tuned circuits used in the I.F. stages of an F-M receiver, we can assume a nominal value of 10,000 ohms for Z_L. With the value of A computed, we may substitute in the formula given above to determine the value of the " Figure of Merit." Table IV contains a list of current pentodes with their relative standing.

The procedure for choosing a tube for use in an amplifier is to tabulate a list of all suitable tubes and then pick the one that has the highest " Figure of Merit."

We have undertaken a fairly detailed inspection of the operation

TABLE IV

Tube Type	Tube Capacitances			g_m (micro-mhos)	A	Figure of Merit g_m/C_{total}
	C_{gp} (mmf)	C_{in} (mmf)	C_{out} (mmf)			
6AB7	0.015	8	5	5,000	50	363
6AC7	0.015	11	5	9,000	90	519
6AG5	0.025	6.5	1.8	5,000	50	524
6AG7	0.06	13	7.5	11,000	110	405
6AK5	0.01	4.3	2.1	5,100	51	737
6AK6	0.12	3.6	4.2	2,300	23	216
6C6	0.007	5.0	6.5	1,226	12.3	110
6D6	0.007	4.7	6.5	1,600	16	141
6R6	0.007	4.5	11	1,450	14.5	93
7V7	0.004	9.5	6.5	5,800	58	358
7W7	0.0025	9.5	7.0	5,800	58	348
6AU6	0.0035	5.5	5.0	4,450	44.5	418
6BA6	0.0035	5.5	5.0	4,400	44	417
6SH7	0.003	8.5	7.0	4,900	49	313

and design of high-frequency I.F. amplifiers because of the importance of these details to those who are going to service or build such amplifiers. Every single component, down to the exact layout of the wiring, must be taken into careful consideration in either repairing or building an F-M receiver. But, without an understanding of the reasons behind this necessity, repairing or construction of sets soon devolves into a mechanical procedure, easily forgotten; certainly, never appreciated. It is only when one has a full appreciation of the task can the best results be obtained.

Commercial I.F. Amplifiers. Schematically, the I.F. amplifier of an F-M receiver (excluding the limiters for the present) does not differ in form from those amplifiers with which we are familiar from sound broadcast receivers. A typical diagram is shown in Fig. 7.6. The general tendency in these higher frequency interstage coupling units is to vary the frequency of the tuned circuit by means of permeability tuning. The threaded core is some magnetic material, generally powdered iron. It is threaded and as it is moved deeper into the center of the coil, it acts to increase the inductance of the coil thereby decreasing the resonant frequency. The advantage of this method of tuning over a variable condenser is that it permits a higher inductance to be used and a wider tuning range to be covered.

The capacitance associated with the inductance, at a high I.F. is kept, as we have already noted, as small as practical. With a small variable condenser only a limited tuning range is possible.

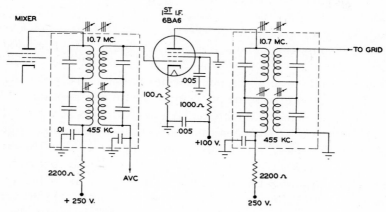

FIG. 7.6. An I.F. amplifier. The symbol above each coil indicates permeability tuning (courtesy RCA).

To cover a greater range, a large capacitance would be required. But to accommodate the larger capacitance, L would have to be lowered. With a decrease in the L/C ratio occasioned by such a

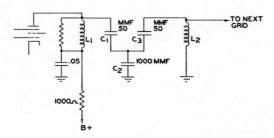

FIG. 7.7. A complex interstage coupling network used in Scott receivers.

procedure, a decrease in gain would occur. Hence, the advisability of permeability tuning. From time to time manufacturers employ complex coupling between stages in place of the usual two coil arrangement shown in Fig. 7.6. Fig. 7.7 is indicative of this type of a circuit and is employed in some Scott receivers. Here L_1 and

L_2 are not inductively coupled to each other. Rather the transfer of energy takes place through the three condensers C_1, C_2, and C_3. C_2 is the common coupling condenser, being common to both circuits. Since the transfer of energy takes place in this manner, the circuits are said to be capacitively coupled. The advantages to be gained through such an arrangement are greater selectivity and a more uniform response throughout the desired range. Its disadvantage is increased cost.

There are many similar combinations possible and probably the reader has encountered some of them at one time or another. Their only difference from the double tuned transformer is in the response they offer and the attenuation imposed on adjacent channel signals. They are widely used in television, where signal bandwidths extend to 6 mc. In such situations, simple coupling devices prove inadequate in maintaining the gain and at the same time presenting uniform response throughout the entire bandwidth. However, in F-M, 200 kc represents a relatively small percentage of the I.F. value, and conventionally coupled circuits are satisfactory.

In order to enhance the sales value of F-M receivers (due to its present restricted use), it is common practice to provide for the reception of standard broadcast and short-wave stations. To keep the total cost of the receiver at a minimum, the same tubes are used for all frequencies, each band corresponding to a different position on the selector switch. One I.F. is employed for the F-M band and one set of I.F. coils for the standard broadcast and short-wave frequencies. To keep connecting wire lengths to a minimum and for space economy, both I.F. transformers are placed within the same can. In some constructions, all windings are placed on the same post. In others, like the one illustrated in Fig. 7.8, there are several posts, each for an individual primary and secondary winding of the tuned circuits. In the composite I.F. transformer shown, an indented area at the underside of the unit contains a stack of silvered mica plates. These are the condensers which resonate the coils to the approximate frequency. The threaded iron core, which is mounted in the hollow center section of each post, then permits adjustment for an accurate alignment. The two primary condensers are silver printed upon one mica disc; the secondary condensers utilize another mica disc. Contact to each silvered surface is made with double-ended metal strips. With two ends, separate lead connections for the chassis wiring and coil terminals may be made. To make the transformer as compact as possible all by-pass condensers associated with that particular section of the circuit are contained within the unit by means of additional mica discs. In this way frequency variations due to temperature changes are limited approximately to a value between 10 and 20 kc. Separate openings at the top of the metallic shield provide access to each iron core.

FIG. 7.8. The compact A-M, F-M, I.F. transformer showing the method of coil arrangement.

No difficulty is encountered by placing the transformers in series with each other, as shown in Fig. 7.6. At any one time only one signal is being received and therefore only one set of I.F. transformers are in use. If the signal is an A.M. signal, the lower set of I.F. transformers in Fig. 7.6 are being used. The upper transformers which are in series with the A.M. units do not affect the A.M. signal because the inductance in the 10.7 mc coils is almost negligible at 455 kc.

When an F-M signal is being received, the upper set of I.F. transformers are used. The 455 kc units do not affect the F-M signal because the condenser shunting the 455 kc I.F. windings acts as a short circuit to the higher 10.7 mc signal, effectively permitting the 10.7 mc signal to pass through the series 455 kc units with negligible loss.

In this respect, here is a service note that may be of interest. Suppose the condenser shunting the primary winding of the 455 kc I.F. transformer located in the plate circuit of the 1st I.F. amplifier opened up. The A.M. sound would come through weakened because of the fact that this winding is now detuned. It might be possible to adjust the iron-coil slug sufficiently to bring the coil back into tune again. But what of the F-M signal? It would now have to pass through the winding of the 455 kc I.F. transformer instead of around it. Since the inductance of this lower frequency winding is considerably greater than the impedance of the 10.7 mc winding above it, most of the F-M signal would appear across the lower winding. The output on F-M then, would be weak and noisy. Only by replacing the open condenser with a good one could the F-M volume be restored.

PROBLEMS

1. What purpose do the I.F. amplifiers serve in a superheterodyne?

2. What advantages are obtained through the use of an I.F. amplifier?

3. What three basic factors must be considered in the design of an I.F. amplifier?

4. Define spurious responses.

5. Which spurious responses prove most troublesome to F-M reception?

6. What governs the choice of an intermediate frequency?

7. Explain image response. Is this phenomenon present in A-M receivers? Explain.

8. What effect does image response have on the choice of an intermediate frequency?

9. How can image response be minimized?

10. How can stations separated in frequency by an amount equal to the receiver I.F. cause interference?

11. What solutions can be employed against this type of interference?

12. What do we mean by the phrase " harmonic spurious responses "? What can be done to reduce their effect?

13. Define the phrase " selectivity of a receiver "? Why is this important?

14. Are the gain and the selectivity of a receiver related? How?

15. What is the difference between the ideal response of a tuning circuit and its actual response? Illustrate by means of graphs.

16. Can interference destroy the desired signal in an F-M receiver? Explain.

17. What relationship exists between the gain of a tuned circuit and the Q of the same circuit?

18. What tends to lower the Q of a tuned circuit?

19. What do we mean by the "Figure of Merit" of a tube? How does this factor influence the design of an I.F. amplifier?

20. Draw a tube symbol and indicate the various capacitances associated with the tube.

21. How is the "Figure of Merit" of a tube obtained?

22. Draw the schematic circuit of an I.F. amplifier.

23. How is one I.F. system used in receivers capable of receiving A-M and F-M signals?

24. What types of interstage coupling is found in the I.F. amplifiers of an F-M receiver?

25. How are most I.F. stages tuned? Why?

CHAPTER 8

LIMITERS

Why Limiters Are Necessary.   The need for limiters in F-M sets arises not from any intrinsic property of an F-M wave but because of the limitations of some of the F-M detectors currently in use.   These detectors are, in varying degrees, sensitive to amplitude variations in an F-M signal.   As a result, the audio output contains voltages due to both the frequency modulation and the amplitude modulation.   The insertion of a total or partial limiter substantially removes the A-M and presents to the detector a wave that is wholly F-M.   Just how much limiting is required will depend upon the type of detector employed.   The Foster-Seeley discriminator requires more than the ratio detector; the locked-in type of F-M detector requires the least amount of limiting, but it is more critical than either of the other two types of detectors and is not widely used.   Until such time as a suitable F-M detector can be developed, limiters, either total or partial, will be used and the serviceman must thoroughly understand their function and operation.

Limiter Operation.   A limiter performs its function of removing amplitude modulation by providing a constant amplitude output signal for a comparatively wide variation in input voltages.   A simple illustration is shown in Fig. 8.1 where the forms of the input and output voltages of a limiter are indicated.   A more exact representation of the ability of a limiter to remove A-M from a wave is given by the characteristic curve of Fig. 8.2.   For all signals possessing more than a certain minimum input voltage at the antenna, the limiter produces a substantially constant output.   In this region, starting at point *B* and extending to the right, the stage is purely a limiter in its action.

In the region from *A* to *B*, however, the stage functions as an amplifier because different input voltages produce different output voltages.   Any signal too weak to drive the limiter beyond (or to the right of) point B will cause amplitude variations in the discriminator output that are in no way part of the original F-M signal. This represents distortion. For proper operation, it is at all times necessary that sufficient amplification be given an incoming signal in

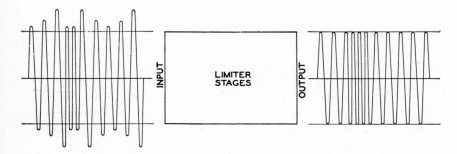

FIG. 8.1. The limiter removes the amplitude variations (modulation) from the input signal.

order that it arrive at the limiters strong enough to drive the tube beyond point B.

Assuming that the F-M signal, as it leaves the transmitter, is wholly frequency-modulated with no amplitude variations, there are two general points in the path of the signal where amplitude variations may be inserted. First, there are atmospheric disturbances, completely random in nature and covering every frequency used for communication. The disturbances may come from natural sources, chiefly electrical storms, or they may come from manmade devices, such as the sparking in automobile ignition systems, trolley lines, electrical machines, etc. Again, there are other stations that may affect the desired

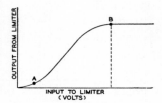

FIG. 8.2. For proper limiting action, the input voltage must be sufficiently strong to operate the limiter at point B or beyond.

signal, although, for the most part, careful assignment of frequencies will minimize such interference. These are all sources external to the receiver and, largely, beyond the control of the set designer.

Within the receiver itself, the unequal response of the tuned circuits is the second important contributing factor toward amplitude variation within an F-M wave. The ideal response curve is a rectangle. This, however is seldom achieved with practical equipment. Economic considerations impose restrictions on the maximum cost of the tuned circuits. As a compromise, the sloping response characteristic is employed with most tuning circuits. An F-M signal applied to a tuned circuit having the response shown in Fig. 8.3 will receive amplification dependent upon the frequency. The center frequency, to which the circuit is peaked, receives the greatest amplification. As the signal frequency moves closer to the ends of the band, the attenuation increases.

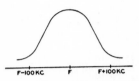

FIG. 8.3. Conventional selectivity characteristics.

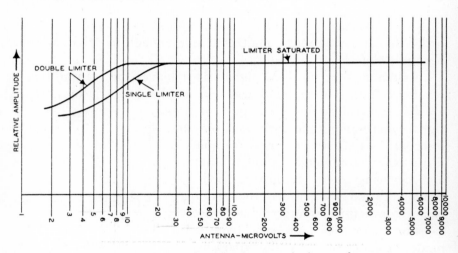

FIG. 8.4. A comparison of the input signal voltage required to produce constant output from single and double limiters.

Influence of Limiters. In order for a limiter stage to be effective, it must function beyond the knee of its characteristic curve for all frequencies of the received F-M signal. In this respect the limiter has a very decided influence over the design and selectivity of the I.F. stages and the amplification that these stages must be capable of providing. Let us consider, for example, the single limiter characteristic shown in Fig. 8.4. According to the graph, the knee of this limiter curve is reached for inputs of 25 microvolts at the antenna. As long as the incoming signal has this value, the

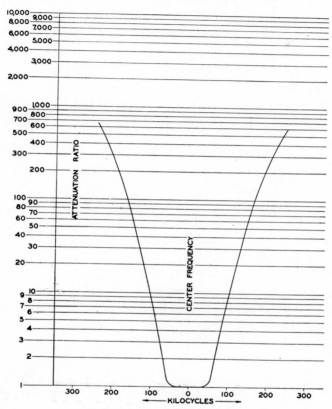

FIG. 8.5. Selectivity curve for an F-M receiver tested.

limiter will function at saturation and no amplitude variations will be obtained at the output. Now consider the curve of Fig. 8.5. This shows the overall selectivity of a typical receiver from the antenna to the limiter. Examination indicates that the farther we move from the mid-frequency to which the receiver is tuned, the greater the attenuation to which the signal is subjected. Thus, at a point 65 kc from the carrier frequency, the signal is subjected to an attenuation rating of 1.25. Glancing back at Fig. 8.4, if 25 microvolts is required at the carrier frequency to give limiter saturation operation, then one and a quarter times this amount, or 31 microvolts, would be needed to produce the same result for that portion of the signal 65 kc off response. Frequencies 75 kc distant are attenuated about two times the mid-frequency value and, at 100 kc, the attenuation ratio is 7. Thus, if we compute the sensitivity of a receiver at points 100 kc off resonance, we find that we need signals of 165 microvolts for complete limiting action. All this is highly important in designing the characteristics of the intervening I.F. stages and the limiter. Beyond ±100 kc, high attenuation of the signal is desirable as this minimizes adjacent station interference.

In practice, with current production limitations for the frequencies near 100 kc, the following gains can be obtained from the various stages of a well-designed F-M receiver.

Directional antenna	5x
Each R.F. stage	8x
Converter	10x
Each I.F. stage (except the one preceding the limiter)	50x
I.F. stage preceding limiter	40x
Single limiter	2.5x
Cascaded limiters	6x

For complete saturation of most limiter stages, an input voltage of 2 volts is necessary. With a 10-microvolt receiver sensitivity (meaning the receiver will reproduce clearly all signals of 10 microvolts or more) an overall gain of 2 volts/10 microvolts, or 200,000 must be available for the signal prior to its application to the grid of the final limiter stage. It then depends upon the designer what combination of R.F. and I.F. stages he will use. Note the relatively poor gain of the R.F. system as compared to each I.F. amplifier. The real usefulness of the R.F. stages lies in their partial discrimination of undesirable signals, and the boosting of weak signals to improve the signal-to-noise ratio. The front end of the receiver is particularly vulnerable to extraneous voltages and anything that will help keep these to a minimum is desirable. However, as far as gain is concerned, it is far more advantageous to add I.F. stages than R.F. stages.

The lower gain obtained from the I.F. amplifier that just precedes the limiter is due to the loading effect of the limiter on the I.F. stage. Grid-current flow in the limiter (as we shall presently see) acts to lower the impedance across the I.F. output coil. The result — a decreased overall impedance with a corresponding lowering in gain. The relationship between amplifier gain and load impedance has been previously given.

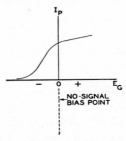

Fig. 8.6. The no-signal bias point for a limiter stage using grid-leak bias.

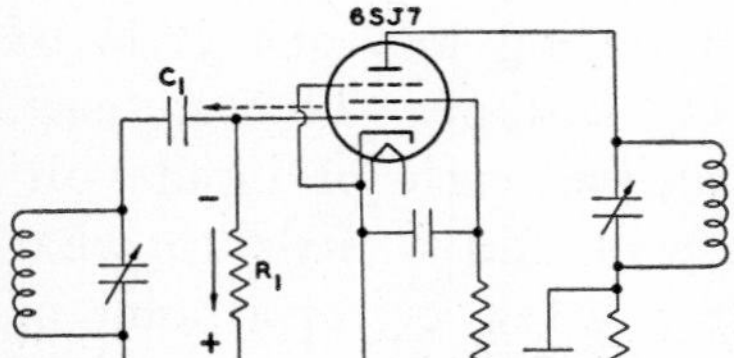

Limiting Methods. There are two widely used methods for obtaining the desirable limiting action. First, we may use grid-leak bias. This limits the plate current on the positive and negative peaks of the incoming signal. Second, we can limit by employing low screen and plate voltages, producing what is known as plate-voltage limiting. Many designers combine both methods in one stage and obtain a better degree of limiting.

Grid-Leak Bias Limiting. The principle of operation of a grid-leak limiter is not difficult to understand. Initially there is no bias and the tube is operating at the zero bias point of its $E_g I_p$ curve. This is shown in Fig. 8.6. Upon the application of a signal, the grid is driven positive and current flows in the grid circuit charging up condenser C_1 (see Fig. 8.7). It is easier for the current to charge C_1 than to attempt to force its way through the relatively high resistance of R_1. The condenser continues to charge throughout the entire portion of the positive half of the incoming signal.

Fig. 8.7. A grid-leak bias limiter stage.

During the negative portion of the input cycle, the accumulated electrons on the right-hand plate of C_1 flow through R_1 and the coil to the left-hand plate. The condenser discharges because it represents a potential difference and as long as a complete path is available, current must flow. The electrons passing through R_1 develop a potential difference with the polarity as indicated in Fig. 8.7. From the moment the input voltage departs from its positive values to the beginning of the next cycle, the discharge of C_1 continues.

At the start of the next cycle, there will be some charge remaining in C_1. Hence, the grid does not draw current again until after the input voltage has risen to a positive value sufficient to overcome the residual negative voltage in C_1. When the input voltage becomes sufficiently positive, current flows, recharging C_1. This sequence will recur as long as an input voltage is present. Because of the fairly long time it takes for C_1 to discharge through R_1, not all the charge on C_1 will disappear during any one cycle of input voltage. Hence, each succeeding cycle of input voltage will add a little to what remains from the previous cycle. After a few cycles a point of equilibrium is reached and the voltage across R_1 remains constant. This establishes the operating bias and the input voltage will fluctuate around this point. The diagram in Fig. 8.8 shows how the tube starts off with zero bias and, after a few cycles, reaches the equilibrium bias point.

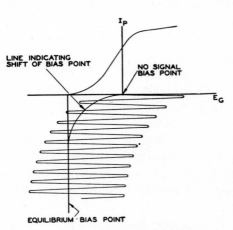

FIG. 8.8. The shift in bias potential during the first few cycles.

The equilibrium bias-point voltage is dependent upon a variety of factors. It depends upon the strength of the input voltage, the voltages on the tube elements, and the time constant of the grid condenser and resistor. For the latter, the time constant is defined as the time, in seconds, for the condenser to discharge 63 per cent of its voltage through R_1. Mathematically, $t = RC$ where

R = resistance in ohms, and C = capacitance in farads. Thus, if we assume values of 0.0001 mf for C and 50,000 ohms for R, we have

$$t = R \times C$$
$$t = 0.0001 \times 10^{-6} \text{ farads} \times 50,000 \text{ ohms}$$
$$t = 5 \times 10^{-6} \text{ seconds}$$

In other words, it requires 5×10^{-6} seconds for the charge on the condenser — no matter what it is — to diminish to 37 per cent of its initial value.

Five $\times 10^{-6}$ seconds, or 5 microseconds, may not appear to be a very long interval but it is long if the input wave has a frequency of 100 mc. At 100 mc, each cycle requires but 1/100 of a microsecond and 500 input cycles will pass in 5 microseconds.

Time Constant of Limiter Grid Circuit. The ability of a grid-bias arrangement to remove amplitude variations from the incoming wave depends upon its ability to change its bias as rapidly as the peak amplitude of the incoming wave changes.

For example, suppose the amplitude of the incoming signal suddenly increases. By increasing the bias developed across R_1, the grid-leak resistor, correspondingly, it is possible to neutralize the rise in signal amplitude. The result is then the same as with a smaller signal and a smaller bias. On the positive peaks, the bias regulates the grid so that it is barely driven positive or just enough to keep the condenser charged and E_g constant. On the negative peaks, clipping by current cut-off occurs. Thus, by the automatic bias regulation, we can force a constant output for varying inputs.

If a variation in amplitude occurs so rapidly that the bias is unable to change with it, and thus neutralize it, then this change will appear in the output. The ability of the bias to change is a function of the time constant of the grid-leak resistor and condenser. As we noted previously, with a condenser of 0.0001 mf value and a resistor of 50,000 ohms, the time constant is 5 microseconds. Compared to the time of one cycle of a 100-mc carrier, 5 microseconds was long. However, even though the frequency of the incoming signal is 100 mc, it rarely occurs in practice that each individual cycle will change in amplitude. Hence, we need not make the time

constant this low.   For *most* amplitude variations, time constants
from 10 to 20 microseconds are more than adequate.   The greatest
difficulty arises when sharp impulses of the staccato variety, such as
we obtain from the ignition system of a car, reach the receiver.   If
the bias is unable to follow the quick rise and fall of the impulse, a
plate current variation will occur and the noise is heard in the
speaker.   In practice, time constants as low as 1.25 microseconds
have been used and the effect of most impulses minimized.   It must
be understood that where the strength of the impulse is greater than
the signal, its effect will still be felt.   However, the limiter tends
to limit the intensity of the impulse and the output noise is not as
strong as that of an unobstructed impulse.

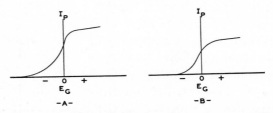

F𝐢𝐠. 8.9.   (A) The normal characteristic curve for a sharp cut-off tube.   (B) The
modified curve obtained with lowered plate and screen voltage.

Limiting with Low Tube Voltages.   The saturation or limiting
effect of low plate and screen voltages is best seen by reference to
the graphs of Fig. 8.9.   In Fig. 8.9A, we have the normal extent
of the $E_g I_p$ curve of a sharp cut-off pentode, say a 6SJ7 or 6SH7.
A sharp cut-off tube is necessary to remove fully the negative ends
of the wave.   It would be quite difficult to obtain a sharp cut-off in
any extended cut-off tube and amplitude variations would be present
on the negative peaks of the wave.

When we lower the plate and screen voltages, the extent of the
characteristic curve is diminished.   This is evident in Fig. 8.9B.
It requires much less input signal now to drive the plate current
into saturation.   An F-M receiver having such a limiter would be
capable of providing good limiter action with weaker input signals
than if the tube were operating with full potentials.

We can, if we wish, operate a tube with lowered electrode

potentials only and obtain satisfactory limiting. However, by adding grid-leak bias it is possible to raise somewhat the electrode voltages (thus providing higher gain) and still obtain good limiting. A typical circuit is in Fig. 8.10.

It was noted previously that, in general, there are two major types of noise which effect a radio wave. One is random or fluctuation noise; the other is the sharp, staccato impulse noise. For the latter type of interference, a low time-constant grid network is best suited to minimize — if not eliminate altogether — the effects

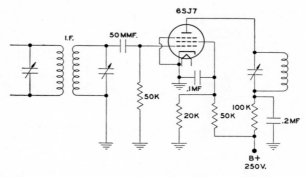

FIG. 8.10. A limiter stage functioning with lowered electrode voltages and grid-leak bias.

of these quick-acting impulses. However, a low-valued capacitance and shunt resistance greatly damp the input tuned circuit and consequently lower the effective value of the signal reaching the grid. In order to develop a large signal voltage across a resonant circuit, a high impedance should be presented to that signal. Shunting a low resistance across the circuit reduces the total impedance. In addition, large input signals cause sufficient grid-current flow in the input circuit actually to detune the resonant circuit. With larger time constants, better regulation of the stage is provided.

Cascaded Limiters. To obtain the advantages that low time constants offer in combating sharp impulses with the better regulation and higher gain of long time-constant networks, some manufacturers have used two limiters in cascade. This is shown in Fig.

8.11.   The first limiter has a time constant of 1.25 microseconds. Because of the higher values possible in the second circuit, the gain of both stages averages around 6.   With only one stage, values of 2.5 are usual.   The increased gain permits the receiver to give full limiter action with weaker input signals.

The advantage can also be seen by reference to the graph of Fig. 8.4.   With two limiters, the knee of the curve is reached by signals of 10 microvolts strength at the receiver input.   With one

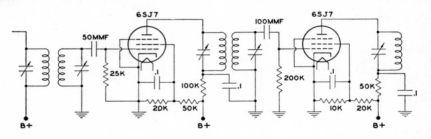

Fig. 8.11.   A two stage (or cascaded) limiter circuit.

limiter, an input signal of 25 microvolts strength is required.   Any signal weaker than 25 microvolts with one limiter does not give complete limiting action.   When the limiter is not operated at saturation, it merely becomes an amplifier and all amplitude noise rides through as readily as the signal itself.   This noise is plainly heard at the outer edges of practically all signals or when tuning between stages.

Commercial Limiter Circuits.   There are two basic limiter circuits in present commercial receivers.   First, there is the single-stage unit similar to the circuit shown in Fig. 8.10.   This functions satisfactorily in sets located near powerful stations where the input signal level is sufficiently strong to provide good limiting.   On weak signals, however, noise will be noticeable unless a high degree of amplification is available in the stages preceding the limiter.   Cascaded limiters may be either resistance-coupled, as shown in Fig. 8.12, impedance-coupled as in Fig. 8.13, or transformer-coupled. If properly shielded and constructed, the transformer-coupled unit possesses the advantage of an additional voltage gain between

circuits, which is not present in the other two circuits. The transformers must be well shielded to prevent feedback and regeneration.

The conventional discriminator is unresponsive to amplitude
modulation when the signal is *exactly* at the center frequency and

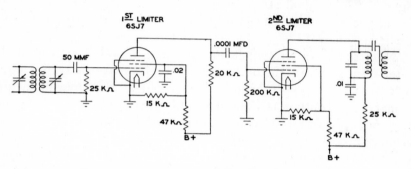

FIG. 8.12. A two-stage resistance-coupled limiter.

the circuits are symmetrical. This is true because the discriminator
consists of two individual rectifiers which are balanced against each
other and the output is the difference between their voltages. At
the center frequency, a correctly balanced circuit yields zero output.

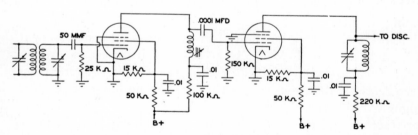

FIG. 8.13. Two limiter stages, impedance-coupled.

To obtain full benefit from this feature, however, it is necessary
that the resonance point of the discriminator coincide with the
resonance points of all the preceding circuits. With strong signals
this is difficult to obtain because the large current flow in the grid
circuit of the limiter acts to detune the network, and the subsequent
loading in the limiter plate circuit produces the same result in the
discriminator. However, with strong signals, it is usually possible

for the signal to override the noise, and any small distortion introduced because of detuning is generally negligible. With weak signals, however, the effect of noise is correspondingly greater. The advantage to be gained by having the circuits properly aligned at low signal strength is important. It is for this reason that servicing manuals urge alignment with weak generator voltages.

Note that it is only when the incoming signal is exactly at the center frequency that the output of the discriminator is zero. Thus, no matter what type of signal is received at that one particular frequency, no output is obtained. However, when the incoming frequency shifts the slightest amount from this midpoint, a limiter becomes necessary. Since the incoming signal is off-center practically all of the time, we find that the limiter is generally employed.

In the choice of a limiter tube, a tube with sharp cut-off characteristics is desirable. In addition, the mutual conductance (g_m) should be as high as possible. A large g_m will provide more current flow for any given strength of signal and permit the tube to cut-off sharply with smaller input voltages.

Tuning in F-M Receivers. Proper reception of an F-M signal is obtained when the signal is perfectly centered in the R.F. and I.F. tuning circuits.

Since satisfactory location of this center point is necessary if the full advantages of F-M are to be enjoyed, it is best to incorporate some form of visual indicator into the circuit. Meters with a zero center scale are useful, but meters are no longer considered in vogue. However, some form of tuning eye or " magic eye " is satisfactory and this is the present trend among manufacturers.

Indications with an electron-ray tube are obtained visually by means of a fluorescent target. The more familiar of these tubes are the 6U5/6G5 and the 6E5. Both contain two main sections: (1) A triode which functions as a d-c amplifier, and (2) a fluorescent screen.

In operation, a positive voltage is applied to both the fluorescent screen, known as the target, and the plate of the triode (see Fig. 8.14.) Electrons from a cathode which is common to both sections of the tube bombard the target and cause a fluorescent glow. The breakdown illustration in Fig. 8.15 illustrates clearly the common cathode extending through the tube.

In order to have a sector of the 360° of the fluorescent screen serve as the indicator, a thin rod extends up from the triode plate (see Fig. 8.15) and projects into the region between the upper section of the cathode and the fluorescent screen. The rod is known as the ray-control electrode. Since it is attached physically and electrically to the triode plate, it assumes the same potentials as the plate. It is on this attachment that the entire operation of the tube depends.

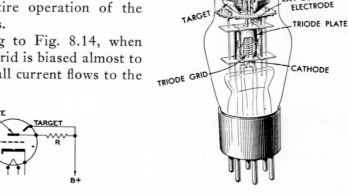

Referring to Fig. 8.14, when the control grid is biased almost to cut-off, a small current flows to the

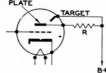

FIG. 8.14. The schematic symbol for a "Magic Eye" tube.

FIG. 8.15. The internal structure of the "Magic Eye" tube.

plate and subsequently through resistor R. The voltage drop across R is very low, placing both the target and the triode plate at almost the same potential. This means, further, that the ray-control electrode projection of the triode plate has practically the same potential as the fluorescent screen.

Electrons leaving the upper section of the cathode are attracted by both the ray-control electrode and the fluorescent screen. Their path is essentially straight, from the cathode to the screen. Thus, the fluorescent screen emits light at all points except directly opposite the thin rod. The electrons are prevented from reaching the screen by the rod and a shadow is observed. This is shown in Fig. 8.16A. When the negative voltage on the control grid is increased further, a slight overlapping appears on the fluorescent screen. This is due to the paths taken by the electrons in passing the ray-control electrode on their way to the fluorescent screen. The electrode is nearer the cathode than the fluorescent plate, and it exerts a greater influence over the electrons. Hence, when the electrode reaches the same potential as the screen, which occurs with no plate current in the triode, it attracts more electrons because it is closer to the cathode. Electrons then flow in the manner shown

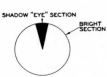

| FIG. 8.16A. The width of the eye when the control grid of the tube is quite negative. | FIG. 8.16B. The electronic paths in the "Magic Eye" tube when an overlapped pattern is produced. | FIG. 8.16C. The eye opening when the grid becomes more positive. |

in Fig. 8.16B and produce an overlapped pattern on the fluorescent screen.

For the opposite set of conditions, when the voltage applied to the triode grid becomes less negative, the current flow through the tube and resistance R increases. This raises the voltage drop across R and places the triode plate at a less positive — or more negative — potential than the fluorescent target. The ray-control electrode also becomes increasingly negative with respect to the fluorescent screen. Electrons leaving the cathode and traveling to the screen will shy away from the ray-control electrode. Thus, very few electrons will impinge on that section of the screen directly behind the ray control. The effect is a dark sector and the " eye " is said to open. The visual effect is indicated in Fig. 8.16C.

In amplitude-modulated receivers, the A.V.C. line is attached directly to the grid and the station tuned in by observing the width of the dark sector on the screen — or, as it is commonly referred to, the shadow. The negative A.V.C. voltage reaches a maximum when the station is correctly tuned in. This is indicated at the electron-ray tube when the width of the shadow is narrowest. On very strong signals the two light ends of the dark sector not only approach each other but actually overlap.

The difference in characteristics between the 6U5/6G5 and the 6E5 is concerned with the triode which closes the shadow angle at a comparatively low value of A.V.C. voltage. The 6U5/6G5 (and also a companion tube, the 6N5) has a remote cut-off triode which closes the shadow only at larger values of negative grid voltage.

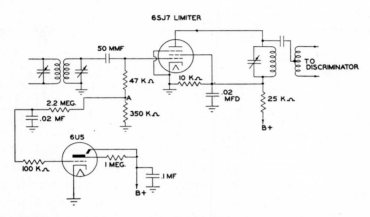

FIG. 8.17. The circuit for connecting a 6U5 tube to the grid of the limiter stage.

Connecting the Tuning Eye in the F-M Set. In an F-M receiver, there are two points where the tuning indicator may be connected. One point is at the limiter grid circuit; the other is at the output of the discriminator.

The simplest arrangement, although not the best, is the attachment of the tuning eye into the grid circuit of the limiter. When two limiters are employed, the connection is generally made in the grid circuit of the first limiter. Here, the negative voltage developed across the grid-leak resistor is directly proportional to the strength of the incoming signal.

A typical receiver circuit is shown in Fig. 8.17. The voltage across the 350,000 ohm resistor is applied to the grid of a 6U5 tuning-eye tube. Since the voltage at point *A* is negative with respect to ground, it is of a suitable polarity to be fed to the grid of the 6U5. The stronger the signal, the more negative

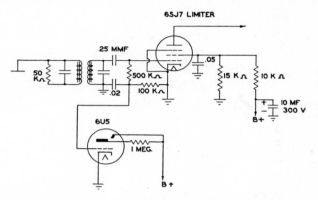

FIG. 8.18. The tuning indicator network in the Howard 718 F-M receiver.

the voltage at point A and the narrower the eye shadow. In tuning, the listener adjusts the dial until the eye shadow closes as far as it

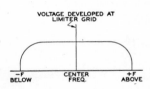

FIG. 8.19. The variation of limiter grid voltage with strong signals.

will go. The 2.2-megohm and 100,000-ohm resistors, together with the 0.02-mf condenser, form a decoupling unit to prevent the alternating components of the input signal from reaching the grid of the 6U5. The edges of the two sections of the fluorescent target become hazy when this occurs. In Fig. 8.18 the circuit in the Howard F-M 718 receiver is practically the same, as above, with a simplification in the decoupling components. Here only the 0.02-mf condenser is used.

The disadvantage of the simple arrangement of obtaining the indicator voltage from the limiter grid circuit is due to the fact that, with strong signals, the voltage developed at the grid of the limiter does not permit exact positioning. Fig. 8.19 shows that there is a wide region about the resonance point where the voltage across the grid-leak resistor of the limiter does not change appreciably. Hence, it becomes possible to tune through a wide range and not obtain a noticeable change in the aperture of the tuning eye. In addition, despite the indications at the grid of the limiter, we still have no way of determining how the discriminator is functioning. Finally, there are receivers which use only partial limiter stages and some other means must be devised if tuning devices are to be used with these receivers.

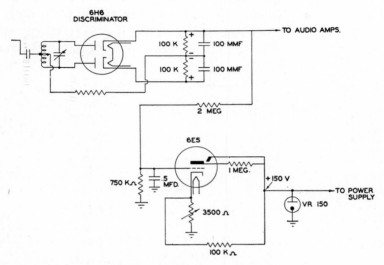

FIG. 8.20.   A 6E5 tube connected to the discriminator output.

One method, found in some sets, employs a 6E5 tuning tube that obtains its input from the discriminator output.   This is shown in Fig. 8.20.   The 6E5 is adjusted to cut-off by variation of the 3500-ohm variable resistor in its cathode circuit.   The VR-150 voltage regulator tube maintains a constant potential of 150 volts. The arm of the 3500-ohm resistor is rotated until the shadow on the fluorescent screen of the 6E5 just closes when no voltage is applied to the grid of the tube.   When the set is detuned in one direction, the output from the discriminator is, say, negative and the shadow overlaps.   Detuning in the opposite direction produces a positive voltage and the shadow becomes wider.   When the receiver is correctly set, the average voltage from the discriminator is zero and the shadows just close.   This is the correct tuning point. The 2-megohm and 750,000-ohm resistors, together with the 0.5-

mf condenser, form a filter that eliminates the audio variations from the discriminator output to the 6E5 and present only an average voltage. The regular audio voltage is still taken from its usual point on the discriminator for the audio stages.

In another arrangement, the tuning indicator is attached somewhat differently to the output of the discriminator. The indicator functions on a combination of voltages taken from both the limiter and the discriminator. The result is a very sharp indication of resonance. The circuit is shown in Fig. 8.21. As far as

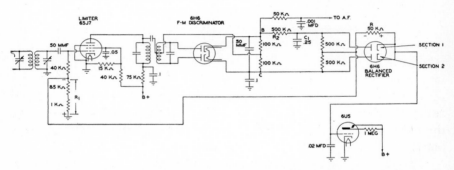

Fig. 8.21. A sharply indicating tuning eye utilizing voltage from the limiter and the discriminator. (Courtesy of Philco.)

the audio frequencies are concerned, the circuit consisting of a 6SJ7 limiter and a 6H6 discriminator is entirely conventional. The tuning indicator, in this network, requires the use of a 6H6 balanced rectifier and the tuning eye tube, a 6U5. Connection into this circuit is also made from a point in the limiter grid circuit.

If we examine the schematic, we find that the grid of the 6U5 receives its potential from essentially two points. First, there is the voltage across resistor R, which is in the cathode leg of the balanced rectifier. A voltage develops across R only when current flows in the balanced rectifier. Second, the grid of the 6U5 receives voltage from the potential across R_1, the 8500- and 1000-ohm resistors in the limiter grid network. Two resistors are used to permit attachment of a test meter. The division, however, has nothing to do with the operation of the tuning indicator. We may disregard the separation and label both as R_1.

When a signal is tuned in, grid current flows in the limiter and a negative voltage is developed on R_1 at the point where the 6U5 control grid is connected. The signal continues to the discriminator and if the station is not correctly tuned in, the *average* voltage across B and C will not be zero. We stress the term " average " because audio voltage is also developed at these points. However, if the station is properly centered, the average voltage developed here will be zero. The output from the discriminator, besides feeding the audio stages through a de-emphasis circuit, is also applied to each plate of the balanced rectifier. Let us see what happens when the station is not properly tuned in.

A signal passing through the set, whether centered or not, will cause a negative voltage to appear across R_1. However, if the station is off-center, a resultant voltage develops at point B which will be either positive or negative with respect to point C, depending upon whether the station is detuned to one side of the center resonant point or the other. It makes little difference to which side the station is detuned. The important point is the off-centered position.

If point B is positive with respect to point C, then section 1 of the balanced rectifier will conduct, causing a voltage to appear across resistor R. This positive voltage will counterbalance the negative voltage presented by resistor R_1, and the eye of the tuning indicator is kept open. If point B is negative with respect to point C, then section 2 of the balanced rectifier conducts, resulting in the same voltage across R. Thus, no matter to which side the set is detuned, the positive voltage developed across R counterbalances the negative voltage across R_1 and prevents full closing of the tuning indicator eye.

When the set is adjusted so that the station is centered, neither section of the balanced rectifier conducts, no counterbalancing voltage appears across R and the full negative voltage from R_1 is present at the grid of the 6U5. The V-shaped shadow of the fluorescent screen becomes smaller and, with large signals, may even overlap. Tuning is sharp and correctly indicated when the shadow is smallest or overlap occurs.

A variation of the above circuit suitable for receivers not

employing a limiter is shown in Fig. 8.22.   The 6E5 tuning indicator is biased approximately to cut-off by the voltage drop across
R_1.   This keeps the shadow on the eye very narrow, almost to the
point where the edges on each side of the shadow overlap.   The
control grid of the indicator is attached to the cathode end of R_2,
a resistor that develops a positive voltage each time one of the
balanced rectifier diodes conduct.   The diodes will conduct only
when a station is not properly tuned in, for only under these circumstances will the average voltage appearing across points A and B

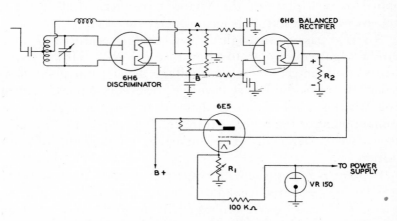

FIG. 8.22.   A circuit similar to Fig. 8.21 but requiring only the discriminator voltage.

be either positive or negative.   Application of positive voltage
from R_2 to the grid of the 6E5 will counterbalance some of the
negative voltage from R_1 and cause the eye to open.   Correct
tuning is indicated when the voltage across R_2 is zero and the eye
is practically closed.

The 6E5 is preferable to the 6U5 in this circuit because of the
sharp cut-off characteristic properties of the 6E5 triode.   Sharper
indications with less voltage are possible.

The Electron-Ray Indicator.   In the last few years, General
Electric has come forth with a new type of tuning indicator (labeled
a 6AL7-GT) which is useful for both A-M and F-M circuits.   It
is an electron-ray tube containing a triode and three deflection plates
and operating on a principle similar to the " Magic-Eye " tubes.

In addition, the tube contains a control grid, located in the triode section of the tube, which can be biased to regulate the brightness of the fluorescent target so that the electron beam can be prevented from reaching the screen when the set is off-station and permitted to reach the screen when the set is tuned to a station. Note that this differs from the action of the control grid in the " Magic-Eye " tubes.

The fluorescent screen of the tube is rectangular-shaped and divided into quarters. (See Fig. 8.23.) Of the four quarters,

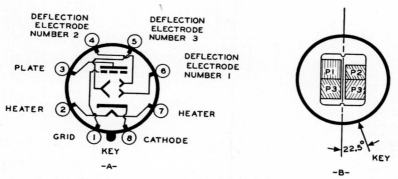

Fig. 8.23. (A) Schematic symbol for the 6AL7-GT tuning indicator. (B) The fluorescent screen used in this tube.

however, the top two (shown as P1 and P2 in Fig. 8.23) connect to separate deflection electrodes or plates while the bottom two quarters connect to the same electrode. This arrangement means that, as far as independent variation is concerned, the top two quarters can be varied in size independently of each other whereas the bottom two quarters, being part of the same electrode, will vary in step with each other. The amount of negative bias applied to each electrode controls the size of that portion of the fluorescent screen. The amount of bias on the control grid varies the brightness (but not the size) of all four sections of the fluorescent screen.

The chart and circuits in Fig. 8.24 illustrate how the 6AL7-GT indicator can be connected into a circuit and the resulting variation of the fluorescent screen area for off-tune and on-tune conditions.

PATTERN SEQUENCE DURING TUNING

CONTROL VOLTAGE SOURCE	SIGNAL	CIRCUIT (SEE BELOW)	OFF CHANNEL (—)	ON CHANNEL OFF TUNE (—)	ON TUNE	ON CHANNEL OFF TUNE (—)	OFF CHANNEL (+)
DISCRIMINATOR	FM	**A & B**					
DISCRIMINATOR AND SQUELCH	FM	**C**					
DISCRIMINATOR AND LIMITER	FM	**D**					
AVC	AM	**E**					

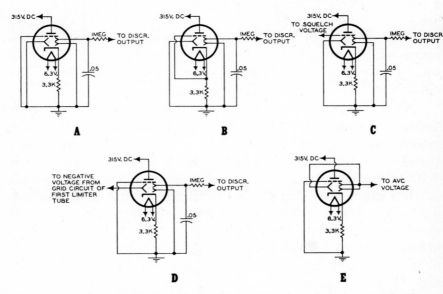

315V. DC → IMEG → TO DISCR. OUTPUT 6.3V. 3.3K .05

A

315V. DC → IMEG → TO DISCR. OUTPUT 6.3V. 3.3K .05

B

315V. DC → TO SQUELCH VOLTAGE IMEG → TO DISCR. OUTPUT 6.3V. 3.3K .05

C

315V. DC → TO NEGATIVE VOLTAGE FROM GRID CIRCUIT OF FIRST LIMITER TUBE IMEG → TO DISCR. OUTPUT 6.3V. 3.3K .05

D

315V. DC → TO AVC VOLTAGE 6.3V. 3.3K

E

Fig. 8.24. Various applications of the 6AL7-GT tube and the patterns appearing on its fluorescent target area. (Courtesy G.E.)

The following explanation will indicate the operation of the tube in each of the circuits shown.

Circuits A and B of Fig. 8.24 show how the tube may be connected so that it operates from the discriminator voltage alone. In each of these two circuits deflection electrodes 1 and 3 are connected to ground, thereby giving them a fixed potential. Hence, none of the fluorescent areas controlled by these electrodes will vary in size, whether the set is tuned to a station or not. This means that P1 and the left-hand portion of P3 will act as a combined reference area. On the other half of the target, a variable P2 is combined with a fixed P3. P2 is connected to the discriminator and its size will vary according to the voltage it receives (either negative, zero, or positive) from this circuit.

When the station is completely off channel, the discriminator voltage is zero, placing P2 at the same potential as P1 and P3. Hence, both halves of the fluorescent screen will be equal in size. This is true whether the set is off-channel above the desired station or below. Furthermore, it is also true when the set is tuned precisely on frequency. This similarity of indications may appear to be confusing, but actually it is not since music or speech will be heard when the set is correctly tuned to a station and only noise will be obtained for both off-channel positions.

When the set is on channel but off-tune, the average output voltage from the discriminator will be negative on one side of the station and positive on the other side. When the voltage is negative, P2 shrinks in size; when the voltage is positive, P2 becomes elongated.

The different connections of the control grid in circuits A and B merely affect the brightness of the total fluorescent area.

In circuit C, we obtain essentially the same tube indications with the exception that a squelch voltage is applied to the control grid, blanking out the fluorescent screen when the receiver is completely off-channel.

In circuit D, P3 receives a negative voltage from the grid circuit of the first limiter tube (if two are used). When the set is completely off-channel, the voltages from the limiter and discriminator are zero, and all electrodes possess the same potential. Hence, the left- and right-hand sides of the target area become equal in size. When the set is on tune, the discriminator voltage is zero, and areas P1 and P2 are equal. At this point, however, the negative voltage from the limiter is quite high, and both quarters of P3 shrink down to practically nothing. On either side of the correct tuning point, the negative grid voltage from the limiter decreases, and the area of P3 increases. However, P2 either will become smaller or larger in size, depending upon which side of the station the set is tuned to.

In circuit E, all deflection electrodes are tied together and all receive the same A.V.C. voltage. Hence, both sides of the target area will vary in step.

Interstation Noise Suppression Systems. As long as a station is tuned in, no difficulty is encountered from background noise. However, as soon as the station is tuned out, the input voltage consists of random noise, too weak to operate the limiter at saturation or beyond. Under these conditions the limiter functions as an amplifier and the amplitude-modulated random voltages produce the familiar loud hiss at the speaker. This is the interstation hubbub, a distracting, hissing, sizzling noise. To eliminate this distraction, many manufacturers have included interstation noise suppression systems — generally some simple arrangement that automatically cuts off one or more audio amplifiers when the input signal decreases below a certain level.

The basic idea behind most of these systems involves the use of a tube that is maintained at cut-off as long as sufficient signal voltage is being received. As soon as the input signal decreases, because of a change of dial setting, the flow of electrons is resumed through the tube. This current is made to flow through the first audio-amplifier cathode resistor and biases the tube to cut-off. This condition is maintained until the signal strength of the input of the receiver again increases.

A simple circuit illustration of this principle is shown in Fig. 8.25. T_1 is the silencer, or squelch tube. T_2 is the first audio amplifier. Both tubes have a common cathode resistor and condenser, R_1 and C_1. As long as T_1 is maintained at cut-off by a negative voltage on its grid, T_2 functions normally. Removal of the negative grid voltage at T_1, or at least a decrease to permit an appreciable current to flow, quickly brings T_2 to cut-off because of the excessive voltage appearing across R_1.   This holding action continues until T_1 is again cut off by the application of a negative voltage.   Tubes capable of high current flow are chosen for the squelch tube, as this permits decisive control with relatively small negative grid voltages.   Triodes like the 6J5 ($g_m = 2500$ micromhos) and the 6L5-G (1900 micromhos) are commonly used. Quite possible, too, is any one of a number of pentodes, although, in their case, provision must be made for screen voltage.

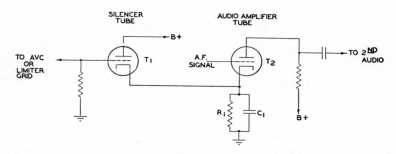

Fig. 8.25.   A simple silencer arrangement.

In an F-M receiver, there are two points where the required negative biasing voltage to control the squelch tube may be obtained. One such point is in the grid circuit of the first limiter stage; the other is at the output of the discriminator.   In a Meissner receiver, shown in Fig. 8.26, the grid of the silencer tube is directly connected into the grid circuit of the 6SJ7 limiter tube.   The negative voltage developed here is sufficient, with signal reception, to keep the 6AC7 at or beyond cut-off.   During these periods, the triode section of the 6SQ7 operates normally as the first audio amplifier.   As soon as the negative voltage is removed from the grid of the 6AC7, a high current flows through R_1 and biases the 6SQ7 to cut-off.   The 6AC7 has a mutual conductance of 9000 micromhos and is capable of large currents with relatively small negative voltage changes on its grid. R_2 and C_1 form a filter to prevent I.F. currents from reaching the 6AC7.   Only the average rectified, or d-c, voltage present on the limiter grid is desired.   A switch is provided in the

cathode circuit of the 6AC7 to permit the listener to cut out the
silencing action if desired.   This cutting-out action, for example,
might be needed on weak signals when the presence of the silencer
could prevent reception.

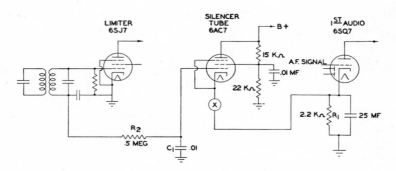

Fig. 8.26.   Another possible silencer circuit.

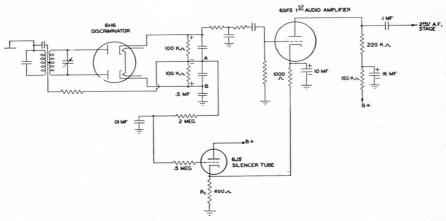

Fig. 8.27.   A silencer functioning on the voltage obtained from the discriminator.

In the Espey model (2170), Fig. 8.27, the d-c voltage available
at the discriminator is utilized for control.   If we examine the
individual polarity across each of the 100,000-ohm discriminator
resistors, we see that point *A* will always be negative with respect
to point *B* as long as a signal is being received.   Note that we are
utilizing only the voltage appearing across the lower resistor and

not across both resistors as is common for the audio output. The voltage obtained from point A consists of an audio component due to the shifting of the frequency of the signal and a d-c component arising from the amplitude of the incoming carrier. As long as the signal possesses sufficient strength to operate the limiters at saturation, the negative voltage present at point A will be strong enough to keep the silencer tube, a 6J5, at cut-off. This will permit the 6SF5, first audio-amplifier, to function normally. However, when the signal is tuned out, the voltage at point A drops, the 6J5 begins to conduct, and the 6SF5 is prevented from operating. R_1 is the resistor common to both triodes. A filter is inserted between point A and the grid of the 6J5 to eliminate the audio component of the voltage at point A and present only a d-c voltage to the silencer.

Silencers and squelch circuits are found usually only in F-M sets using the limiter and discriminator type of arrangement. The ratio detector and the locked-in oscillator, which require less limiting action, do not generally use a silencer system because the noise level is quite low between stations.

Automatic Volume Control (A.V.C.). Automatic volume control is a common feature in the standard broadcast sound receiver. It helps maintain a fairly constant level of output volume and largely counteracts normal changes in signal intensity due to external sources. Within the receiver, A.V.C. also helps to prevent overloading of the I.F. stages. In F-M receivers, the need for A.V.C. is not quite so urgent. As long as the signal is sufficiently strong, it will operate the limiters at saturation, and any change in signal strength beyond this point will have no effect on the output audio fidelity or strength. Also, the I.F. stages preceding the limiter are operated at maximum gain in order to insure saturation at the limiter of all desired signals. Any signal stronger than the average will suffer only amplitude limitation before it reaches the limiter, but this will not affect its frequency modulation. Since the I.F. amplifiers are operated at maximum gain, signals that are too weak to saturate the limiter are being received below the rated sensitivity of the receiver, and the inclusion of A.V.C. would not prove helpful. As long as the amplitude of the signal being received is of no consequence beyond a certain point, there is little need for A.V.C.

Practically the same reasoning applies to receivers possessing the other types of detectors. In the Philco lock-in oscillator circuit, the minimum I.F. input signal required to operate the detector is approximately one-half volt rms for full deviation. The voltage required for other off-center frequencies varies linearly with deviation. Thus, if a minimum of one-half volt is required for full deviation, correspondingly less voltage is needed for smaller frequency swings. Inclusion of an A.V.C. voltage could only decrease, not increase, the sensitivity of the receiver, and thus little is gained by its inclusion. One possible advantage, perhaps, of an A.V.C. voltage is to decrease the possibility of overloading in the R.F. stages, which can serve as a source of spurious response. This was mentioned previously. Receivers employing ratio detectors (see Chapter 9) have a ready source of A.V.C. voltage, and, therefore, advantage is taken of this to apply this control voltage to the R.F. stage and the first I.F. amplifier. In receivers utilizing other forms of detectors, where the A.V.C. voltage is not as readily obtained, most manufacturers omit the A.V.C.

PROBLEMS

1. Why are limiters necessary in F-M receivers?

2. Do all F-M receivers require limiters? Explain.

3. In what section of the F-M receiver are limiters placed? Could they be placed elsewhere in the circuit? Explain.

4. Describe the operation of a limiter.

5. How does noise affect the F-M signal? Does it affect an A-M signal in a similar manner? Why?

6. What advantage do double limiters possess over single limiters?

7. Are limiters always effective in reducing interference? Explain.

8. How much gain can be normally expected from each stage preceding the F-M detector? What is the significance of this gain at the limiter? How is the total gain for a receiver computed?

9. Draw the circuit for a grid-leak bias limiter stage.

10. Explain the operation of a grid-leak bias limiter.

11. In what other circuits in radio do we find grid-leak bias?

12. What do we mean by " time constant "? Where is it used? How is it computed?

13. Why is the time constant of the limiter grid circuit important?

14. What effect does the use of lowered voltages have on tube operation?

15. Draw the schematic diagram of a limiter using grid-leak bias and lowered tube voltages. The grid circuit has a time constant of 50 microseconds.

16. Draw the schematic diagram of a two-stage, transformer-coupled limiter circuit. Assign values to all parts, using a 5-microsecond time constant in the

grid circuit of the first limiter and a 25-microsecond time constant in the grid circuit of the second limiter.

17. What advantage would a 2-stage transformer-coupled limiter possess over a 2-stage resistance-coupled unit? What disadvantage?

18. Are special tuning devices necessary in F-M receivers for proper reception of signals? Explain.

19. What types of tuning devices are used? How do they function?

20. Draw the circuit of a simple tuning device connected to the limiter.

21. Explain how the circuit drawn in Question 20 operates.

22. What limitations does this method of connecting a tuning device possess?

23. Draw the schematic diagram of a tuning device connected to the discriminator output.

24. Explain the operation of the circuit drawn for Question 23.

25. Why are interstation noise suppression systems used? What is the basic idea behind most of these systems?

26. Draw the schematic diagram of a simple silencer circuit and explain its operation.

27. What type of tube would be most desirable in silencer networks? Why?

28. Does the silencer network function when a loud burst of interference is being received? Explain your answer.

29. Draw the schematic circuit of the I.F. and limiter section of an F-M receiver. Use two I.F. stages, two resistance-coupled limiter stages, and a tuning device.

CHAPTER 9

F-M DETECTORS

Discriminator Action. The heart of the F-M receiver, where the frequency variations are reconverted to intelligible sound, is at the discriminator. Since the intelligence is contained in the different instantaneous positions of the carrier frequency, the demodulating or detecting device must be such that its output varies with frequency. This is the bald, overall action of a discriminator. A closer inspection of the present discriminator will disclose that it is a balanced circuit, producing its frequency discriminations by properly combining the outputs of essentially two circuits. Whereas this form of discriminator does not readily indicate its mode of operation, its forerunner does, and we will investigate it first. The circuit is shown in Fig. 9.1.

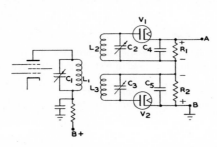

Fig. 9.1. An early form of discriminator. The secondary contains two separate windings.

L_1 and C_1 form the plate load of the last limiter stage preceding the discriminator. The tuning circuit is broadly tuned to the I.F. center value, broad enough to pass the 200 kc required by a frequency-modulated signal. L_1, L_2, and L_3 are all inductively coupled and the energy contained in L_1C_1 is transferred to L_2C_2 and L_3C_3. Each of the two secondary circuits is a detector circuit in itself, complete with diode rectifier and load resistor. They are placed end to end, as shown in Fig. 9.1, in order that their output may combine to provide both the negative and the positive half cycles of the audio wave.

To obtain the frequency discriminating action, L_2C_2 is peaked to a frequency approximately 75 to 100 kc below the center I.F.

value, while C_3L_3 is peaked to a frequency the same number of kilocycles above the I.F. center point. It makes little difference which circuit is above or below, provided both are not peaked to the same point. In Fig. 9.2A, the frequency response curves of both tuned circuits are shown with respect to frequency. In Fig. 9.2B, they have been arranged — as the circuit wiring is arranged — to produce either a negative or positive output. If there is any doubt of this, trace the flow of current through V_1 and V_2 and through their respective load resistors, R_1 and R_2. From the polarities obtained (Fig. 9.1) it can be seen that the polarity of the voltage

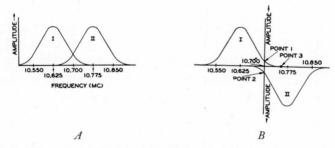

A B

FIG. 9.2. (A) The secondary response curves. (B) The same curves as in (A) in a position corresponding to the voltage developed across the load resistor.

obtained at the output terminals A and B will depend upon which resistor develops the larger voltage. If the voltage appearing across R_1 is larger than the voltage at R_2, the output polarity will be positive. If, however, E_{R2} is greater than E_{R1}, the output voltage will be negative. Now we can discuss the discriminating action.

Each secondary resonant circuit is tuned to a different peak, and the amplitude of the voltage developed across R_1 or R_2 will depend upon the frequency of the signal present at that particular instant. For example, suppose that the incoming carrier is at the mid-point frequency, hence containing no modulation. From Fig. 9.2B, the amount of voltage developed across L_2C_2, at this frequency, is shown by point 1 on its response curve. Assuming no loss of voltage in the tube, this same voltage will be developed across R_1, with the top end of the resistor positive. L_3C_3 will also respond to this frequency, the amount of voltage indicated from the response curve by point 2.   This, too, will be the amount of voltage present across R_2, but of such a polarity as to oppose E_{R1}.   The output, because of the cancellation of voltages, will be zero.   This is as it should be, for with no frequency modulation no output should be obtained.

When modulation is present and the frequency of the carrier begins shifting above and below the center frequency, then a definite output voltage will appear.   Suppose, for example, that the carrier frequency shifts to point 3, which is above the normal center frequency.   The voltage across L_3C_3 will be greater than that present across L_2C_2 because the frequency of the carrier is now close to the resonant peak of L_3 and C_3.   Hence, while some voltage may be present across R_1 to cancel part of the voltage at R_2, there will still be considerable voltage remaining at R_2.   This will appear across terminals A and B.   As the frequency of the carrier shifts back and forth, at a rate determined by the frequency of the audio note that produced the modulation, the output will rise and fall, through positive and negative values, and the frequency variations will be converted into their corresponding audio variations.

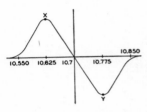

FIG. 9.3.   The resultant curve derived by combining both separate curves of Fig. 9.2B.

Since the output voltage represents the difference between the potentials present across R_1 and R_2, we can combine both response curves into one resultant curve.   This has been done in Fig. 9.3. If properly designed, the response curve will be linear throughout the operating range X to Y and no distortion will be introduced when the F-M signal is converted to audio voltages.   Should the extent of the linear operating section X-Y be so small that the signal variations extend into the curved sections beyond, then a good reproduction of the audio signal will not be obtained.   To guard against this, it is customary in practice to design a discriminator that is linear for a range greater than the required ± 75 kc.   In most cases, the curve extends to ± 100 kc.   The methods for aligning a discriminator are given in Chapter 11.

Condensers C_4 and C_5, Fig. 9.1, are for the purpose of by-passing the intermediate frequencies around the load resistors to prevent them from reaching the audio amplifiers. In choosing these condensers, care must be taken to see that they are not made so large as to by-pass the higher audio frequencies. Usual values range around 0.0001 mf. This is large enough for the I.F., but too small for the highest audio notes. R_1 and R_2 may be about 100,000 ohms.

In this discriminator, we have essentially two separate actions in converting the F-M to audio signals. First, within the tuned circuits, the frequency modulation is changed to the corresponding

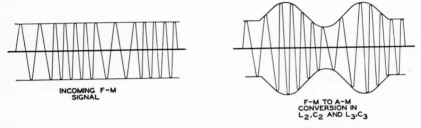

INCOMING F-M
SIGNAL

F-M TO A-M
CONVERSION IN
L_2, C_2 AND L_3, C_3

FIG. 9.4. The first step in the process of converting the F-M signal to the final audio voltage.

amplitude modulation. If we were to picture the waveform change, it would look as shown in Fig. 9.4. As yet, however, we cannot hear any audio signals because the A-M wave is at the I.F. values. By inserting an amplitude detector — a diode — we reconvert the A-M to audio. Thus we change F-M to A-M and then obtain — with a conventional A-M detector — the audio output. It is for this reason that limiters are necessary before the discriminator. Since part of the discriminator relies on amplitude demodulation and since this type of detector is sensitive to amplitude differences, we must use a limiter to present to the discriminator a pure F-M signal. Only in this way can we be sure that the A-M obtained is completely derived from the F-M and not from any extraneous, unwanted signals that may have found their way into the circuit. It will be shown later that with a ratio detector it is possible to reduce the effect of amplitude modulation with less limiting.

A Modified Discriminator. The foregoing discriminator contains one primary and two secondary condensers. A more compact unit, one that requires only two adjustments, is the discriminator shown in Fig. 9.5. Actually, what has been done here was to combine both secondary windings into one coil and use a single condenser to peak the secondary to the mid-frequency of the I.F. band. Now, the discriminator output voltage does not depend on the different response of two tuned circuits to an incoming frequency; instead, the voltage applied to each diode depends upon the phase of the voltage in the secondary winding as compared to the phase of the primary voltage. In other words, by using a single secondary circuit, we must rely upon phase variations within that circuit to discriminate against different frequencies. In the previous discriminator, each secondary reacted separately to each frequency, their rectified outputs combining to give the audio signal. Now, each different frequency alters the phase response of the secondary network and this, in turn, causes each diode to receive a different amount of voltage. As before, the rectified voltage across R_1 and R_2 gives the proper output.

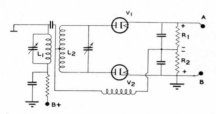

FIG. 9.5. A modified discriminator in widespread use today.

Fundamentals of Coupled Circuits. Before we proceed with the explanation of this circuit, let us review some fundamental considerations of resonant circuits and the phase relationships of coupled circuits. In Fig. 9.5 we have two circuits that are inductively coupled. Energy from the left-hand coil is transferred to the right-hand coil through the alternating lines of force that cut across from one coil to the other. The energy in L_2 appears as a voltage within the coil and, if a complete path is available, current will flow because of the pressure of the induced voltage. To determine the phase of the current flowing in the circuit with respect to the induced voltage, we must know the frequency of the induced voltage, since a resonant circuit responds differently to each frequency. This, incidentally, is the reason resonant circuits are useful in receiving one station to the exclusion of all others.

When a voltage is induced into a coil, such as in the resonant circuit shown in Fig. 9.5, the current that flows will develop across the coil a voltage that does not necessarily have to possess the same phase and amplitude as the induced voltage. This is very important and merits additional investigation. Consider, for example, two coils inductively coupled, as shown in Fig. 9.6. Because of the primary current in L_1, a voltage appears across L_2. If L_2 is an open circuit, there is no current flow, and the voltage appearing across L_2 is exactly the same voltage — in phase and amplitude — as the induced

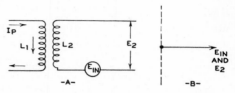

FIG. 9.6. The induced voltage in L_2, due to I_p, is in phase with the voltage appearing across L_2.

voltage. If now we connect a resistor across L_2, as in Fig. 9.7A, permitting current to flow, then the voltage appearing across L_2 will differ from the induced voltage — both in phase and amplitude. The voltage that is induced in the secondary coil has a complete

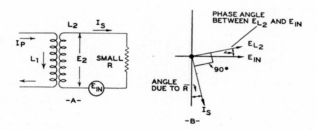

FIG. 9.7. The current and voltage phase relationship in the secondary circuit.

circuit consisting of the coil and the resistor. The opposition to the flow of current consists of the inductive reactance of L_2 and the resistance of R. If R is small in comparison to the inductive reactance, the current flowing in the circuit will be governed almost completely by the inductive reactance and will lag the voltage by slightly less than 90° (this from elementary electrical theory). This is shown graphically by the two vectors, E_{in} and I_s, in Fig. 9.7B.

Now this current, in flowing around the circuit and through L_2, will develop a voltage drop across L_2 because of the coil's inductive reactance.   As is true of every coil, the voltage will lead the current by 90°.   On the vector graph it can be placed in the position marked E_{L_2}, 90° ahead of I_s.   Thus we see the extent of the phase difference between E_{L_2} and the induced voltage E_{in} that produced it.

The two voltages also differ in amplitude because the voltage drop across the coil plus the voltage drop across the resistor must add up, vectorially, to equal E_{in}.

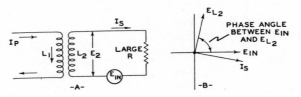

FIG. 9.8.   The same circuit as shown in Fig. 9.7 except that R is now large.   Note the difference in the phase angle between E_{in} and E_{L2}.

Following the same line of reasoning, we get the vector graph of Fig. 9.8 when the inserted resistance is high in comparison to the inductive reactance.   Note that because of the high resistance, the current flow is more nearly in phase with E_{in}.   However, no matter how close the voltage, E_{in}, and the circuit current approach each other in phase, the voltage drop across the inductance, L_2 (or any inductance), is always 90° out of phase with the current through it.

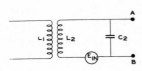

FIG. 9.9.   A secondary resonant network.

Secondary Resonant Circuit.   The next step is to replace the resistor, R, with a condenser, C_2 (see Fig. 9.9).   This is now a resonant circuit and the frequency of the induced voltage will determine the phase of the secondary current with respect to the voltage.

As far as the induced voltage is concerned, the coil and condenser form a series circuit.   But if we consider the output terminals of the circuit, points A and B, then we have a parallel circuit.   At the moment only the current *within* the circuit is of interest.   Hence, we shall regard this as a series-resonant circuit.

The impedance offered to the circulating current will depend upon the frequency of the induced voltage. If the resonant frequency of the circuit is the same as the frequency of the incoming signal, a large current will be obtained. At the resonant frequency, the series impedance of the circuit is low because the inductive and capacitive reactances completely cancel each other. Above and below resonance, the reactances no longer cancel, and the resultant of the two, together with any coil and wiring resistance, presents a greater opposition to the current.

The nature of the current flow — for any one given induced voltage — is shown by the familiar curve of Fig. 9.10. At the resonant

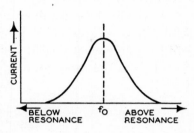

FIG. 9.10. The variation in current in a series resonant circuit.

frequency, f_o, the opposition is least and the current largest. On either side of the resonant point the current decreases because the circuit impedance increases.

Fig. 9.10 shows only the variation in current amplitude with frequency. Now let us determine how the phase angle between the current (I_s) and the induced voltage (E_{in}) varies, as the frequency changes. At resonance, the sole opposition to the current arises from the incidental resistance in the circuit. Hence, with pure resistance alone, I_s and E_{in} are in phase. Vectorially, this is shown in

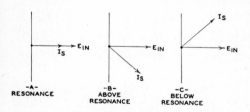

FIG. 9.11. The phase displacements between the induced voltage and the secondary current for different signal frequencies.

Fig. 9.11A. At frequencies *above* resonance, the opposition of the coil increases, because inductive reactance (X_L) is equal to $2\pi fL$. Capacitive reactance, on the other hand, decreases with frequency according to the relation $1/2\pi fC$. Hence, *above resonance,* the X_L predominates and the current will *lag* E_{in}. This is is illustrated by Fig. 9.11B. Below resonance, the opposite occurs, and the current *leads* E_{in}. See Fig. 9.11C.

The foregoing phase shifting with frequency is the basis of operation of the discriminator shown in Fig. 9.5. By properly utilizing these phase variations, we can convert F-M to audio, obtaining the same results as we did in the previous discriminator.

Discriminator Development. In order to utilize these phase shifts within the secondary resonant circuit, it is first necessary to establish a reference level. At this reference level, which is the mid I.F., no output should appear across the output terminals A and B. This is the same now as it was before, namely, no output with

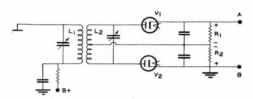

Fig. 9.12. Development of the modern discriminator. The inclusion of a center-tapped secondary and two separate rectifiers produce a balanced network.

an unmodulated carrier. On either side of the reference point we must unbalance the voltages applied to V_1 and V_2 in order that a resultant voltage will appear across A and B. Above resonance, for example, we might have R_1 develop the greater voltage; below resonance, E_{R2} would predominate. In this manner, swinging above and below the center frequency, we obtain positive and negative output audio voltages.

A simple resonant circuit, by itself, is unable to provide the balanced differential output we desire. Hence, some modifications must be made. First, by center-tapping the secondary coil and connecting a diode to each end, as shown in Fig. 9.12, we can obtain a balanced arrangement. This will permit a balancing of one tube against the other to give zero output at mid-frequency. The circuit, however, is still incomplete because there is nothing to unbalance the voltages applied to V_1 and V_2 above and below the center frequency. In the present circuit, V_1 and V_2 will have at *all* frequencies exactly the same applied voltage because L_2 is center-tapped and each tube receives exactly half of any voltage developed across L_2. As a result, the rectified voltages across R_1 and R_2

will be equal, and, because of their back-to-back placement, opposite
in polarity.   No resultant will ever appear at terminals A and B.
To produce the proper unbalance, C_3 and L_4 are added, as shown
in Fig. 9.13.   If we compare
this arrangement with the discriminator circuit of Fig. 9.5,
we note they are identical.

Discriminator Operation.
The circuit of V_1 includes L_2,
which is half of the secondary
coil, choke L_4, C_4, and R_1.
The other half of the balanced secondary includes V_2,

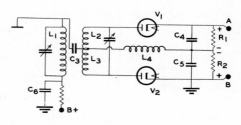

FIG. 9.13.   The complete discriminator.

L_3, L_4, C_5, and R_2.   Note that L_4 is common to both V_1 and V_2
and is introduced to provide the reference voltage in order that
an unbalance will occur at frequencies above and below the mid-
frequency.   One end of L_4 attaches to the top of L_1 through C_3
whereas the other end reaches ground through C_5 or, what is the
same thing, the bottom of L_1. L_4 then is in parallel with L_1.
C_3, C_5, and C_6, which aid in placing the choke L_4 across L_1, have
negligible opposition at the high I.F. values.   Hence, all of E_{L_1}
appears across L_4.   Thus, the reference voltage for the discriminator is the voltage across the primary coil, L_1.   More on this in
a moment.

The secondary coil is divided into two equal sections, L_2 and
L_3.   Whenever current flows through the coil, we know that one
end becomes positive with respect to the other end.   The tap, being
in between both ends, will be negative with respect to the positive
end and positive with respect to the negative end.   We could, if we
wished, arbitrarily call this point *zero*.   Both secondary circuits
connect to the center terminal, and we can indicate the polarity of
the voltage applied to each tube with respect to this center terminal.
This is shown in Fig. 9.14.   The arrow pointing up is the positive
voltage, E_2; the arrow pointing down is the negative voltage, E_3.
Both are taken with respect to the center tap.   Now let us add L_4
with its voltage.   We shall assume that a mid-frequency signal is
being received.   Hence, the current that flows through the second-

ary resonant circuit is in phase with the induced voltage. Later we shall extend this to include all conditions.

The incoming signal causes a current to flow through L_1, the primary coil. The magnetic flux, due to the primary current, extends to the secondary winding and gives rise to the induced voltage, E_{in}. The greatest voltage is induced in the secondary when the primary flux is changing most rapidly. The flux changes most rapidly when the current does. In an a-c wave, this change occurs when the current is passing through zero, going from

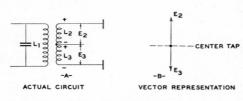

FIG. 9.14. Effect of center-tapping the secondary coil in the discriminator.

one polarity to another (see Fig. 9.15A). However, the induced voltage is zero when the primary current is not changing, or at those times when the primary current has just reached the peak positive or negative points. If we plot these facts, we see that the current and induced voltage differ by 90°, with the current leading. This is shown in Fig. 9.15B.

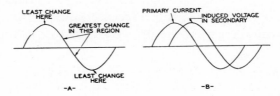

FIG. 9.15.   (A) The regions of least and greatest change in an a-c wave.   (B) The phase relationship between primary current and induced secondary voltage.

The voltage, E_1, developed across L_1 will always be 90° ahead of the current through L_1. This, of course, is true of any inductance. If we put E_1 on a vector plot, as in Fig. 9.16A, then it must be placed 90° ahead of I_1, the current through L_1. E_{in}, on the same vector graph, must be placed 90° behind I_1 as determined above. Hence, we see that the primary voltage and the induced secondary voltage differ by 180°. This is true at all frequencies. Remember that we are discussing E_1 and the *induced* secondary voltage. We have not, as yet, mentioned the voltage across the secondary coil. Most radio men are no doubt familiar with the results which we have just evolved. But, for the sake of clarity, this was methodically determined in order to show how these principles are used in the discriminator.

We can replace E_1 by E_{L4} because, as has been already shown, E_{L4} is in parallel with E_1 and is the same voltage. Also, we can drop the primary current vector, it having already served its purpose. The result is merely E_{in} and E_{L4}, shown in Fig. 9.16B. To the vectorial diagram, we must still add E_2 and E_3 and then combine

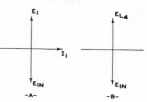

FIG. 9.16. (A) The phase differences between E_1, E_{in} and I_1. (B) E_1 replaced by its equivalent E_{L4}.

them with E_{L4}. Fig. 9.13 shows quite definitely that the voltage acting at V_1, for example, is the combination of E_{L4} and E_2. Likewise, the voltage at V_2 is E_{L4} and E_3. From their relative magnitudes we can determine which will predominate, and this will indicate the output voltage.

To cover fully the operation of the discriminator, frequencies above, below, and at the mid-point value must be considered. The first illustration will cover the operation with mid-frequency signals. This represents the case of no modulation. Secondly, we will use a frequency above the center point; lastly, a frequency below. Thus, the entire range of an F-M signal will be covered. The output voltage from the discriminator will give the circuit response to input frequency variations.

When the incoming frequency is at the I.F. mid-point, the induced voltage, E_{in}, produces a current in the secondary circuit which is in phase with E_{in}. At the resonant frequency, the impedance presented to any voltage is purely resistive. Hence, current and voltage are in phase. On the vector diagram, Fig. 9.17A, we can indicate the in-phase condition by drawing E_{in} and I_s (I_s, the secondary current) along the same line. The length of each vector differs because of the resistance in the circuit.

The voltage developed in L_2 and L_3, because of I_s, differs in phase from I_s by $90°$. Again, this condition is true of any inductance. On the vector diagram, we can insert E_2 and E_3, the voltages developed across L_2 and L_3, both 90° from I_s. E_2 and E_3 are on opposite sides of I_s, because of the center tap on the secondary coil (see Fig. 9.14). E_2 and E_3, taken with reference to the center tap, are 180° out of phase with each other. To show this graphically, in Fig. 9.17A, they are placed pointing in opposite directions.

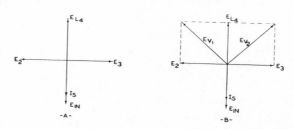

FIG. 9.17. (A) Vector diagram for an unmodulated signal. (B) The vector addition of E_2 with E_{L_4} and E_3 with E_{L_4}.

We can now combine E_2 and E_{L_4} to arrive at E_{V_1}, the effective voltage applied to tube V_1. Also E_3 and E_{L_4} to derive E_{V_2}, the voltage applied to V_2. It is evident from Fig. 9.17B that E_{V_1} and E_{V_2} are both of equal amplitude. Hence, the same current will flow through each tube and the same voltage will appear across R_1 and R_2. Since the voltages across these two resistors are in opposition, no output will be obtained. For an F-M signal containing no modulation, no output is derived.

Conditions with Higher Input Frequency. Consider next the circuit conditions when the modulated F-M signal swings to a higher frequency. At any frequency, the voltage induced in the secondary of the discriminator will be 180° out of phase with the voltage across the primary. Hence, to start the vector diagram, we can insert these two voltages (see Fig. 9.18A). Again, for E_1 we can substitute E_{L_4}, and thus far the conditions are the same as for the previous case.

A voltage having a frequency higher than the resonant frequency of the secondary circuit will encounter more opposition than a voltage at the resonant frequency. Also, because this is a series-resonant circuit (at least, as far as the induced voltage is concerned), the higher frequency will meet more opposition from the coil than the condenser. Hence, in the present instance, the coil will cause the current to lag behind E_{in} (see Fig. 9.18A). Now we can draw in E_2 and E_3, since they differ from the current (I_s) by 90°. I_s is responsible for E_2 and E_3 appearing across the secondary coil, and there is always a 90° phase difference between voltage and current in a coil.

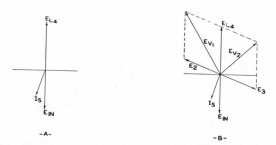

FIG. 9.18. Circuit phase conditions when the signal frequency is above the I.F. center value.

Adding E_2 and E_{L4}, E_3 and E_{L4}, vectorially, we see that the resultant vectors are no longer equal. In this case, E_{V1} is greater than E_{V2}. Consequently, R_1 will develop a larger voltage than R_2, and the output voltage will be positive with respect to ground. The amount by which I_s will differ in phase from E_{in} depends upon the incoming frequency. The farther this frequency is from the mid-frequency or resonant point of the secondary circuit, the more I_s and E_{in} will differ in phase. As the position of I_s changes, the positions of E_2 and E_3 will likewise change. Several off-frequency conditions are shown in Fig. 9.19, illustrating the phase shifting that occurs.

Input Frequency Below Mid-Frequency. The phase analysis when the frequency swings below the mid-frequency value is just as readily accomplished. We can draw in immediately the vectors E_{in} and E_{L4}. I_s follows next. Its position is ahead of E_{in} because, as the frequency drops below resonance, the capacitive reactance of the condenser becomes greater than the impedance of the coil. In a capacitive circuit, current leads voltage. This places I_s ahead of E_{in}. E_2 and E_3 are 90° out of phase from I_s, and these can be added to the vector diagram.   Addition with E_{L_4} shows the unbalance of voltages, this time favoring V_2 (see Fig. 9.20).   The output voltage from the discriminator now becomes negative.

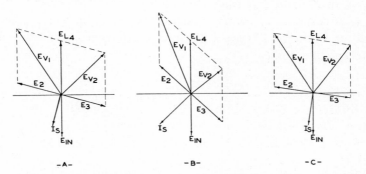

FIG. 9.19.   Several additional off-frequency conditions.   The input frequency is high.

As a summary of the overall picture, the following points are evident:

1. At the resonant frequency, which is the mid-frequency of the carrier, no output is obtained from the discriminator.

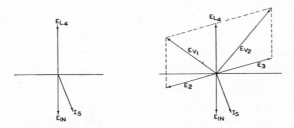

FIG. 9.20.   The shift in vectors when the signal is below the I.F. midpoint.

2. At frequencies off resonance, an unbalance is created in the circuit, and an output voltage is obtained.

The unbalance that arises from the shifting frequency is made linear with respect to frequency in order that the audio output will be a faithful reproduction of the modulation as effected at the transmitter.   The same discriminator S-shaped curve derived for the previous discriminator (Fig. 9.3) is obtained again.   The linear section of the curve X-Y generally extends for 200 kc, although the frequency shifts are restricted to a maximum of 75 kc on either side of the carrier. The extension is added protection to insure faithful reproduction.

Other Discriminators. Although the preceding discriminator is widely used, slight variations have been introduced by certain manufacturers. A modified dis-criminator employed in many sets is shown in Fig. 9.21. The difference between this unit and the preceding circuit is to be found in the elimina-tion of L_4 and the use of only one condenser across the out-put instead of two. It may appear that E_{L4}, the reference voltage so necessary for the

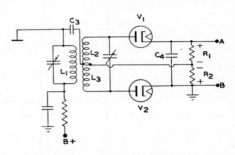

FIG. 9.21. A modified discriminator.

proper operation of the discriminator in Fig. 9.13, has been elimi-nated. Actually this is not so. The reference voltage is still present, but in a slightly altered position.

If we trace the circuit from the top of L_1 through C_3 and R_2 to ground, we see that R_2 is in parallel with L_1 and hence E_1 appears across R_2. If we travel around the network containing V_2, we find that both E_3 and E_1 (from across R_2) act on V_2. This is identical with the preceding case, except that the E_1 voltage was obtained from choke L_4. Now we have eliminated L_4 and placed E_1, the reference voltage, across R_2. Thus, in this circuit, R_2 per-forms double duty. Not only does it develop the rectified voltage for V_2, but it also serves to apply E_1 to V_2.

In the V_1 network, R_1 is also found to be in parallel with L_1. The circuit extends from the top of L_1 through C_3 to R_1, to the top of R_1, then through C_4 to ground. Both C_3 and C_4 offer slight opposition to any high I.F. Thus, R_1 is substantially in parallel with L_1. Hence, R_1 is to V_1 what R_2 is to V_2. No unwanted intermediate frequencies reach the following audio stages because of C_4. Its low reactance to intermediate frequencies by-passes from point A. However, being only on the order of 0.0001 mf or so, it does not provide an easy path for the rectified audio frequencies, and these reach the audio amplifiers.   Aside from these changes, the operation of this circuit is identical with the preceding network.

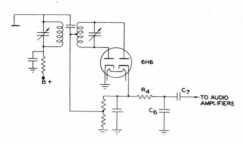

FIG. 9.22.   The same discriminator as shown in Fig. 9.21, but slightly rearranged.

The advantage of the circuit lies only in the fewer parts required. R_1 and R_2 must be kept as high as possible because they are in parallel across L_1.   A low value would decrease the impedance of L_1 with a subsequent decrease in gain.   With the choke, R_1 and R_2 are isolated from L_1, and their effect is not as marked.   As a general rule, R_1 and R_2 may be higher in value in the unit of Fig. 9.21 than that of Fig. 9.13.

The circuit diagram of Fig. 9.21 may be drawn in many ways, one variation being shown in Fig. 9.22.   At first glance there appears to be no relationship between the two circuits.   On tracing out the wiring, however, it becomes evident that exactly the same discriminator is used.   Each manufacturing firm draws schematics along its own peculiar lines and sometimes it requires a little patience to recognize the similarity of identical units.

C_6 and R_4 of Fig. 9.22 form a de-emphasis network to return the signal to its correct values.   It will be recalled that pre-accentuation or pre-emphasis is used at the transmitter in order to raise the relative intensity of the higher audio frequencies in an attempt to better the signal-to-noise ratio.   At the receiver the reverse action must be instituted to bring the signal back to its proper form. C_7 is a coupling condenser.

A Modified Discriminator.   In standard A-M broadcasting receivers, it is customary to use a duo-diode triode or pentode for the dual function of detector and first audio stage.   If we attempt to use the same tube for an F-M receiver, we run into difficulties because the duo-diode section of the tube contains a common cathode (see Fig. 9.23).   Although there are two separate diode plates, there is only one common cathode.   In the discriminator circuits

thus far encountered, each cathode of a diode rectifier was connected to a different portion of the circuit.   Hence, a conventional
circuit could not be handled by a duo-diode.   General Electric has,
however, employed such tubes in their F-M
sets with a modified discriminator circuit.

The basic circuit is shown in Fig. 9.24.
C_1 and L_1 form the primary tuner, L_2, L_3
and C_3, the secondary resonant circuit.
The bottom of L_2 and the top of L_3 are
connected by means of a small 200-mmf
condenser.   This condenser presents essentially no opposition to high I.F. and the

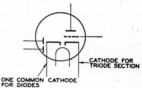

CATHODE FOR TRIODE SECTION

ONE COMMON CATHODE FOR DIODES

Fig. 9.23.   A typical duo-
diode tube.

bottom of L_2 and the top of L_3 may be considered as at the same
potential.   At the audio frequencies, the opposition of the 200-mmf
condenser is high, and one side is not at the same audio potential
as its other side. R_1 is the load resistor for V_1; R_2 is the load
resistor for V_2.   As before, V_1 and V_2 form two distinct and
separate rectifier circuits.

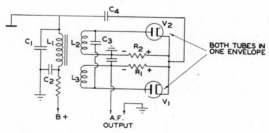

BOTH TUBES IN ONE ENVELOPE

FIG. 9.24.   A discriminator suitable for use with duo-diode tubes, containing a common
diode cathode.

A ground is placed at the left-hand side of R_2, this being equivalent to the ground at one end of R_2 in the previous discriminator
circuits.   It represents one output terminal, and placement of a
ground connection at this point shown has absolutely no effect on
the operation of the circuit.   The other output terminal, just as we
had before, is taken from the opposite end of R_1.   Here, too, the
output represents the difference between the audio voltages developed across R_1 and R_2.

The one outstanding departure from the other conventional design is the method of introducing the primary reference voltage into the secondary circuit. This is accomplished by C_4. For tube V_1, E_1 is brought to the secondary through C_4 and R_2. Since C_4 offers very little opposition to these high intermediate frequencies, the full primary voltage E_1 appears across R_2. For V_1, the path is from the top of L_1, through C_4 and R_1 to ground. Again, in this path, only R_1 offers any appreciable resistance, and the full primary voltage E_1 appears across R_1. It is to be noted that R_1 and R_2 are both in parallel with L_1, as in the discriminator circuit of Fig. 9.21.

In operation, the circuit is exactly equivalent to either of the other two discriminators. At resonance, no output is obtained, whereas above and below resonance, the output voltage will vary, the polarity being dependent upon the position of the incoming frequency. The rate at which the output voltage changes depends upon the rapidity with which the frequency changes position.

F-M Ratio Detector. The inherent limitations of the preceding discriminators necessitated a limiter stage. The limiter removed all traces of amplitude modulation and presented a pure F-M wave to the discriminator. The disadvantage of employing a limiter is the excessive amplification that must be given to the signal before it reaches the limiter. This is necessary in order that the weakest desired signal be brought up to the point where it will drive the limiter to saturation.

If a detector could be built which would develop an output that was independent of amplitude variations in the incoming signal, then a great simplification in circuit design could be affected. It would mean that perhaps one, at most two, I.F. stages would be needed. Recently, the ratio detector was developed which does not respond as readily to amplitude variations as the Foster-Seeley circuit itself, without a limiter.

To see why a ratio detector is more immune to amplitude variations in the incoming signal, let us compare its operation with that of the Foster-Seeley discriminator.

In the discriminator circuit of Fig. 9.13, let the signal coming in develop equal voltages across R_1 and R_2. This would occur, of course, when the incoming signal is at the center I.F. value. Suppose that each voltage across R_1 and R_2 is 4 volts. When modulation is applied, the voltage across each resistor changes, resulting in a net output voltage. Say that the voltage across R_1 increases to 6 volts and the voltage across R_2 decreases to 2 volts. The output voltage would then be equal to the difference between these two values, or 4 volts.

However, let us increase the strength of our carrier until we have 8 volts, each, across R_1 and R_2, at mid-frequency. With the same frequency shift as above, but with this stronger carrier, the voltage across R_1 would rise to 12 volts and that across R_2 decrease to 4 volts. Their difference, or 8 volts, would now be obtained at the output of the discriminator in place of the previous 4 volts. Thus, the discriminator responds to both F-M and A-M. It is for this reason that limiters are used. The limiter clips off all amplitude modulation from the incoming signal, and an F-M signal of constant amplitude is applied to the discriminator.

When unmodulated, the carrier produced equal voltages across R_1 and R_2. Let us call these voltages E_1 and E_2, respectively. With the weaker carrier, on modulation, the ratio of E_1 to E_2 was 3 to 1 since E_1 became 6 volts and E_2 dropped to 2 volts. With the stronger carrier, on modulation, E_1 became 12 volts and E_2 dropped to 4 volts. Their ratio was again 3 to 1, the same as with the previous weaker carrier. Thus, whereas the difference of voltage varied in each case, the ratio remained fixed. This demonstrates, in a very elementary manner, why a ratio detector could be unresponsive to carrier changes.

An elementary circuit of a ratio detector is shown in Fig. 9.25. In this form the detector is similar to the detector of Fig. 9.1 where each tube has a completely separate resonant circuit. One circuit is peaked slightly above the center I.F. value (say T_1); the other is peaked to a frequency below the center I.F. value (say T_2). The output voltage for V_1 will appear across C_1, and the output voltage for V_2 will be present across C_2. The battery, E_b, represents a fixed voltage. Since C_1 and C_2 are in series directly across the battery, the sum of their voltages must equal E_b. Also, due to the manner in which the battery is connected to V_1 and V_2, no current can flow around the circuit until a signal is applied.   Now, although E_1E_2 can never exceed E_b, E_1 does not have to equal E_2.   In other words, the ratio of E_1 to E_2 may vary.   The output voltage is obtained from a variable resistor connected across C_2.

When the incoming signal is at the I.F. center point, E_1 and E_2 will be equal.   This is similar to the situation in the previous discriminators, especially Fig. 9.1.   However, when the incoming signal rises in frequency, it approaches the resonant point of T_1, and the voltage across C_1 likewise rises.   For the same frequency

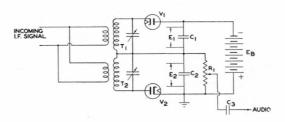

Fig. 9.25.   Preliminary form of the ratio detector.

the response of T_2 produces a lower voltage.   As a consequence, the voltage across C_2 decreases.   However, $E_1 + E_2$ is still equal to E_b.   In other words, a change in frequency does not alter the total voltage but merely the ratio of E_1 to E_2.   When the signal frequency drops below the I.F. center point, E_2 exceeds E_1.   Again, however, $E_1 + E_2$ equals E_b.   The audio variations are obtained from the change of voltage across C_2.   Condenser C_3 prevents the rectified d-c voltage in the detector from reaching the grid of the audio amplifier.   Only the audio variations are desired.

The purpose of E_b in this elementary explanatory circuit is to maintain an output audio voltage which is purely a result of the F-M signal. E_b keeps the total voltage $(E_1 + E_2)$ constant, while it permits the ratio of E_1 to E_2 to vary.   As long as this condition is maintained, we have seen that all amplitude variations in the input signal are without effect.

The problem of deciding upon a value for E_b is an important one.   Consider, for example, that a weak signal is being received.   If E_b is high, the weak signal would be lost because it would not possess sufficient strength to overcome the negative polarity placed by E_b on the tubes, V_1 and V_2. The tubes, with a weak input voltage, could not pass current. If the value of E_b is lowered, then powerful stations are limited in the amount of audio voltage output from the discriminator. This is due to the fact that the voltage across either condenser — either C_1 or C_2 — cannot exceed E_b. If E_b is small, only small audio output voltages are obtainable. To get around this restriction, it was decided to let the average value of each incoming carrier determine E_b. Momentary increases could be prevented from affecting E_b by a circuit with a relatively long time constant.

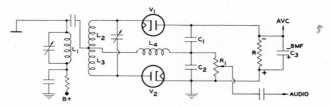

FIG. 9.26. Practical form of the ratio detector.

The practical form of the ratio detector is shown in Fig. 9.26. It uses the phase-shifting properties of the discriminator of Fig. 9.13. R and C_3 take the place of E_b, and the voltage developed across R will be dependent upon the strength of the incoming carrier. Note that V_1 and V_2 form a series circuit with R (and C_3) and any current flowing through these tubes must flow through R. However, by shunting the 8-mf electrolytic condenser across R we maintain a fairly constant voltage. Thus, momentary changes in carrier amplitude are merely absorbed by the condenser. It is only when the *average* value of the carrier is altered that the voltage across R is changed. The output audio frequency voltage is still taken from across C_2 by means of the volume control.

Since the voltage across R is directly dependent upon the carrier strength, it may also be used for A.V.C. voltage. The polarity of the voltage is indicated in Fig. 9.26. With this detector, it becomes possible to design an F-M receiver containing only two I.F. stages. The reduction in costs is considerable and permits marketing F-M sets in a range comparable to the present A-M receivers. The detector possesses the disadvantage of being more difficult to align, and greater care must be taken to obtain a linear characteristic. Distortion tends to become more noticeable at high input voltages, although this can be minimized by special compensations of the circuit.

Ratio Detector Modifications.   The ratio discriminator shown in Fig. 9.26 represents but one form of this circuit.   In Fig. 9.27 there is a modification which possesses greater symmetry.   Furthermore, it has the advantage of making available a voltage which can be used, in conjunction with a tuning eye, to indicate when the

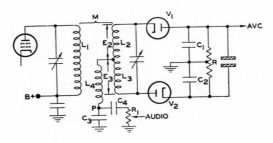

Fig. 9.27.   A symmetrical ratio detector.

station is properly tuned in. L_1, L_2, and L_3 are inductively coupled, which is similar to the previous discriminators.   However, in place of the former, direct capacitive connection between L_1 and the secondary coil center-tap, we now have L_4.   It will be remembered that it is due to the presence of E_1 in the secondary as a reference voltage that this circuit is able to function.   In Fig. 9.27, we have, by using L_4, substituted it for the previous method of obtaining this reference potential. L_4 consists of several turns of wire which are closely coupled to L_1.   Hence, the voltage induced in L_4 will remain constant so long as the primary voltage is constant. Since E_{L4} depends upon E_1 and not upon the secondary circuit, it can be used as the reference voltage in place of the previous arrangement.   If E_{L4} is varied, it would not affect the *relative* amplitudes or phases of any of the secondary voltages.

To understand better the other modifications, the circuit of Fig.

9.27 has been rearranged (see Fig. 9.28). The path from the center tap on the secondary coil to the connection between C_1 and C_2 contains L_2 and C_3. Disregard C_4 and R_1 for the moment, as they are merely placed across C_3 to feed the audio output to the following amplifiers. The voltage which is applied to V_1 consists of E_{L4} and E_2. Across V_2 we have E_{L4} and E_3. At the center I.F. value, both tubes receive the same voltage, with C_1 and C_2 charging to the same potential. But what of the potential across C_3?

At this moment it is zero. The reason can be found if we trace the current paths for each tube. The current in V_2 flows up through L_3, through L_4 to C_3 and C_2. Current will flow in this

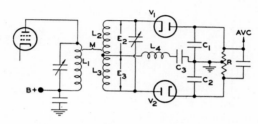

FIG. 9.28. The circuit of Fig. 9.27 rearranged to better indicate its mode of operation.

path until the voltage across C_3 and C_2 equal the voltage across the tube. Then the flow ceases. The current from V_1 will flow from its plate to C_1 and C_3, then L_4 and finally up through L_2 to V_1 again. As before, there will be a movement of electrons around this path until C_1 and C_3 charge to the potential at the tube. Note, however, that the current from V_2 flows through L_2 and C_3 in a direction *opposite* to the current produced by V_1. Hence, what actually happens is that these two currents in the middle branch buck each other. At mid-frequency the resultant is zero. The voltage across C_3, then, is also zero. Hence, the current in the circuit flows from V_2, through L_3 to V_1 and through C_1 and C_2 back to V_2. At mid-frequency, point P, Fig. 9.27, is zero with respect to ground.

At other frequencies, the voltage applied to each tube will differ with the result that a net current flows through C_3 and L_4. Which way the current flows will depend upon which tube receives the greater voltage.   It is thus evident that the potential variations across C_3 will vary directly with frequency and consequently represent the audio or demodulated voltage.   By means of a coupling condenser and a volume control, we can feed these audio variations to the succeeding amplifiers.

Since the voltage at point P is zero when the mid-frequency is received and either positive or negative at other frequencies, it can be used to control a tuning-eye indicator.

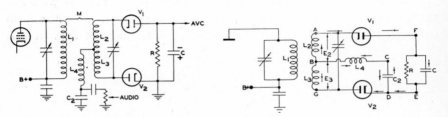

FIG. 9.29A.   Another form that the   FIG. 9.29B.   A rearrangement of
ratio detector can assume.   Fig. 9.29A.

Another arrangement of the ratio detector is shown in Fig. 9.29A.   This is similar to the circuit of Fig. 9.26 except that condenser C_2 has been retained and C_1 has been eliminated.   The audio voltage is obtained from C_2, the same as in Fig. 9.26. L_4 is coupled to L_1 and furnishes the reference voltage which causes the potentials applied to V_1 and V_2 to change with frequency.

In order to understand the operation of the circuit without C_1, it must be kept in mind that the voltage across C_2 is determined by:

1. The potential of R and C.   This, in turn, is fixed by the average amplitude of the incoming F-M signal.

2. The frequency of the incoming signal.

3. The *relative* currents flowing through V_1 and V_2.   This, of course, depends upon No. 2.

To demonstrate better the various current paths in the secondary network, the rearranged diagram of Fig. 9.29B will be used. Note that no connections have been altered, merely the relative placement of several components.

The voltage applied to V_2 is the vector sum of E_{L_4} and E_3 (see Figs. 9.18 and 9.20).   Similarly, the voltage active across V_1 is composed of E_{L_4} and E_2. As the frequency shifts in response to modulation, the total voltages at V_1 and V_2 will follow suit. This has already been noted in previous paragraphs.

Consider, now, the current paths for each of the tubes. V_1 is part of the complete path $AFEDCBA$. Its current can also flow through path $AFEDGBA$. For V_2, the two paths are: $GBAFEDG$ and $GBCDG$. In other words, currents from each tube can flow around the outer path ($GBAFEDG$) or part of each can be diverted through L_4 and C_2 of the center path.

When the total voltages applied to each tube are equal (at mid-frequency), no current flows through L_4 and C_2. This is true in all ratio detectors. At points other than mid-frequency, however, the current of one tube is greater and a portion of it does pass through L_4 and C_2. Hence, the voltage across C_2 will be a function of frequency. Due to the fact that each tube is connected into the circuit in an opposite manner, their currents (from V_1 and V_2) flowing through L_4 and C_2 will likewise be opposite. Consequently, E_{c_2} will possess one polarity for frequencies above resonance and the opposite polarity for frequencies below resonance. By attaching a potentiometer across C_2, we can obtain an audio voltage for the audio amplifiers.

It may not be amiss at this point to note again the difference between the ratio detector and its predecessor in Fig. 9.5. The latter unit operates on the difference of the output voltages of two diode detectors. The diode load resistors are connected with their voltages opposing each other. The resultant of these two then becomes the output audio voltage. The response of this discriminator to amplitude modulation requires that a limiter (at least one) always precede it. Consequently, a comparatively large amount of amplification must be available so that the signal can be in a position to drive the limiter to saturation. Economically, this requirement raises the price of the receiver.

In the ratio detector, the two diodes are connected in series, and a controlling voltage is established in the circuit which is dependent upon the average value of the incoming carrier. Because of the long time-constant of the R-C filter in the network, instantaneous changes in signal amplitude are prevented from affecting the audio output voltage.   Furthermore, this control voltage sets the limit to the maximum audio voltage that can be obtained.   The ratio detector is more immune to amplitude modulation than the Foster-Seeley discriminator if the latter is considered by itself, without any limiter.   However, when a limiter is added, the Foster-Seeley circuit possesses a slight edge in performance.   The ratio detector, however, is more desirable economically since the amplification required ahead of this stage is less and advantage can be taken of this fact to reduce the number of stages in the I.F. system.   Many manufacturers attempt a compromise by having the I.F. amplifier preceding the ratio detector operate as a partial limiter.   While this reduces the gain of the I.F. system, it does improve the performance of the detector for F-M signals possessing large amounts of amplitude modulation.

FIG. 9.30.   A block diagram of the Beers receiver.

The Beers Receiver.   The ratio detector was one attempt to simplify the construction of the F-M receiver.   There is yet another solution available.   This is the locked-in oscillator arrangement developed by G. L. Beers.   A block diagram of the receiver is shown in Fig. 9.30.   Note that the conventional limiters have been eliminated and in their place a locked-in oscillator has been substituted.   A discriminator closely resembling the discriminator of Fig. 9.13 is used, except that the linear range of response of this unit is considerably less than the 200 kc of the former unit.   Besides these two units, the F-M receiver is similar to any previously discussed.

The locked-in oscillator is frequency-modulated by the incoming F-M signal.   In other words, the incoming signal causes the locked-in oscillator to shift in frequency in exact step with the frequency variations of the incoming signal.   However, the locked-in oscillator operates at one-fifth the frequency of the incoming I.F.

signal.   This reduces not only the center I.F. but also the deviation of the F-M signal about its central point.   Thus, the ±75-kc swing of the incoming signal is reduced to a ±15-kc swing at the oscillator output.   Because of this, the following stage — the discriminator — can operate over a reduced range.   In the process, the rate at which the frequency of the incoming signal shifts from one point to another is not altered in the output.   This, of course, is the modulation frequency and has nothing to do with the compression

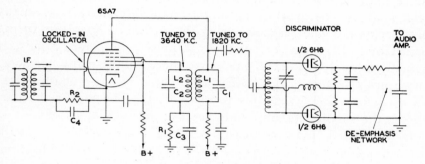

Fig. 9.31.   The locked-in oscillator and discriminator.

of the frequency swing of the signal.   A limiter is unnecessary in this circuit because the output from the locked-in oscillator to the following discriminator remains constant for a wide range of input voltages.   However, if the input signal does not attain a certain minimum value, the oscillator is not " locked-in " by the incoming signal and no output is obtained.

A diagram of a lock-in oscillator is shown in Fig. 9.31.   The output of the I.F. stages is applied to the oscillator tube, a 6SA7, at grid 1.   The frequency here would be any of the current I.F. values, say 9.1 mc, or 9100 kc.   In the output circuit, the plate tank (L_1 and C_1) is tuned to one-fifth of the I.F., or 1820 kc. L_1 and C_1 are coupled to L_2C_2, the latter being tuned to the second harmonic of 1820 or 3640 kc.   Grid 3 receives this voltage and, with the plate, forms the oscillator.   As we shall see presently, the coupling between L_1 and L_2 forces the oscillator to lock-in with the I.F. signal. C_3 and R_1 provide grid-leak bias for the oscillator. C_4 and R_2 do the same for grid 1.   The reduced-range discriminator is identical with the discriminator in Fig. 9.13. For the discriminator we obtain the familiar S-shaped curve, except that the linear portion extends for a range one-fifth the linear distance of an ordinary discriminator. Following the discriminator is a de-emphasis network leading to the audio amplifiers.

Operation of Locked-In Oscillator. Oscillations in any oscillator will, after a few moments, reach a steady state. With grid-leak bias, the oscillating voltage will, on each positive peak, drive the grid positive and cause grid current to flow. The grid-leak condenser becomes charged and establishes an average steady bias across the grid resistor during the continued operation of the oscillator. The grid current flows in pulses, and, since a pulse is actually a highly distorted sine wave, there will be many harmonic frequencies present in the oscillator output. This is true of almost all oscillators employing this form of bias. The higher the harmonic, the smaller its amplitude because the impedance offered to it by the tuned circuit decreases. When the impedance is small, less voltage is developed for feedback and subsequent amplification. However, with care in design, strong harmonics up to the 6th or 8th can be obtained.

In the absence of any incoming signal, the oscillator will produce the strongest output at 1820 kc. This is fed to the discriminator, but since the discriminator is designed to give no output at 1820 kc, no voltage is forwarded to the succeeding audio amplifiers.

Suppose that an I.F. signal at 9100 kc, the 5th harmonic of 1820 kc, is received. Present also in the oscillator is the 4th harmonic of 1820 kc, or 7280 kc. The fourth harmonic will beat with the incoming 9100 kc to produce a difference frequency of 1820 kc in the plate circuit. Because of the coupling between L_1 and L_2, the difference frequency voltage will appear in the oscillator to lock-in with the incoming signal. When two signals lock-in, a fixed, unchanging relationship is maintained between them. Thus, for example, in a television receiver, the incoming synchronizing pulses trigger oscillators at the same point in each cycle. The frequency of the oscillators is kept fixed by the pulses.

When the incoming signal is unmodulated, its I.F. is exactly at 9100 kc. The output from the locked-in oscillator, under this condition, is 1820 kc. However, since 1820 kc represents the center frequency of the discriminator, no audio output is obtained. It is only when the oscillator shifts above and below 1820 kc that an audio voltage will appear at the discriminator output terminals.

Consider, now, an incoming signal at, say, 9130 kc. When this voltage mixes with the 4th harmonic of 1820 kc, we obtain a difference frequency which is greater than 1820 kc. The effect of the latter voltage is to introduce an out-of-phase component into the oscillator-plate tuned circuit. As a result, the out-of-phase current either will aid or oppose the reactive current already flowing in the circuit. For example, if the incoming frequency has increased, the current introduced into $L_1 C_1$ due to the mixing of the incoming signal with the fourth harmonic will aid the inductive current already flowing in the circuit. The result is the same as if we had added some additional inductance in parallel with L_1. As is well known, the total value of inductances in parallel is less than either one. Decreasing the total inductance in any tuned circuit raises its operating frequency. Thus, when the incoming frequency rises, the oscillator frequency also rises. The oscillator is thus kept " locked-in " with the arrival signal.

It is a simple matter to determine the extent of the oscillator increase. If the incoming signal changes from 9100 kc to 9130 kc, then the oscillator increases from 1820 kc to 1826 kc. We know this because the incoming signal mixes with the 4th harmonic of the oscillator to produce the oscillator frequency. One-fifth of a 9130-kc signal is 1826 kc. The fourth harmonic of 1826 is 7304 kc and subtracting 7304 kc from 9130 kc gives us the required 1826 kc at which the oscillator is now functioning.

When the incoming signal drops below 9100 kc, the effect on $L_1 C_1$ is as though the capacitance had increased. The oscillator frequency decreases. $L_2 C_2$ follow increases and decreases of frequency in step with $L_1 C_1$. In this way the output frequency fed to the discriminator is an exact duplicate of the incoming signal, but with less frequency deviation about the center point. From 9.1 mc ± 75 kc we get 1.82 mc ± 15 kc.

It may occur to many that actually the 6SA7 functions as a reactance tube. The shifting phase of the plate current causes the frequency of the oscillator to shift. Within limits, the oscillator will follow and lock-in with the incoming signal. However, if the incoming frequency moves too far in either direction, we find that the oscillator snaps out of control and returns rapidly to its natural resonant frequency of 1820 kc. In a sense this is an advantage because it eliminates interference from adjacent channel stations — something which the conventional discriminator is unable to do. In design, care must be taken to make certain that the oscillator will lock-in over the proper range. Such items as the type of tube, the amount of input signal, and the loading effect of the discriminator, all have a direct bearing on the range of the oscillator lock-in.

The tube must have a high mutual conductance between grid 1 and the plate and a fairly high plate current. It is the purpose of the tube to supply the reactive current which produces the oscillator frequency shift. If a small change in voltage at grid 1 causes a relatively large change in plate current (high g_m), then the range over which the oscillator is locked-in will be increased. The important point in the lock-in operation is the production of a fairly large 4th harmonic component to mix with the incoming signal to produce the oscillator frequency. Large pulses of plate current will do this. In addition, it is helpful if L_2C_2 resonate at twice the frequency of L_1C_1. If L_2C_2 resonated at the same frequency as L_1C_1, then the 4th harmonic would be quite small. However, by designing L_2C_2 to resonate to the 2nd harmonic of L_1C_1, a greater amount of 4th harmonic voltage is produced. The reason for the increase is due to the fact that the 4th harmonic is only twice removed from the resonant frequency of L_2C_2. If L_2C_2 had been designed for optimum operation at the fundamental, the 4th harmonic would be four times removed and, consequently, less voltage would have developed.

The Philco Single-Stage F-M Detector. There has recently appeared an F-M receiver which utilizes a locked-in oscillator in a manner somewhat similar to the Beers receiver. However, due to the nature of the feedback between the mixer section of the unit, and the oscillator, no discriminator is required. Instead, the audio output is obtainable directly from the plate-current variations of the mixer tube.

The basic circuit of the F-M detector is shown in Fig. 9.32. The tube, which was specially designed for this purpose, is a heptode. The cathode and the first two grids serve as an electron-coupled oscillator with grid 2 as the plate. Grids 2 and 4 are connected together, but both grids are at I.F. ground potential. The input I.F. signal is fed in at grid 3, whereas the feedback or quadrature circuit is connected to the plate of the tube. Both the oscillator and the quadrature circuit are resonant to the I.F. In order to insure the proper kind of feedback, the quadrature circuit

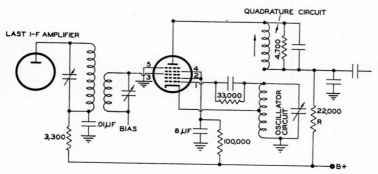

FIG. 9.32.   The Philco single-stage F-M detector.

is damped with a relatively low resistor (4700 ohms) so as to have a bandwidth which is roughly six times that required by the F-M signal.

The oscillator grid is closest to the cathode, and it will exert the greatest influence over the flow of electrons. The oscillator functions class C and permits electrons to flow past grid 1 only in short pulses. Throughout the remainder of the cycle the grid is biased beyond cut-off. The second controlling element in the tube is grid 3. Its voltage will determine how much of the pulse passed by the first control grid reaches the plate. There are thus two factors controlling the amount of plate current that flows to the quadrature circuit. As we shall see presently, it is through this dual control that the circuit is able to function.

The basic operation of the circuit depends upon the fact that the pulses of current that the oscillator grid permits to flow are further modified in magnitude by the second (or signal) control grid 3. If, at some instant, the potential of grid 3 is more positive than its normal value, an increased plate current will flow through the quadrature coil. Conversely, if grid 3 is more negative, less than the average current will flow. Through the interaction of the oscillator and the quadrature coils, the change in current will alter the frequency of the oscillator. From the oscillator frequency variation, F-M demodulation occurs. Essentially, then, lock-in between the oscillator and the frequency variations of the incoming F-M signal must occur. In this respect, the circuit is similar to the Beers receiver. However, here the similarity ends.

The circuit consists of three main sections: the oscillator, the quadrature circuit, and the second control grid (No. 3) where the incoming signal is applied. The oscillator is a Hartley, designed to generate a frequency equal to the center frequency of the I.F. band as long as there is no signal voltage. However, when a signal appears (assume for the moment that it is not modulated), the oscillator adjusts itself to lock-in with the signal. Throughout the lock-in range, the frequency of the oscillator and the signal will be identical.

The lock-in of the oscillator is brought about by the transfer of energy (coupling) between the oscillator coil and the quadrature coil. The quadrature coil is designed so that its impedance does not appreciably change over the range of frequencies of the incoming signal. To insure this, the coil is made to possess a bandwidth approximately six times that which is actually required. This is the reason for the low-valued damping resistor (4700 ohms).

The quadrature coil is inductively coupled to the oscillator and any change in plate current in the quadrature circuit is reflected immediately into the oscillator. The reflected impedance consists of two parts, a resistive component and a reactive component. The resistive loading remains constant because of the low-valued resistor. The reactive component, however, will vary directly with the plate current. It is this reflected component which causes the oscillator frequency to vary. It is important that only the reactive feedback vary; otherwise, the amplitude of the oscillator signal will fluctuate producing an additional A-M component which is not part of the original signal.

The incoming signal controls the flow of plate current, which, in turn, because of the quadrature circuit, affects the oscillator frequency and causes it to lock-in with the incoming signal. The oscillator frequency is thus kept the same as the signal.

The control of the plate current by the signal grid (No. 3) is illustrated in Fig. 9.33. In A of Fig. 9.33, the incoming signal has the same frequency as the oscilla-tor, and the pulse of current passes through the tube when the signal grid is going through zero. Under this condition the two frequencies are locked together, and the aver-age plate current (of the pulses) is such as to maintain this condition. If, upon application of the signal, the exact phase relationship be-tween the signal and the oscillator pulses is not as shown in Fig. 9.33A, then the average value of the plate current will change suffi-ciently to swing the oscillator into line. Thereafter, the two are locked in synchronization, and the situa-tion shown in Fig. 9.33A prevails.

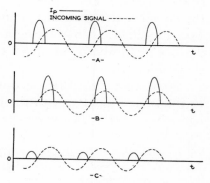

FIG. 9.33. Interaction between the sig-nal voltage and the oscillator pulses to regulate the oscillator frequency. In (A) the two signals are identical; in (B) and (C) the signal frequency is either slightly higher or lower than the oscillator.

When the incoming signal changes frequency — with modula-tion — the phase of the signal voltage (with respect to the pulses of plate current) changes, either increasing or decreasing the average value of the current. This change, reflected in the oscil-lator circuit, appropriately increases or decreases its frequency to the new value. When the new frequency is attained, the phase between signal voltage and oscillator is again as shown in Fig. 9.33A.

Now the question is: How do these variations in oscillator frequency bring about demodulation of an F-M signal? Simply this — the average value of the current over any cycle is directly proportional to the peak value of the fundamental component of the pulse. (A pulse will contain a strong fundamental and many weaker harmonics. The fundamental, of course, is the oscillator frequency.) Now, if the signal frequency rises, so will the oscillator frequency, and the average value of the plate current will change. In this circuit, the current decreases. (See Fig. 9.34.) Conversely, if the signal frequency decreases, the oscillator frequency will decrease. This time Fig. 9.34 indicates that the plate current rises. Thus, plate current will vary with frequency, and the circuit is designed so that the current varies in a linear manner (see Fig. 9.34). By placing a resistor in the plate lead, R of Fig. 9.32, we can obtain an audio voltage to feed the audio amplifiers that follow.

Note that the entire action will prevail only so long as the oscillator is locked-in with the incoming signal. If the signal voltage is too small (below one-half volt for full 75-kc deviation) or the signal frequency shift too large, then the oscillator will slip out of control and return to its free-running frequency. This is shown in Fig. 9.34 by the series of broken dashes at the extremes of the discriminator response curve. An advantage of the requirement of a minimum voltage needed for control of the oscillator is the elimination of interstation noise. This is common with the conventional limiter discriminator arrangement. Its disadvantage is the loss of control that may occur with weak signals. However, weak signals tend to be noisy (even with F-M) and therefore the loss may not be too disadvantageous. With sufficient strength, amplitude variations in the signal do not cause change in the average plate current. What happens is that with a change in signal amplitude, the oscillator phase readjusts itself slightly to maintain the plate current required for that frequency.

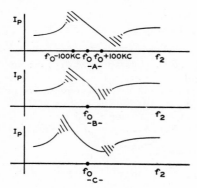

FIG. 9.34. (A) The proper response characteristics from the demodulator. (B) and (C) are the result of an improper adjustment.

Adjustment of the circuit consists in aligning the quadrature circuit for a linear response characteristic, Fig. 9.34A. If the circuit is detuned, the nonlinear curves of Figs. 9.34B and 9.34C are obtained.

The 6BN6 Gated-Beam Tube. A new approach to a combined limiter-discriminator combination, one that differs considerably from any of the previous circuits, is provided by the 6BN6 gated-beam tube. This tube, designed by Dr. Robert Adler of the Zenith Radio Corporation, possesses a characteristic such that, when the grid voltage changes from negative to positive values, the plate current rises rapidly from zero to a sharply defined maximum level. This same maximum value of plate current remains, no matter how positive the grid voltage is made. Current cut-off is achieved when the grid voltage goes about 2 volts negative.

The reason for this particular behavior of the tube stems from its construction. (See Fig. 9.35.) The focus-electrode, together with the first accelerator slot, form an electron gun which projects a thin-sheet electron stream upon grid 1. The curved screen grid, together with the grounded lens slot and aided by the slight curvature of grid 1, refocuses the beam and projects it through the second accelerator slot upon the second control grid. This grid and the anode which follows are enclosed in a shield box. Internally, the focus, lens, and shield electrodes are connected

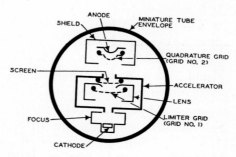

FIG. 9.35. The internal construction of the beam-gated tube.

to the cathode. The accelerator and the screen grid receive the same positive voltage because both are connected internally.

The foregoing design is such that the electrons approaching the first grid do so head-on. Hence, when grid 1 is at zero potential or slightly positive, all approaching electrons pass through the grid. Making the grid more positive therefore, cannot increase the plate current further. When, however, grid 1 is made negative, those electrons that are stopped and repelled back toward the cathode do so along the same path followed in their approach to the grid.

Because of the narrowness of the electron beam and its path of travel, electrons repelled by the grid form a sufficiently large space charge directly in the path of other approaching electrons, thus causing an immediate cessation of current flow throughout the tube. In conventionally constructed tubes, the spread of the electron beam traveling from cathode to grid is so wide that those electrons repelled by the grid return to the cathode without exerting much influence on other electrons which might possess greater energy and therefore be able to overcome the negative grid voltage. It is only when the control grid voltage is made so negative that no emitted electrons possess sufficient energy to overcome it that current through the tube ceases. These differences between tubes may be compared to the difference between the flow of traffic along narrow and along wide roads. Along the narrow road, failure of one car to move ahead can slow down traffic considerably; along the wide road, more room is available and the breakdown of one car has less effect.

The electron beam leaving the second slot of the accelerator approaches grid 2 also in the form of a thin sheet. Thus, this section of the tube may also serve as a gated-beam system. If this second grid is made strongly negative, the plate current of the tube is cut off no matter how positive grid 1 may be. Over a narrow range of potentials in the vicinity of zero, the second grid can control the maximum amount of current flowing through the tube. However, if the second control grid is made strongly positive, it also loses control over the plate current, which can never rise beyond a predetermined maximum level.

So much for the operating characteristics of the tube. Now let us see how it can be made to function as a limiter-discriminator. A typical circuit is shown in Fig. 9.36.

It has been noted that when F-M signals reach the discriminator they contain amplitude variations. When the 6BN6 gated-beam tube is used, these signals are applied to control grid 1. If the signal has received sufficient prior amplification, it will have a peak-to-peak value of several volts. Upon application to grid 1, current through the tube will start to flow only during the positive part of the cycle and will remain essentially constant no matter how positive the signal may become or what amplitude variations it may contain. Thus, signal limiting is achieved in this section of the tube, the electron beam being passed during the positive half-periods of the applied signal and cut-off occurring during negative half-periods. The groups of electrons that are passed then travel through the second accelerator slot and form a periodically varying space charge in front of grid 2. By electrostatic induction, currents are made to flow in the grid wires. A resonant circuit is connected between this grid and ground, and a corresponding voltage of approximately

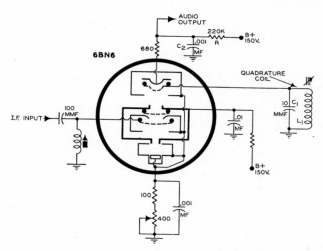

FIG. 9.36. The beam-gated tube connected as a limiter-discriminator.

5 volts is developed at grid 2. The phase of this voltage is such that it will lag the input voltage on grid 1 by 90°, assuming that the resonant circuit is tuned to the intermediate frequency. (Because of this 90° difference between grid voltages, grid 2 is often referred to as the quadrature grid.)

The idea of electrostatic induction, while it has not been labeled as such, was encountered in the previous discussion of the 6A8 pentagrid converter. Whenever a group of electrons approach an element in a tube, electrons at that element will be repelled, resulting in a minute flow of current. By the same token, electrons receding from an element will permit the displaced electrons to

return to their previous positions.   Again, a minute flow of current
results, this time in a direction opposite to that of the first flow.
If sufficient charge periodically approaches and recedes from an
element, the induced current can be made substantial.   This is
precisely what occurs at grid 2 in the 6BN6.

In the gated-beam tube, both control grids (No. 1 and No. 2)
represent electron gates.   When both are open, current passes
through the tube.   When either one is closed, there is no current
flow.   In the present instance, the second gate lags behind the first.
Plate-current flow starts with the delayed opening of the second gate

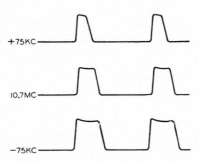

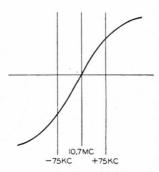

FIG. 9.37. The variation in current
pulse duration in the beam-gated
tube with frequency modulation.

FIG. 9.38. Discriminator response of the beam-gated
tube when connected as
shown in Fig. 9.36.

and ends with the closing of the first gate.   Now, when the incoming signal is unmodulated, and L_1C_1 of Fig. 9.36 is resonated at
the I.F. frequency, the voltage on grid 2 will lag the voltage on grid
1 by 90°.   However, when the incoming signal is varying in frequency, the phase lag between the two grid voltages will likewise
vary.   This, in turn, varies the length of the period during which
plate current can flow.   (See Fig. 9.37.)   Thus, plate current
varies with frequency, and the circuit is designed so that the current
varies in a linear manner.   By placing a resistor in the plate lead,
R of Fig. 9.36, we can obtain an audio voltage to feed the audio
amplifiers that follow.   A typical discriminator response for an
F-M receiver with a 10.7-mc center frequency is shown in Fig. 9.38.

Note that this curve does not possess any sharp bends (such as Fig. 9.3 does, for example) at frequencies beyond the range of normal signal deviations. This makes the receiver easier to tune.

In the circuit of Fig. 9.36, a 680-ohm resistor is inserted between the load, R, and the plate of the tube. By-passing of the I.F. voltage is accomplished by C_2, but since this condenser is placed beyond the 680-ohm resistor, a small I.F. voltage appears at the anode of the tube. Through the interelectrode capacitance that exists between the anode and grid 2, the I.F. voltage developed across the 680-ohm resistor is coupled into $L_1 C_1$. The phase relations existing in this circuit are such that this feedback voltage aids in driving the tuned circuit.

Bias for control grids 1 and 2 is obtained by placing a resistor in the cathode leg of the tube. Since A-M rejection, especially at low input signals near the limiting level, is a function of the correct cathode bias, the cathode resistor is made variable. This permits adjustments to be made in the field in order to compensate for tube or component changes.

PROBLEMS

1. Contrast the purpose of an A-M detector with that of an F-M detector. State clearly why each should differ.

2. Draw the schematic diagram of an early type of discriminator which employed two secondary windings.

3. Explain the operation of the circuit drawn for Question 2.

4. Would the foregoing discriminator function if one of the diodes became inoperative? Give the reasons for your answer.

5. Draw the response curve for this early type of discriminator. What would be the effect on the curve if the two tuned secondary circuits were brought closer in frequency? How would this affect the reception of a fully-modulated F-M signal?

6. Draw the circuit of a modified discriminator (Foster-Seeley type) widely used today.

7. Describe the operation of the modified discriminator circuit briefly.

8. Describe the exact function of each component in the discriminator.

9. Are there any modifications that can be made in the circuit? Explain.

10. Draw the schematic diagram for an F-M discriminator using a duo-diode tube having a common cathode.

11. What limitations of the Foster-Seeley type of discriminator resulted in the development of a ratio detector?

12. Draw the circuit of a ratio detector.

13. Explain briefly the operation of a ratio detector.

14. Describe the operation of the Beers locked-in discriminator circuit.

15. Why does the discriminator used with this arrangement possess a limited frequency range?

16. Draw the schematic circuit of the Beers F-M discriminator system.

17. What is the purpose of the 6SA7 tube used in the Beers arrangement?

18. What happens in the Beers discriminator when the incoming signal deviates too far from its center frequency? How does this affect the audio output? Contrast this with the effect obtained on the Foster-Seeley discriminator using the same off-frequency signal.

19. Which of the foregoing arrangements does the Philco F-M detector resemble? Why?

20. Draw the circuit diagram for the Philco F-M detector.

21. What is the purpose of the quadrature circuit in the Philco circuit?

22. Explain the operation of the Philco F-M detector.

23. Can the Philco circuit and the Beers arrangement be used interchangeably? Explain your answer.

24. Explain briefly the operation of a beam-gated limiter discriminator circuit.

CHAPTER 10

AUDIO AMPLIFIERS AND HIGH FIDELITY

AUDIO AMPLIFIERS

High Fidelity. To many people, both in and out of the radio profession, the great advantage of F-M lies in its ability to reproduce the full range of audio frequencies. For sales appeal, the term " high fidelity " was popularized and everything desirable was associated with it. And yet, like everything else that has been oversimplified, unwarranted assumptions have been made. High fidelity represents not one but a host of ideas, and what may appear to be high fidelity to one person may not be so to another. To a large extent, high fidelity involves the listener, and thus any complete consideration of the meaning of this phrase must not only include the technical details of the electrical system but the relationship of the listener himself to this system. It is because of this latter aspect that we find any one precise definition of high fidelity impossible. Nonetheless, we may still investigate the contributing factors which add up to provide good reproduction of a broadcast. Briefly, these factors include the electrical system (receiver and transmitter), the loud-speaker, the surrounding acoustics of the room where the reproduction occurs, and, finally, the aural capabilities of the listener.

In considering the listener, we find that the human ear has a frequency response characteristic that varies not only with each individual but also with age and even slightly with the length of time that the ear is subject to the music or speech of any one continuous listening. As an example of the average frequency characteristics of the ears, consider Fig. 10.1. Here we have the different intensities which each frequency must possess in order to sound the same to our ears as the 1000-cycle note. An example will perhaps make this clearer. Dealing with the bottom curve, we note that a 50-cycle note must be 50 db stronger than a 1000-cycle signal in order for both sounds to *seem* equally intense to us.   Each curve represents the response at different sound levels. Thus, the bottom curve is for very soft sounds, almost at the threshold of audibility.   The top curve represents situations where the sound is so loud or intense that hearing involves pain.   The other curves are for intermediate degrees of intensity.   In each curve, the 1000-cycle frequency is taken as the level of reference.

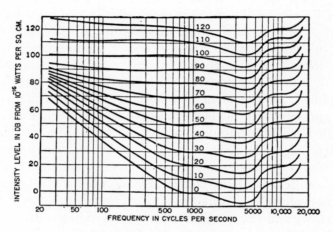

FIG. 10.1.   Frequency and loudness characteristic curves of the ears.

From these curves, several important general conclusions may be drawn.

1. The best response occurs around 3000 to 4000 cycles.

2. The low frequency response is poorest at low intensity levels. Thus, when the volume is turned down low the low frequency notes suffer the most.   Many manufacturers incorporate compensation for this in their tone controls.

3. The overall ear response is flatter as the volume increases. Note that the curves near the top of Fig. 10.1 tend to be fairly flat.

Although not indicated in the diagram, individual hearing ability decreases with age.   As one grows older, the ability to hear any of the audio frequencies deteriorates, with the higher frequencies subject to the greatest loss.

To consider only one of the foregoing conclusions, provision must be made in the radio receiver to compensate for the change in hearing response at different volume levels. As mentioned, most manufacturers incorporate low frequency compensation on volume controls at the lower level. Beyond this, however, very little has been done and the listener is obliged to resort to his tone controls for further adjustments.

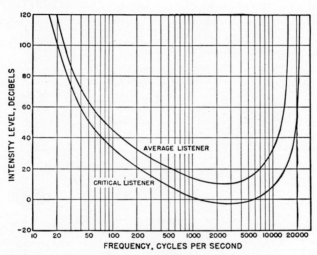

FIG. 10.2.   A comparison between the hearing ability of average and critical listeners.

The dependence between volume and the frequency response is indicated more clearly in Fig. 10.2.   Two curves are shown, one for the average listener and one for the more critical listener.   The data for the average-listener curve were obtained using people of all ages and both sexes.   We see that when the sounds are very loud, the frequency range for the average person extends from 20 to 15,000 cycles.   As this volume is decreased, both ends of the curve drop and the frequency response becomes narrower.   As before, the ear is most sensitive to frequencies between 3000 and 4000 cycles.

In the discussion of these curves, no mention was made of noise, which is present to a certain degree in all homes. The surrounding, or (as it is more technically known) ambient, noise will be most noticeable when the volume is turned down low.   It will tend, also, to mask the low and high frequencies because as we have seen from the charts, these require greater intensity to produce the same aural sensation.   It has been discovered that the average residential noise level is 43 db.   In many homes, with children romping about, the noise is considerably higher and the ability of a person to hear is that much more impaired.

The Loud-speaker.   As the translator of electrical currents into acoustic sounds, the speaker is as much an integral part of this

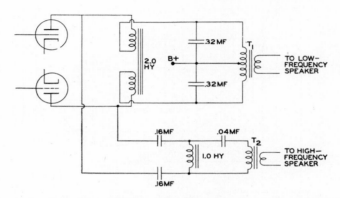

FIG. 10.3.   A frequency-dividing network designed to feed two speakers.

system at the listener.   In midget sets the small diameter cones are capable of a restricted range with best response at the frequencies between 4000 and 5000 cycles.   Since it requires a large cone area to reproduce effectively the low frequencies, high fidelity reproduction from these small sets is impossible.   In console receivers one solution to the problem of efficient reproduction has been through the use of two speakers.   A frequency-dividing network, shown in Fig. 10.3, separates the frequencies as they come from the output transformer and thus permits each speaker to respond only to frequencies within its designed range.   Another recent innovation has been the use of a coaxial speaker, where one small cone is positioned at the center of a much larger cone (see Fig. 10.4).   Again, frequency-dividing networks provide each speaker with its proper band of frequencies.   The name " coaxial " is derived from the similarity of this arrangement to the coaxial cable where one conductor is located at the center of an outer hollow conductor.

Balance. It is common belief that everything less than the full frequency coverage of 30 to 15,000 cycles leaves us short of our goal of high fidelity. Extensive tests have indicated, however, that of greater importance than trying to establish the maximum range is the balance achieved between the highs and the lows. By

FIG. 10.4. A coaxial type of speaker.
(Courtesy of Jensen.)

balance, we refer to the low and high frequency limits of our system. If we take a system and extend the high frequency response without providing a corresponding extension at the low frequencies, we find that the results do not tend to be as pleasing despite the fact that, from a true fidelity viewpoint, we are now in a position to receive more of the audible frequency range. The aural effect of extending the high frequency end, for example, without similar compensation at the low frequency end is to give the speaker response a shrill tone. Small radios possess speakers that accentuate the higher frequencies. This requires frequent use of the bass portion of the tone control to produce a compensating mellow effect.

The concept of balance has not been reduced to a definite mathematical formula, but it has been suggested that a good, empirical test is to have the product of the high and low frequency limits of the band fall approximately between 500,000 and 600,000. Thus, as an illustration, a band that starts at 90 cycles at the low frequency end should extend up to 6000 cycles at the high end in order to pre-

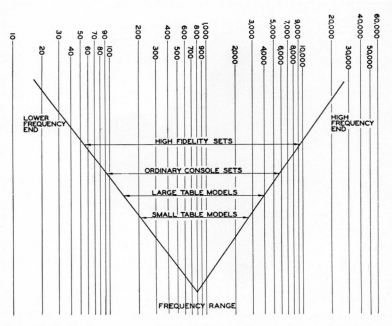

FIG. 10.5. Desirable frequency ranges for various types of receivers in order to obtain the proper tonal balance.

serve the balance between the upper and lower limits. The chart in Fig. 10.5 shows how the limits vary from a small table model to a large console radio with a proper balance maintained in all instances.

Bandwidth Limits. It has been assumed throughout the foregoing discussion that the receiver networks are fully capable of passing all the signal sidebands. Although this may readily be accomplished if the manufacturer takes the proper precautions in design, the simple fact remains that this is not so in many instances. The proper bandwidth response must be maintained in the R.F. and

I.F. transformers, in the audio amplifiers, the output coupling transformer and, finally, in the loud-speaker itself. In the tuned coupling transformers of the R.F. and I.F. stages, the usual arrangements result in the familiar, rounded response. With this response, the lower audio frequencies which are closest to center of the carrier (and hence closest to the center of the curve) receive the greatest amplification. The higher frequencies, situated farther away, receive correspondingly less amplification. Hence, even if the signal is properly balanced at the set input, by the time it reaches the second detector the balance is distorted because of unequal amplification accorded the various frequencies. These are the present conditions in A-M receivers. With an F-M receiver, unequal response in the R.F. and I.F. circuits does not greatly affect the signal as long as its strength is sufficient at the limiter to cause saturation. However, in an F-M receiver, the bandpass of each tuning circuit must be wide enough to permit reception of the full 200 kc, and the discriminator must be capable of converting F-M to A-M linearly. Careful design and construction are needed to balance all these factors — a fact that frequently varies in direct proportion to the price of the receiver. The latter statement is not meant to be an indictment of present practice but merely a recognition of some of the commercial considerations that often waylay high fidelity.

We have touched briefly on the subject of high fidelity to indicate some of the highly personal factors that combine to form this concept. It is because individual tastes differ that we find an extensive use of tone controls in most F-M receivers. Some of the common methods of achieving this tone variation will be taken up in a later section.

Phase Inverters and Push-Pull Amplifiers. In order to be able to produce the full range of audio frequencies at full volume without undue overloading, push-pull output amplifiers are required. Advantages of push-pull amplifiers are (1) the cancellation within the stage of second harmonic distortion, (2) greater permissible drive at the input producing a stronger output with less odd-harmonic distortion, and (3) smaller output transformers and less supply voltage filtering. The last advantage reduces hum and permits a greater dynamic range from the loud-speaker.   At low volumes, hum can be very disturbing, and the current practice of accentuating the bass response of a receiver by special cabinet construction tends to accentuate hum further.   In a balanced push-pull

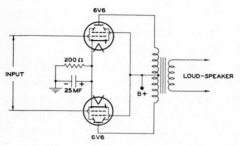

FIG. 10.6.   A push-pull amplifier.

amplifier, a-c ripple from the power supply is eliminated in the plate transformer.

If we use a push-pull stage, such as the typical unit shown in Fig. 10.6, then the input voltages to each tube must be 180° out of phase with each other. The simplest, although not

the cheapest, means of accomplishing this is by using input transformers.   Ordinary transformers, however, have a poor frequency response, and compensated transformers are quite costly.   The

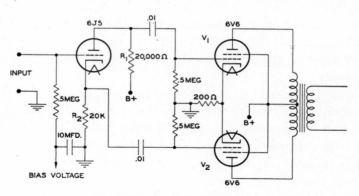

FIG. 10.7.   Phase inversion supplied by a single triode.

best solution is the use of a phase inverter whereby a portion of the signal is taken and inverted so that it becomes 180° out of phase with its input signal.   This makes available two properly phased signals for the push-pull input.

Present phase inverters fall into two general classes.   The simplest arrangement is shown in Fig. 10.7, where a single triode

(6J5, 6C5 etc.) supplies both out-of-phase voltages. One push-pull amplifier receives its excitation from the plate of the phase inverter; the other push-pull tube receives its signal from the inverter cathode. That these two signals are 180° out of phase can be noted by tracing the current through the circuit. Electrons reaching the plate of the 6J5 must pass through R_1 and R_2 in series, with the top end of R_1 always opposite in sign with respect to the cathode end of R_2. Perhaps a better way of visualizing the inverting action is by considering the path for the a-c component in the circuit. In Fig. 10.8 the circuit is redrawn slightly to emphasize this aspect. Now we see that, as far as the signal is concerned, R_1 and R_2 are electrically

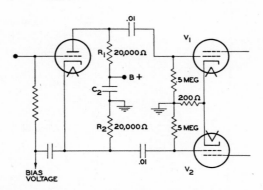

FIG. 10.8. Fig. 10.7 rearranged to emphasize the balance of voltage across R_1 and R_2.

connected at their common intersection to ground (through C_2). Each signal voltage is then taken from the remaining two ends and fed to each grid of the push-pull amplifier. Thus we have a balanced arrangement against ground.

In this inverter, R_1 and R_2 must always be equal in order that equal voltages are fed to V_1 and V_2. Because R_2 is in the cathode leg of the 6J5 and unby-passed, the tube functions as a degenerate amplifier. The a-c voltage developed across R_2 opposes the input signal, decreasing its effectiveness at the grid. As a result, the gain of the stage, grid to grid at the push-pull amplifier, is approximately 1.8 to 2 times the input signal to the phase inverter. Consequently, if a large voltage is needed to drive V_1 and V_2, this arrangement is not very feasible. It does, however, possess the advantages of simplicity, low distortion due to the degenerative feedback, freedom from changes in tube emission, and the ability of always developing equal signals for the push-pull amplifier.

Two variations of the circuit are given in Fig. 10.9. In Fig. 10.9A the degeneration is eliminated by feeding the input signal between R_2 and R_3. R_2 is fully by-passed by C_1 to provide the proper bias for the tube. Hence, no audio voltages appear across

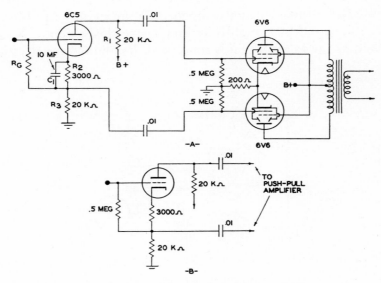

Fig. 10.9. Two alternate phase-inverter circuits.

R_2. R_g, the grid input resistor, is connected to the top of R_2 and, since no degeneration appears between this point and cathode, full input voltage is effective in varying the current through the phase inverter. The gain of this network is higher than in the previous circuit, but its fidelity is not as good because of the removal of the degeneration.

In Fig. 10.9B, the smaller cathode resistor is left unby-passed to provide a small amount of negative feedback. This aids the stability of the phase inverter and provides a better high and low frequency response.

The second basic phase inverter circuit is shown in Fig. 10.10.

Here, either V_1 or V_2 may be separate tubes or else each may be part of a duo-triode (6C8, 6F8, 6N7, 6SC7).   The output of the first triode, V_1, is fed to one grid of the push-pull amplifier.   A portion of this voltage, however, is also applied to the grid of the second triode (V_2) and the output from this tube applied to the grid of the other push-pull amplifier tube.   Since the input and output voltages of V_2 differ by 180°, we have the output voltage of V_2 differing from the output voltage of V_1 by 180°.   In this way each grid of the push-pull amplifier receives its voltage in proper phase

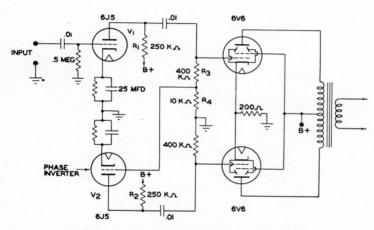

FIG. 10.10.   Phase inversion using a separate tube.

relationship.   Since V_2 is used for the sole purpose of taking a portion of the output voltage of V_1 and reversing it in phase, it is actually the phase inverter.

The amount of voltage that is fed to the grid of V_2 depends upon the ratio of R_4 to $R_3 + R_4$ and the amplification of V_2. Thus, for the voltage amplification at V_2 to be 40, the voltage tapped off at R_4 should be 1/40 of the total voltage across $R_3 + R_4$.   With this method, each grid of the push-pull amplifier tubes receives the same input voltage, and the circuit is balanced. In the present circuit, the ratio of R_4 to $R_3 + R_4$ should equal 1/40, and substitution of the given values for R_3 and R_4, 10,000/410,000, shows this to be approximately true.

Unlike the previous phase inverters, this circuit is capable of fairly high gain. Its greatest disadvantage, however, is the unbalance that occurs whenever the amplification of either triode changes. Both triodes are unrelated and any change that occurs in one section is not automatically compensated for by the other triode. Hence, unless care is taken to measure the characteristics of each tube from time to time (and making compensations therefore), some unbalance will always be present.

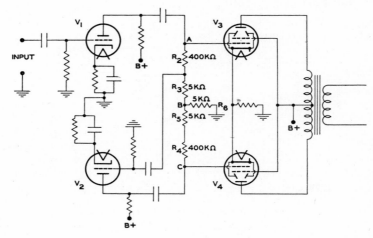

FIG. 10.11. A modified phase inverter to produce automatic balancing.

Partial compensation for unbalance is obtained by the circuit of Fig. 10.11. A change has been introduced in the grid circuit of the push-pull amplifiers by the insertion of the common resistor, R_6. Since R_6 is also in the input circuit of the phase-inverter tube, V_2, any changes here will also affect this tube's operation. V_2 receives its input voltage from R_3 and R_6, whereas its output voltage appears across R_4, R_5, and R_6. For V_1, the output signal is developed across R_2, R_3, and R_6.

To understand how the compensation is accomplished, let us suppose that both V_1 and V_2 are functioning normally. The voltage for tube V_3 appears between point A and ground; for tube V_4, between point C and ground. The voltage present at R_6, under normal conditions, is zero because the output voltages from V_1 and

V_2 are out of phase and hence cancel across this common resistor. But, now, let us suppose that the amplification of one tube decreases, say V_1. Thus, if point A went positive, say 8 volts at one instant, point C (with respect to ground) might be 10 volts negative because of the greater amplification of V_2. Under these circumstances, the net voltage appearing across R_6 would not be zero but some small negative value. Since the voltage applied to the grid of V_2 is composed (at the moment) of the positive voltage of R_3 and the small negative voltage of R_6, the net voltage acting at the grid of V_2 is slightly less than it ordinarily would be. As a result, the output voltage of V_2 is decreased, counterbalancing the increased amplification of this tube.

Conversely, if V_2 should decrease in amplification, a greater voltage would be applied to its grid, giving a correspondingly larger output. Within limits, the common resistor R_6 tends to maintain a balanced circuit, although at a small sacrifice in overall gain.

Negative Feedback. The beneficial effects of feeding back some voltage which is out of phase with the input voltage was mentioned briefly above in connection with phase inverters. Actually in the case of Fig. 10.7, the degeneration (or negative feedback, as it is known) was unintentional. It was necessary to leave R_2 unbypassed in order that the alternating voltage developed across it could be transferred to the next stage. However, in many amplifiers, the negative feedback is purposely introduced. Its advantages are:

1. Improvement of the frequency response of the amplifier.

2. Decrease in distortion in an amount depending upon the percentage of voltage fed back.

3. Increased stability, with less tendency for regeneration (whistles or howls) to appear.

It is true, of course, that these advantages are not obtained without a loss — in this case, gain. For as the degree of negative feedback increases, the gain of an amplifier decreases. However, for most amplifiers, especially those used in radio receivers and small amplifiers, the amount of available gain exceeds the need, and a slight loss for the advantages noted above is voltage well spent.

In negative feedback, a certain proportion of the output voltage is fed back to a previous stage in opposition to the input voltage that is present at this point. The circuit in Fig. 10.12 illustrates the principle. R_1 and R_2 form a voltage divider across the output of V_1. Through the connection from point A to point B, a portion of the audio voltage that is developed at R_L is fed back to the grid circuit of V_1. Now let us determine whether the voltage fed back is in phase opposition to the incoming voltage appearing across R_2.

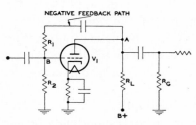

FIG. 10.12. A simple negative feedback circuit. R_1 and R_2 form a voltage-divider network across R_1.

If the incoming signal to V_1 at any instant is going in the positive direction, then the voltage at point A is going negative. This action is due to the increased current through the tube, resulting in a greater voltage drop across R_L, leaving the top end (point A) more negative (or less positive because of the increased voltage drop in R_L) than it was before the application of the signal. By connecting points A and B together, the voltage from R_L (E_L) will cancel part of the positive incoming audio voltage at point B. This cancellation is the essential principle of negative feedback. When the incoming signal is strong, more voltage is fed back from A to B and a greater cancellation occurs. With a weak signal, the opposition of the feedback voltage is correspondingly reduced. Thus, the negative feedback voltage acts to maintain a constant output. Again, if distortion is introduced between points B and A, the voltage transferred back will contain this distortion. However, because the voltage fed back from point A to point B is opposite in phase to the signal passing through V_1, the feedback voltage will introduce this distortion in a manner opposite to that produced by the tube. When the signal, with this reverse distortion, passes through the tube, the impact of the tube distortion is partially nullified. The result — a decrease in the overall distortion as seen in the output.

The amount of feedback in the circuit of Fig. 10.12 is determined by the ratio of R_2 to $R_1 + R_2$. ($R_1 + R_2$ parallel R_L

and the output is developed across them.)   This voltage is divided
between them in direct proportion to their relative resistances, with
the larger resistor obtaining a larger percentage of the voltage.   If
R_2 is large, a greater percentage of voltage will be transferred to
point B.   This, in turn, will lower the gain considerably.   Generally
a compromise is reached, where the gain is still appreciable but
sufficient feedback is developed
to afford good stability with low
distortion.

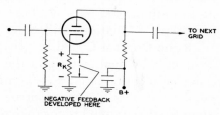

One very simple form of negative feedback is obtained by removing the cathode by-pass condenser (see Fig. 10.13).   The
a-c portion of the plate current
must now flow through the cathode resistor R_k instead of being

Fig. 10.13.   Negative feedback obtained
from an unby-passed cathode resistor.

by-passed.   As a result, an alternating voltage is developed across
R_k which opposes the input signal.   To illustrate, suppose the grid
of V_1 is made positive by an incoming signal.   The plate current

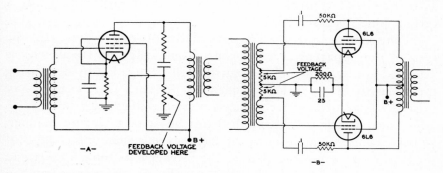

Fig. 10.14.   Two additional methods for obtaining negative feedback.

through V_1 will increase, increasing the voltage drop across R_k with
the polarity as noted.   However, the voltage at the grid that
caused the increased flow of current through the tube is the grid-to-
cathode voltage.   Since, in this instance, the cathode becomes more
positive, part of the positive signal voltage rise at the grid is
counterbalanced by the positive voltage rise at the cathode.

There are many other possible arrangements and several of the more common methods are shown in Fig. 10.14. In each instance the opposition of the voltage being fed back may be noted by following the procedure outlined above. Feedback may occur from the plate of one stage to its grid, or it may extend over several stages. Whatever the method, care must be taken to see that the feedback is degenerative, not regenerative. Regenerative feedback means voltage fed back in phase, not out of phase, and under these conditions oscillations will occur.

Tone Control Circuits. It is due to a recognition of the variation in individual tastes plus the fact that radios are used in widely differing locations that tone controls are incorporated into a large number of sets. Tone control permits the listener to vary the amplification applied to a range of frequencies and in this way cause a definite accentuation or boosting within this range. For the reception of music, for example, many listeners prefer to turn their tone control to the point where the bass frequencies predominate. For speech, the adjustment is made toward the higher frequencies. Whatever the preference, we are more interested in this discussion as to how tone control is electrically achieved rather than why a certain tone is preferred.

Tone-control systems are essentially of two types. In one system, the apparent accentuation of one range of frequencies is achieved not by an actual boost within this range but by decreasing the strength of the other frequencies present. For example, to raise the level of bass frequencies, most manufacturers provide an adjustment which will accomplish this boost in a relative manner, by decreasing the intensity of the treble frequencies. The effect of the high frequency decrease upon the listener is as though there had been an accentuation of the bass tones. The second system involves an actual boosting of the frequencies that we desire to accentuate.

Simple Bass-Boost Control.. A simple tone control that is found in many sets is shown in Fig. 10.15. It is placed in the plate circuit of one of the audio amplifiers and functions through its ability to decrease the relative strength of the high frequencies that are permitted to reach the speaker. When the center arm of the resistor is at the end nearest the condenser, the decrease of the high frequencies is maximum because only the condenser is opposing their passage around the plate circuit.   At these times the bass output will seem strongest; moving the center arm to the opposite end of

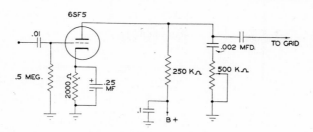

FIG. 10.15.   A simple bass-boost tone control.   The variation of control is accomplished with the 500,000-ohm potentiometer, but the entire tone control circuit includes also the 0.002-mf condenser.

the resistor permits a greater percentage of the highs to reach the output because the by-passing path's resistance has been increased.

Treble Control.   The opposite effect can be achieved by replacing the series condenser of Fig. 10.15 with a series choke coil,

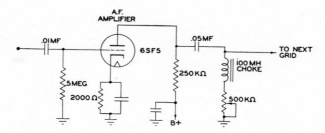

FIG. 10.16.   A simple treble tone control.

as shown in Fig. 10.16.   Now we have a path for the low frequencies to be shunted away from the output.   When the center arm is at the end of the resistor nearest the coil, the maximum shunting effect is imposed on the low frequencies.   The position would correspond to greatest treble output from the set.   When the center arm is at the opposite end of the resistor, the opposition to the lows has increased, providing more frequencies from this range for the output.   If we wish to combine both circuits, obtaining a more flexible control, we have the arrangement of Fig. 10.17. This unit is particularly useful at low volume levels because it tends to provide a more uniform response over the entire audio range. It was

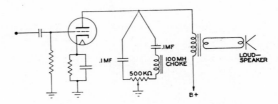

FIG. 10.17. A combination "treble-bass" tone control.

noted from the response curves of the ear in Fig. 10.1 that, as the volume is decreased, the high and low frequencies decrease more rapidly than the middle-range frequencies. In the control of Fig. 10.17, the middle frequencies are attenuated more than those at

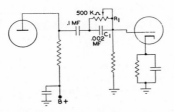

FIG. 10.18A. A series treble tone control.

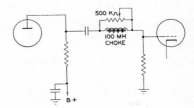

FIG. 10.18B. A series bass-boost tone control.

either end of the audio range. The overall result is a more uniform distribution.

Instead of placing the tone control in shunt across the circuit, it is also possible to place it in a series branch. For low frequency attenuation, the circuit of Fig. 10.18A is possible. The low frequencies lose more voltage across the condenser C_1 than the higher frequencies. Hence, when R_1 is completely in the circuit, the greatest amount of loss occurs at the low frequencies. By gradually shunting out a part of R_1, we can raise the intensity of the lows at the output. As a treble attenuator, the condenser can be replaced by a choke (see Fig. 10.18B).

Tone Control by Inverse Feedback. Tone variation can be also accomplished by inverse or negative feedback methods. Two popular methods are shown in Fig. 10.19. In Fig. 10.19A, the negative feedback effect is incorporated in the cathode leg of the tube. R_1 and C_1, in series, provide the degenerative effect. The value of C_1 determines the frequencies at which the effect first becomes noticeable. If C_1 is small in value, the decrease in output occurs at the middle and low frequencies; if C_1 is large, the output

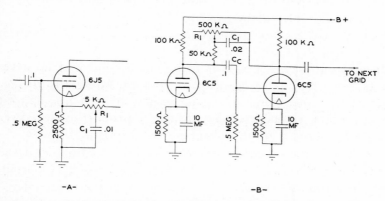

FIG. 10.19. Two common methods of applying negative feedback to obtain tone control.

decreases only for the very low frequencies. The whole operation of this network depends upon the fact that if the cathode bias resistor is not adequately by-passed, the voltage across it will vary and tend to counteract the effect of the input voltage. When C_1 is small, only the higher frequencies are readily by-passed, the middle and lower frequencies producing a variable drop across C_1 because of the substantial impedance offered them by the condenser. The variable cathode bias (for the frequencies mentioned) will partly counteract input voltages of the same frequencies. The result is that the higher frequencies remain untouched and appear more strongly at the loud-speaker. As C_1 is made larger in value, its opposition to even the lower frequencies decreases. Hence, these, too, pass through undiminished. The inclusion of the additional frequencies lessens the aural effect of the highs, and the tone becomes deeper. R_1 is inserted to provide a variable adjustment.

Another approach to the problem of negative feedback tone control is the plate-to-plate connection illustrated in Fig. 10.19B. Actually, what we do here is to feed back a voltage from the plate of the second 6C5 to the grid of the same tube. We use the plate-to-plate connection to keep the positive B+ voltage of the 6C5 from reaching its grid. C_c isolates the voltage from the grid. In the circuit, C_1 and R_1 combine to regulate the high frequency voltage that is fed back from the plate to the grid. Since the high frequencies return out of phase, they decrease other incoming high frequencies, permitting the lows to dominate at the output. The position of the center arm of R_1 determines how much high frequency degeneration occurs.

In all of these circuits, it is to be understood that no network permits one range of frequencies to pass, excluding all others. It is merely that one range of frequencies is offered less opposition than any other frequencies and, hence, a proportionately greater amount of voltage from this range passes through.

All of the preceding tone-control circuits have been so designed that in order to obtain either a high or low frequency output response, the opposite range of frequencies was attenuated. The circuits have the advantages of economy in construction and simplicity of design. Much more complex are the booster arrangements whereby an actual boost or increase is given to the section of frequencies that we desire to accentuate. A typical circuit is shown in Fig. 10.20. The separate triodes of the 6C8 receive the input signal equally. However, in the second triode section, high frequency negative feedback from the plate to the grid causes the signal that reaches R_2 to be predominantly low in frequency. The 0.002-μf condenser in the plate circuit of the first triode of the 6C8 attenuates the low frequencies. Hence, R_1 is the treble control booster, whereas R_2 controls the bass response. By proper manipulation of each of these controls, we can derive almost any desired tone in the loud-speaker. The two tone controls, R_1 and R_2, vary the amount of voltage that is applied to each triode section of the 6F8. This, in turn, will determine what percentage of the total output voltage contains either the high or the low frequencies. In the plate circuit of the 6F8, a common load resistor, R_3, recombines the two sections of the signal again.

Automatic Tone Compensation. Before we leave the subject of tone controls, there is one commonly used network that provides a fixed amount of tone compensation at the volume control. In Fig. 10.21 a series resistor and condenser are tapped across the lower section of the volume control. When the volume is turned up high, the tone compensation network has no appreciable effect. At low volume levels, however, when the center arm of R_1 is near the lower

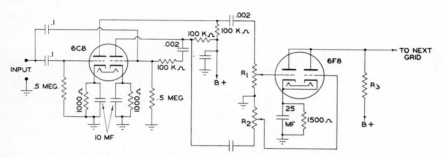

FIG. 10.20.   A circuit in which the high or low frequencies may be varied independently of each other.

end of the volume control, R_2 and C_1 become effective. Their purpose is to attenuate somewhat the amount of middle and high frequencies that reach the succeeding amplifiers. The need for the compensation is due to the fact that at low volume levels the human ear is least sensitive to the low frequencies. Partially to offset this limitation, some of the higher frequency voltage is by-passed by C_1 and R_2. The aural effect is an apparent increase in low frequencies at low volume.

Speaker Cross-Over Networks. In an attempt to obtain as high a degree of faithful reproduction as possible, many F-M receivers employ two loud-speakers in place of the customary one. One speaker is designed to respond especially to the high frequencies, whereas the other responds to the low frequencies. Recently, there has become available a dual speaker constructed as one unit and known as a coaxial speaker (see Fig. 10.4). The name is derived from the placement of the smaller, high frequency speaker at the center of the larger, low frequency unit. Although mounted as one unit, both speakers are entirely distinct of each other.

To transfer the output from the audio amplifier to each of the speakers, a special cross-over network is used. This circuit separates the high and low frequencies and applies them to their respective speakers. The point of separation, or the cross-over point, as it is known, is placed generally near 400 cycles. From the common terminals in the network, Fig. 10.3, a low-pass filter admits all frequencies from 30 to 400 cycles, whereas frequencies over 400 cycles are quickly attenuated. On the other side, we have a sharp cut-off,

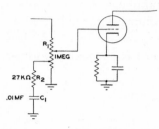

FIG. 10.21. A fixed-tone compensation circuit.

high-pass filter, and frequencies from 400 to 10,000 cycles are directed along this path. The high-pass filter is designed to cut-off quite sharply below 400 cycles in order to prevent the formation of undesirable harmonics. This form of distortion has been found to occur when frequencies below the accoustic cut-off are permitted to reach the speaker.[1]

PROBLEMS

1. State briefly what factors must be taken into consideration in any discussion of high fidelity.

2. How do the properties of the human ear affect high fidelity? Describe some of these properties.

3. What have radio manufacturers done in recognition of the frequency and loudness characteristics of the human ear?

4. Describe what is meant by " frequency balance."

5. Draw the diagram of a frequency-dividing network designed to feed signals to special high and low frequency speakers.

6. What are the advantages of push-pull amplifiers over single-ended amplifiers?

7. Must push-pull amplifiers always be transformer-coupled to the previous amplifiers? Explain.

8. Draw the circuit diagram of a push-pull amplifier.

9. What is a phase inverter? Why is it useful?

10. Draw the circuit diagram of a single phase inverter tube driving a push-pull amplifier.

[1] Paul W. Klipsch, *Electronics,* Nov., 1945, Vol. 18, No. 11, p. 144.

11. Why can a single tube be used to provide two out-of-phase voltages?

12. What are the advantages and disadvantages of using a single tube to drive a push-pull amplifier?

13. Draw the circuit schematic of a single amplifier and a separate phase inverter driving a push-pull amplifier.

14. What is negative feedback?

15. What are the advantages of negative feedback?

16. Describe several methods for achieving negative feedback.

17. What precautions must be observed when using negative feedback?

18. What type of tone control is used on most receivers? What other type is there? Which is the most desirable?

19. Draw the diagram of an audio amplifier containing a simple bass-boost tone control.

20. Illustrate the differences between bass and treble tone controls.

21. Explain how negative feedback can be used to obtain tone control.

22. Draw the diagram of a circuit using negative feedback to obtain tone control.

23. What is automatic tone compensation? Why is it used? How is it achieved?

CHAPTER 11

F-M RECEIVER ALIGNMENT

The ability of F-M to reduce interference depends to a great extent upon the proper centering of the signal within the bandpass channel of the receiver's tuned circuits. This, in turn, requires that the tuned circuits of the receiver be correctly aligned. When a station is tuned in manually on an F-M receiver, the speaker output gradually increases in volume, accompanied by much more noise than is customarily heard with A-M receivers. However, if the dial rotation is continued, a point is reached where the station program comes through loud and clear with all background noise completely absent. Interstation noise, unless removed by a special noise-limiter circuit, is much greater with F-M than A-M receivers. The reasons for this have been discussed previously.

Two methods for aligning F-M receivers are currently in use. The better and faster method is by the use of an F-M signal generator and an oscilloscope. The alternate method requires less extensive equipment — merely a single-signal generator and either a sensitive current meter or a high-ohmage voltmeter. Since both methods are likely to find wide usage, both will be considered in detail. The serviceman can then choose the one best suited to his purpose.

At the present time, commercial F-M receivers can be divided into four categories. First, we have the familiar limiter and discriminator combination. Second, there is the ratio detector, a circuit developed by RCA. Third, there are those receivers that achieve F-M demodulation with some form of a synchronized oscillator. At present only one large manufacturer is using this method and it is difficult to gauge how widespread its use will become. Finally, there is the recently developed 6BN6 gated-beam tube. Thus far this tube has not been used in any A-M–F-M receiver, although it has appeared in the F-M sound section of one television receiver. The method of aligning this detector is given also in this chapter.

To systematize the alignment presentation for the various types of detectors, we will first examine the alignment of those receivers containing the limiter and discriminator type of detector. Furthermore, since the alignment can be achieved by either of the methods previously mentioned, we will begin with the method requiring the least amount of equipment and then progress to more extensive visual procedure.

LIMITER-DISCRIMATOR RECEIVERS

Point-to-Point Method. For the purpose of alignment, the receiver can be divided into three main sections: the R.F. stages, the I.F. and limiter stages, and the discriminator. Some manufacturers recommend alignment of the discriminator first, whereas others give first attention to the I.F. and limiter circuits. Actually, experience has indicated that it makes little difference which is adjusted first, provided a final test is made on both sections to check their correspondence over the total bandpass. It is very important that zero output from the discriminator occur at the mid-frequency of the I.F. system. Negligence in this respect will greatly impair the noise-reducing properties of the F-M system.

To align the discriminator, the signal generator is connected to the grid of the last limiter stage (if more than one is employed) preceding the discriminator. The indicating device, either a voltmeter or a microammeter with a high-valued series resistor, is placed across AB or BC, as shown in Fig. 11.1. The meter must be connected with observance to polarity. Other than this, however, either load resistor may be used. The signal amplitude at this point in the alignment need not be kept at any particular level.

The signal generator frequency is set at the I.F. carrier value, say 10.7 mc. Then the primary tuning slug or trimmer condenser of the discriminator transformer is adjusted until the voltmeter reading is maximum. With the signal generator untouched, place the indicator across both load resistors, or between A and C, Fig. 11.1. Adjust the secondary trimmer screw until the indicator reads zero. The voltage across both load resistors must be equal to obtain this indication and this is the proper output at the center I.F.

The foregoing adjustments should cause the discriminator transformer to produce the response characteristic shown in Fig. 11.2.

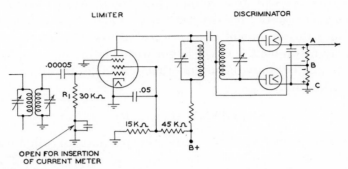

FIG. 11.1. A typical limiter-and-discriminator circuit illustrating the placement of indicators.

However, a test should be made of the discriminator linearity, at least up to ±75 kc. Most manufacturers design the discriminator

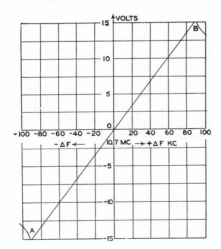

FIG. 11.2. The proper output characteristic of a discriminator.

transformer to be linear up to ±100 kc, but ±75 kc will suffice. Vary the frequency of the signal generator to obtain several points such as ±20 kc, ±40 kc, ±60 kc, and ±75 kc, about the chosen carrier frequency, 10.7 mc. The meter across the load resistors should indicate equal readings (although of opposite polarity) for each set of frequencies. Thus 10.7 mc + 20 kc should produce the same deflection as 10.7 mc − 20 kc. If these tests indicate that the response is not linear, then the primary winding trimmer must be readjusted. The linearity of the discriminator response is a function of the primary trimmer, whereas the cross-over point (or symmetry) of the curve is determined by the secondary trimmer.

I.F. System Alignment. In the adjustment of the I.F. stages, the limiter comes first. If two tuned limiters are present, the indicating meter should be put in the grid circuit of the second tube, as shown in Fig. 11.3. If the coupling between the limiters is untuned, the indicator is placed in the grid circuit of the first limiter. A current meter is inserted in series with the grid resistor. If the resistor is high in value, a microammeter is necessary; if the resistor is small, a milliammeter may be used. In the absence of an am-

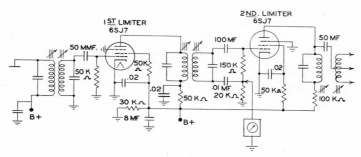

FIG. 11.3. When two tuned limiters are used, the indicator is placed in the grid circuit of the second tube.

meter, it is possible to connect a high-resistance voltmeter from the grid to ground. A low-resistance voltmeter will change the characteristics of the grid circuit considerably unless the signal level is kept very low. Most limiters function by having a certain amount of grid current flow on the peaks of the input signal. However, this flow of current lowers the impedance presented by the tube to the input circuit. Thus, there is a shift in the resonant peak of the tuned circuit. The smaller the resistance of the voltmeter shunted from grid to ground, the greater the circuit loading and the greater the possibility of frequency shift with even low testing signals. Some manufacturers provide a low-valued resistor in series with the grid-leak resistor. The low-resistance voltmeter may then be placed across the smaller resistor without seriously affecting the input circuit (see Fig. 11.4). At all times it is best to use as low an input signal as possible, consistent with good results. The stages will thus be aligned for maximum response at low signals. Upon the application of strong voltages, a certain shifting in the peak of the limiters will result, producing some distortion.   However, strong signals can deal more effectively with interference and distortion, and the effect of this peak shifting is then far less noticeable than it would be if the shifting occurred on weak signals.

If two limiter stages are used and they are coupled by means of tuned circuits, the signal generator is placed at the grid of the first limiter and the meter is kept in the grid circuit of the second limiter.   The signal generator is still at the I.F. carrier value — the previously mentioned 10.7 mc.   The tuned transformer between the limiters is then adjusted for maximum meter indication.

When the coupling between the two limiters is not adjustable — perhaps because of resistance-capacitance coupling — then the sig-

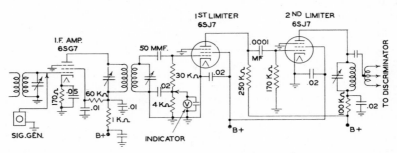

Fig. 11.4.   Placement of the signal generator and indicator with a two stage R-C network.

nal generator is inserted at the grid of the last I.F. stage preceding the limiters.   (See Fig. 11.4.)   The indicator is in the grid circuit of the first limiter.   It must be cautioned again that at no time in the alignment of the I.F. system should the input signal become so strong that either limiter (if two are used) is driven into saturation. In this event, attempting to peak the transformers for sharper maximum response on the meter becomes impractical.

The alignment is continued, working back stage by stage until all of the I.F. stages have been peaked.   To align the first I.F. stage, attach the signal generator to the grid of the mixer tube. Since the mixer-grid tuned circuit is resonant to the much higher input signal, its impedance to the I.F. will be low.   Consequently, a very high setting of the signal generator amplitude control will be required to push a small amount of signal into the I.F. system. The best method is to unsolder the lead of the grid of the mixer tube and substitute a 100,000-ohm resistor from the mixer grid to ground. The signal generator voltage is then applied across this resistor. The actual operation requires less time than it takes to describe it, and the results are good.

The question is often asked as to whether the high-frequency oscillator should be disconnected — or prevented from functioning — during this period of alignment. For clear-cut results, it is better to stop the oscillator. We can remove the oscillator tube if a separate oscillator is used or short the plates of its tuning condenser, providing we do not ground out the B+. In crystal oscillators, removal of the crystal itself will prevent operation of the oscillator.

Overall Check on Alignment. The entire I.F. system and the discriminator have now been adjusted. As a final test we should check the spread about the center point to determine whether the discriminator, in conjunction with the I.F. circuits, is symmetrical about the center frequency. It will be sufficient if three to five frequencies on either side of the center position are used for checking. Leave the signal generator at the grid of the mixer tube, remove the meter from the grid circuit of the limiter, and place a voltmeter across the load resistors of the discriminator, points A and C of Fig. 11.1. Next, set the signal generator to a frequency 20 kc above the center I.F. value. Note the reading on the voltmeter. Lower the signal generator frequency to a point 20 kc below the center frequency of the I.F. system. Again note the reading (with the meter leads reversed). If the circuits are in proper alignment, the two readings should be identical. Follow the same procedure for various other frequencies about the center position, noting each time whether equal indications are obtained for equal frequencies above and below the center frequency. If this is so, the system is in complete alignment. If not, it becomes necessary to readjust first the discriminator and then the I.F. circuits.

Overcoupled I.F. Transformers. There are in use many I.F. transformers which possess a double peak, due to overcoupling, in order to obtain a wide-band characteristic. (See Fig. 11.5.) For these, a slightly modified approach is necessary. When an over-coupled stage is to be aligned with an A-M signal generator, it is necessary to use loading networks. The network loads the circuit so that the transformer is effectively below critical coupling. In this condition, the transformer can be peaked. The loading net-

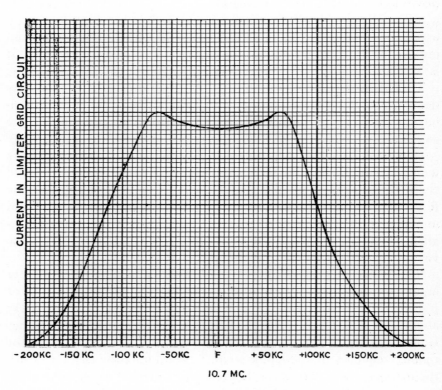

FIG. 11.5. A double-peak response curve for an F-M, I.F. system.

work to be used will be specified by the manufacturer and may consist of a single resistor or a resistor and condenser in series. When aligning a loaded stage, a greater signal is required from the signal generator and the stage will tune broadly. If it is found that the generator does not possess sufficient strength, it will be necessary to increase the size of the loading resistor in order to reduce the effect of the loading.

Where the manufacturer's service data is not available, or the size of the loading resistor is not known or specified, a resistor of 680 ohms may be used.

To align an overcoupled transformer, place the loading network across one of the windings, and peak the unloaded winding at the intermediate frequency. After this has been done, the loading network is switched to the other side of the transformer, and the winding, which is now unloaded, is peaked. Both sides of the transformer are now aligned. Remove the loading network, and adjust the windings of all the other transformers in similar manner.

When connecting the loading network across a transformer winding, use leads which are as short as possible. We are dealing here with relatively high frequency networks and there may exist enough inductance in the connecting leads to affect appreciably proper circuit operation. Hence the need for connecting leads which are as short as possible.

Alignment of R.F. Section. The procedure for aligning the R.F. portion of the receiver is similar, in many respects, to the methods in use for present commercial sets. In addition, nearly all R.F. tuned circuits are single-peaked, requiring that we adjust the various trimmers merely for maximum response.

To start the alignment, connect the signal generator to the input terminals of the receiver. (Unless the circuits are completely out of alignment it is perfectly feasible to adjust all the R.F. circuits and the oscillator at the same time.) The indicating meter is placed in the grid circuit of the limiter. Set the signal generator to some frequency at the high end of the band, say 104 or 105 mc. Adjust the front dial of the receiver accurately to read the same frequency. With the signal generator on, peak the oscillator until the maximum indication is obtained. Next, adjust the R.F. trimmers, while at the same time rocking the dial knob. Rocking consists of adjusting the R.F. trimmers while rotating the dial a small amount back and forth through peak output. The purpose is to find the maximum peak. If the point of maximum response occurs at a reading of the dial other than that of the incoming frequency, the oscillator trimmer will have to be adjusted while the dial is gradually brought back to correct position. Once at the correct position, the R.F. trimmers are aligned for maximum response.   As previously mentioned, it is important to remember that the indicating meter, in its present position, will give usable readings only if the signal does not saturate the limiter.   Keep the signal generator output at its lowest point consistent with readable indications on the meter.

Next, decrease the frequency of the signal generator to the low frequency end of the band (say 88 or 90 mc).   Again turn the dial of the F-M receiver until it reads the same frequency.   Adjust the trimmers of the oscillator and R.F. circuits for maximum indication at the meter.   If only one trimmer is available for each unit, a compromise position will have to be determined — one that gives the most uniform reading over the dial.

Visual Alignment.   Without doubt, adjustment of any receiver can be accomplished more quickly and more efficiently with an F-M signal generator and an oscilloscope than by means of the substitute point-by-point procedure.   In one case we are viewing the complete response whereas in the other we obtain several points and the remainder of the response is assumed.   Results of the adjustments of the various trimmers may be viewed immediately, whereas, in the point-by-point method, the effect of an adjustment can only be ascertained by its effect at the particular frequency, and its effect on the overall response must remain unknown.

The Oscilloscope.   The oscilloscope, shown in Fig. 11.6, is a voltage indicator.   Hence, in order to obtain any indications on the screen, the plates (or the input terminals) must be placed across two points in a circuit where a difference of potential exists.   If we desire to determine the form of the current wave, it becomes necessary to pass the current through a resistor and then to obtain the waveform of the voltage across the resistor.   Only through this indirect method is it possible to determine the current variations present.

For alignment of an F-M receiver, we still use the points indicated previously.   In the grid circuit of the limiter, we obtain the necessary voltage for the oscilloscope from across the grid resistor. At the output of the discriminator, the other indicating point used, the substitution of the oscilloscope introduces no problem.

In connecting the oscilloscope, the vertical input and ground leads are placed across the two points whose voltage waveform is to be viewed. At the points mentioned, one end is usually at ground potential, and it is best to connect the ground terminal of the scope

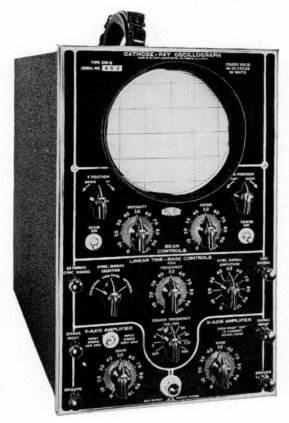

FIG. 11.6. A modern service oscilloscope. (Courtesy of DuMont.)

to the grounded point. This places the scope ground at the same potential as the set ground and avoids shock. If both points at which the voltage is to be measured are above ground, care will have to be exercised that one does not come in contact with the case of the oscilloscope, this usually being at oscilloscope ground. Remember that the so-called " ground " of one system does not necessarily

have to be at the "ground" of another system, unless both are
directly connected with a conductor.

In order to use the oscilloscope to its fullest extent, it is essential to have a good understanding of the type of indications that
will appear. Unless the proper interpretations are made from the
observed results, very little benefit will be derived from its use.

We know, from the previous discussion, that an S-shaped curve
represents the characteristic response of the discriminator. The
usable region, between points *A* and *B* (Fig. 11.2), must be made
linear if amplitude distortion is to be avoided during the F-M
demodulation process. Beyond the two points the characteristic
may curve considerably without affecting the response in any way.

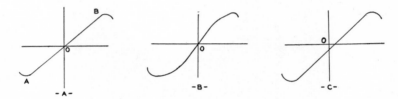

Fig. 11.7. Several response curves obtained from a discriminator: (A) correct alignment; (B) improper primary adjustment; (C) incorrect secondary trimmer setting.

With an F-M signal generator sweeping over the entire band,
the full S-shaped curve will be obtained on the screen of the scope.
If the entire I.F. system is properly aligned, the signal generator
may be placed at the grid of any of the tubes from the first I.F.
stage to the last limiter. If the discriminator is aligned before the
other stages, the signal generator must be placed at the grid of the
limiter preceding the discriminator. The vertical input terminals
of the scope, for discriminator alignment, connect between point *A*
and ground (Fig. 11.1).

With the signal generator in operation, the curve that should
appear on the scope screen is shown in Fig. 11.7A. If the secondary of the discriminator input transformer is properly aligned, but
not the primary, the linearity of the curve between points *A* and *B*
will be distorted, perhaps producing the result shown in Fig. 11.7B.
The primary winding controls the linearity of the response, and it
should be adjusted until the operating portion of the curve is linear.

Misalignment of the secondary, with the primary winding properly adjusted, shifts the cross-over point (point *O*, in Fig. 11.7A) from its normal position (see Fig. 11.7C). Adjustment is required until both sections of the curve are symmetrical with respect to the center point.

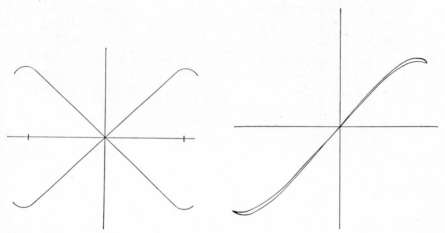

FIG. 11.8. A double discriminator response as seen on the oscilloscope screen.

FIG. 11.9. A discriminator characteristic obtained with a sine-wave sweep.

Although we require but one S-shaped curve, we sometimes get two. The curves may appear either as shown in Fig. 11.8 or Fig. 11.9, depending upon the system used by the F-M signal generator. In the signal generator shown in Fig. 11.10, the 60-cycle sine-wave input from the power line is used to modulate the reactance-tube modulator. At the same time, a portion of this sine-wave voltage is brought to an outlet at the signal generator panel. From this point it is connected to the horizontal input terminals at the oscilloscope by means of a cable. In other words, we replace the saw-tooth sweep of the indicating scope with this 60-cycle sine-wave voltage.

A saw-tooth voltage, shown in Fig. 11.11, when applied to the horizontal deflection plates of an oscilloscope, will cause the electron beam to move slowly from left to right and then, at the retrace, to

FIG. 11.10. A signal generator covering the F-M and television bands.

swing rapidly back to the left-hand side of the screen. With a 60-cycle sine-wave deflecting voltage, such as that obtained from the foregoing F-M signal generator, the action of the beam is entirely different.

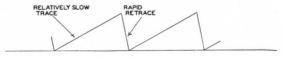

FIG. 11.11. The application of a saw-tooth wave to the deflecting plates of a scope causes a relatively slow left-to-right motion and rapid retrace.

Sine-Wave Deflection. In Fig. 11.12 we have the familiar sine wave, with letters from A to E inserted at convenient points to aid in the explanation. At point A, the voltage is zero and, if applied to the horizontal deflection plates, would not affect the beam. Hence, when the sine wave of Fig. 11.12 is applied to the deflecting plates, and the voltage is zero, the electron beam will pass through the center of the deflecting system unaffected and strike the fluorescent screen at its center.

From *A* to *B*, the voltage is increasing, and the beam is deflected to one side, say the right. From *B* to *C*, the deflecting voltage is decreasing, and the beam is gradually returning to the center of the screen. It arrives at this position when point *C* is reached.

From *C* to *D*, the voltage has reversed itself, and the beam is now shifting to the opposite side of the screen. At *D*, the maximum left-hand position has been reached. From *D* to *E,* the beam returns to the center of the screen again.

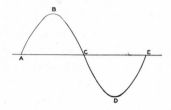

Fig. 11.12. A sine wave.

Now let us apply the output from the signal generator to the grid of the last limiter tube. The generator output is varied by the same 60-cycle sine wave. This means that the output frequency starts from its center position (which is indicated by the dial on the front panel), shifts to a higher frequency, reverses and returns to its center position, drops to a lower frequency, and finally returns to the carrier or resting position to end the cycle.

When we apply the F-M signal to the discriminator circuit, one S-shaped curve is traced out on the left to right motion of the beam, and a similar S-shaped curve is traced out as the beam travels from right to left on the screen. Remember that with this signal generator we are using a sine-wave sweep; the saw-tooth sweep of the oscilloscope itself is in the off position and without effect. If the discriminator circuit were perfectly balanced, the left-to-right trace of the electron beam would follow the exact same path as the right-to-left trace. However, with even a slight amount of unbalance, one trace is slightly displaced from the other, producing two S-shaped curves, as shown in Fig. 11.9. A slight distortion in the output from the signal generator will produce the same displacement in the beam traces.

The foregoing double trace represents one of two possible types. There is yet another form that the double trace may take and this is shown in Fig. 11.8. In one instance, a sine sweep is employed, causing the electron beam to trace forward and then backward. The second trace form is obtained when, in place of a sine sweep, we use the saw-tooth sweep generated in the scope itself. To understand how the double sweep of Fig. 11.8 is obtained, let us analyze the action of the overall system.

Saw-Tooth Deflection. With signal generators which utilize the oscilloscope saw-tooth deflecting voltage, a linearly rising and falling modulating voltage is driving the reactance-tube modulator and producing the frequency modulation. (Whether or not a reactance-tube modulator is used makes little difference. The important aspect of the discussion is the frequency deviation produced by a saw-tooth driving voltage.) In one cycle, the frequency output of the signal generator will swing twice across the frequency range to be covered. As an illustration, suppose we desire a signal from the generator of 90 mc, with a frequency variation of ±150 kc. Then in one cycle of the modulating voltage, we would obtain from the signal generator a sweep from 89.850 to 90.150 mc and then back to 89.850 mc again. In sweeping from 89.850 to 90.150 mc, the discriminator response will produce one S-shaped curve, while, in sweeping back from 90.150 to 89.850 mc, another S-shaped curve will be obtained.

Two S-shaped response curves appear on the oscilloscope (Fig. 11.8) because the saw-tooth deflecting voltage retraces rapidly when it reaches the right-hand side of the screen. Thus, in the interval when the frequency is swinging from 90.150 to 89.850 mc, after one S-shaped curve has been traced on the screen, the electron beam does not move slowly from right to left; rather it snaps back to the left-hand side of the screen and traces out the discriminator characteristic for the frequency range, 90.150 to 89.850 mc. The first and second S-shaped curves are shown in Fig. 11.13. When both these curves are placed on one screen, we obtain the result shown in Fig. 11.8.

Note that, although both curves are placed along the same horizontal axis, both do not have the same frequency values. When the beam traces forward on the first frequency sweep, the horizontal axis represents an increasing frequency (see Fig. 11.13A). On the second trace, the frequency is decreasing (see Fig. 11.13B). In the actual alignment this shift in axis values is unimportant as long as the S-shaped curve is sufficiently linear and the proper frequency bandwidth is obtained.

To summarize: F-M signal generators may have one of two types of output. In one instance, the signal frequency variation occurs sinusoidally. In the other instance, the variation rises and falls linearly. With a sinusoidal variation, the oscilloscope deflecting voltage is obtained from the generator. With a linear

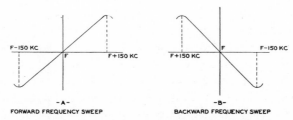

FIG. 11.13. The forward and backward frequency sweeps when saw-tooth deflection is employed.

frequency change, the saw-tooth deflecting voltage of the oscilloscope itself is used. A sine-wave deflecting potential produces two curves one slightly displaced from the other but otherwise similar at all points. For saw-tooth wave deflection, the two curves are mirror images of each other.

When the signal generator employs sinusoidal frequency variation, it generally also contains a phase control knob on its front panel. The need for this control arises from the fact that, although the driving voltage which is used to deflect the beam in the oscilloscope is obtained from the same source as the voltage applied to the sweep generator oscillator, it does not necessarily follow that these voltages are still in phase with each other when they actually reach the beam or the modulator tube. The voltages are transferred from point to point by means of condensers and resistors, and such networks will alter the phase of a voltage.

The effect of such phase shift is the appearance of a double trace on the oscilloscope screen. Thus, in Fig. 11.14A, we have the discriminator response pattern when the two driving voltages are essentially in phase with each other at their point of application and

in Fig. 11.14B the same response when the voltages are out of
phase with each other.   Either type of pattern may be used by the
serviceman to align a set visually, but the pattern in Fig. 11.14A is
easier to work with.   Toward that end, a phase control adjustment
is provided on the frontal panel of the signal generator and, when a
double trace is obtained, the serviceman adjusts the control setting
until the two patterns blend into one, as nearly as possible.

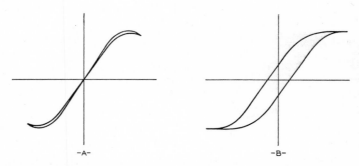

FIG. 11.14.   Discriminator response pattern on the screen of an oscilloscope.   (A) Phase
control on generator properly adjusted.   (B) Phase control improperly adjusted.

Visual Discriminator Alignment.   To align the discriminator
input transformer visually, connect the output terminals of the
signal generator between grid and ground of the last limiter tube.
Attach a wire from the " Vertical " post of the oscilloscope to
terminal A of Fig. 11.1.   The other end of the discriminator load,
usually ground, is connected to the ground terminal of the oscilloscope.   In addition, an outlet is provided on practically all F–M
signal generators (see Fig. 11.10) to permit a portion of the modulating voltage to be tapped off and applied as synchronizing voltage
to the terminal labeled " External Sync " on the oscilloscope front
panel.   (See Fig. 11.6.)   In this way it is possible to synchronize
the sweep of the oscilloscope with the modulating voltage of the
signal generator and obtain a stationary pattern on the oscilloscope
screen.

Set the generator to the I.F. value, say 10.7 mc, and adjust the
sweep control so that the output frequency sweeps for about 1 mc
about 10.7 mc.   This will produce the complete response pattern

on the screen plus a good indication of the circuit response beyond the desired spread about 10.7 mc. The primary and secondary trimmers (or cores) of the discriminator coil are adjusted now until the desired curve is obtained. This curve is shown in Fig. 11.7A. When this curve has been achieved, the discriminator circuit is aligned.

It is understood that synchronization is required only when the saw-tooth deflection voltage of the oscilloscope itself is utilized. For sine-wave deflection, the F-M signal generator furnishes the deflecting voltage, and no additional synchronizing is needed.

Visual Alignment of I.F. Stages.   For the visual alignment of the I.F. system, the vertical input leads of the oscilloscope are placed across the grid-leak resistor in the grid circuit of the last limiter stage. The signal generator is placed between grid and ground of each successive tube working from the tube just preceding the last limiter back to the grid of the mixer stage. At each position, the interstage transformer nearest the signal generator is adjusted until the desired bandpass response curve is obtained on the screen. If double peaking is used, care must be exercised to adjust each stage for the symmetrical curve of Fig. 11.5. The peaks must be positioned at equal distances from the center, or carrier-frequency, point. With single peaking, the midpoint of the peak should occur directly at the central carrier point. The level of the input signal is kept as low as possible in order not to drive the limiter beyond saturation.

Double curves may be seen on the oscilloscope screen, just as in the alignment of the discriminator. The remarks made at that time apply equally here.

R.F. System Alignment.   Alignment of the R.F. stages is achieved as follows: Attach the signal generator to the antenna terminals of the receiver, leaving the oscilloscope connected across the grid-leak resistor of the limiter stage.   Just how to connect the signal generator leads to the receiver will generally be specified by the manufacturer. Philco, for example, states that two simple dipole aerials should be constructed using 30-inch lengths of rubber-covered wire.   One dipole is connected to the receiver antenna terminals and one dipole is connected to the output terminals of the

signal generator. The two dipoles are then spaced several feet
apart and the signal transfer affected in this manner. Other manufacturers specify that the signal generator output leads should connect to the receiver antenna terminals through series resistors.
The value frequently chosen is 270 ohms.

The sweeping range of the generator is set for approximately
1 mc and the center output frequency adjusted to 108 mc. Set the
dial of the receiver to the same frequency. Now adjust the oscillator and input trimmer condensers (as indicated by the manufacturer) until the response curve seen at the oscilloscope is sym-

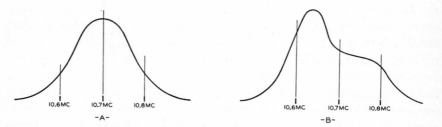

FIG. 11.15. (A) The response characteristic of a correctly aligned I.F. system. (B) A
distorted response indicating circuit misalignment.

metrical and at a maximum.   Note that, since the oscilloscope is
placed in the limiter grid circuit, the signal generated by the signal
generator will first have to pass through the I.F. system before it
reaches the oscilloscope.   Hence, the response pattern seen on the
oscilloscope will be that of the I.F. system.   (See Fig. 11.15A.)
However, if the R.F. stages are not properly adjusted, the response
pattern will become distorted, one possible shape shown in Fig.
11.15B.   The R.F. stages are correctly adjusted when the I.F.
response curve observed on the oscilloscope screen possesses its
proper form with a maximum amplitude.

The same procedure is repeated at 88 mc.   Practically all R.F.
coils are of single-peak design, and the foregoing method of adjusting for one maximum response at each test point is sufficient.

Marker Frequencies.   In using the oscilloscope, it would aid
considerably if the frequency at specific points on the curve seen
on the screen were identified in some manner by special markers.

Such indicators are known as marker frequencies or marker points. Some signal generators, like the one shown in Fig. 11.10, produce internal marker points at either 1-mc or 10-mc points. The indication on the screen of these points is either a slight wiggle in the curve being viewed or a slight break in the curve at that point. Both indications are illustrated in Fig. 11.16.

With the signal generator shown in Fig. 11.10, two crystal oscillators generate fundamental frequencies of 1 and 10 mc. These oscillators are designed, however, to produce outputs that are rich in harmonics. Hence, 1-mc and 10-mc marker points appear over the entire range of the unit.

It might seem that the identification of the various marker points would be extremely difficult, but this is not so when the dial reading is taken into account. Suppose, for example, that a signal of 90 mc is applied to the F-M receiver, along with 10-mc marker points. A marker indication should appear at the center of the scope screen, this being the ninth harmonic of the original funda-

Fig. 11.16. Two marker indications; (A) a slight wiggle and (B) a break in the curve.

mental 10-mc oscillator, or the pip at 90 mc. If we also inject the 1-mc marker pips, we can locate all the points on either side of the 90-mc marker, such as 87 mc, 88 mc, 89 mc, 91 mc, 92 mc, etc. Several moments spent in becoming familiar with the dial markings of the signal generator and observing the change in position of the 10-mc marker pips will readily familiarize one with the identification of the various frequency locations on any curve produced on the screen of the oscilloscope.

The disadvantage of the foregoing system is that marker pips cannot be placed at points which are intermediate to the 1-mc and 10-mc values mentioned. The F-M intermediate frequency value is 10.7 mc, and a marker pip cannot be obtained at this point.

There is, however, still another method whereby we may obtain a marker indication at any point, but it requires the use of an A-M signal generator. This second generator may be connected in parallel with the sweep (or F-M) generator or it may be placed somewhere along the path through which the signal from the sweep generator must pass.* The second generator is then set at the frequency at which we wish the marker indication to appear. The result on the screen of the oscilloscope will be a small wiggle at the proper point in the characteristic curve.

As an illustration, suppose the I.F. system of the receiver is being aligned. For a double-peaked response, it is necessary that each peak be equidistant from the center frequency. Connect the F-M signal generator across the grid circuit of the first I.F. stage (or the mixer stage) and, at the same time, connect the generator that will supply the marker frequency in parallel with the F-M generator. (Place an isolating resistor of 270 ohms in series with each lead from the A-M signal generator. This will keep interaction between the two generators to a minimum. Also keep the output of the A-M generator as low as possible while still being able to observe a wiggle in the response curve.) Let the F-M generator sweep over the band in the usual manner. Set the A-M generator — which develops a single signal at each dial setting — to the frequency of one of the peaks. The oscilloscope, connected into the grid circuit of the limiter stage, will indicate a wiggle at the point where one of the peaks should be located. By changing the A-M generator output to the other peak frequency, we can determine whether or not the system has been properly adjusted.

The marker indication is also good when aligning the discriminator. It may be used to indicate the two end points of the S-shaped discriminator curve plus the cross-over or central point. These are just a few of the uses of the marker points. The serviceman, in dealing with the equipment, will undoubtedly find many more.

ALIGNMENT OF F-M CIRCUITS CONTAINING THE RATIO DETECTOR

To align F-M receivers that do not use the Foster-Seeley discriminator but have another type of detector, such as the ratio

---

* Some sweep generators have an auxiliary A-M signal generator built in. Injection of the marker signal is then accomplished by simply flipping a switch and setting A-M generator to desired frequency.

detector, for example, it is necessary to modify the process some-what. Furthermore, ratio detectors fall into two categories, balanced and unbalanced, and this introduces slight variations in the alignment procedure. We will start first with the unbalanced ratio detector, using an A-M signal generator and a vacuum-tube voltmeter.

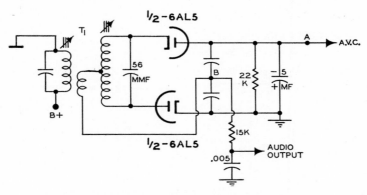

FIG. 11.17. An unbalanced ratio detector.

An unbalanced ratio detector is shown in Fig. 11.17. Connect the output lead from the A-M signal generator through a .05-mf condenser to the control grid of the I.F. amplifier tube just preceding the detector. Set the signal generator to the I.F. value (10.7 mc, usually). This signal should be unmodulated. Connect the vacuum-tube voltmeter between point A and ground. This con-nects the meter across the 5-mf condenser and the 22,000-ohm resistor. (Point A is where the negative A.V.C. voltage is obtained.)

With the equipment thus set up, adjust the primary core of T_1 until maximum voltage is indicated on the vacuum-tube voltmeter. To zero-adjust the secondary winding of T_1, it becomes necessary to balance artificially the detector. This balancing is done by con-necting two 68,000-ohm resistors (within 1 per cent of each other) in series, from point A to ground. (See Fig. 11.18.) Connect the common lead of the vacuum-tube voltmeter to the junction of these resistors, and the d-c probe to point B. The signal generator remains where it was, with the same dial setting. Now adjust the secondary winding core in T_1 for zero meter reading.

Detector linearity can be checked by shifting the signal frequency above and below 10.7 mc and noting whether equal readings are obtained for frequencies which are equally above and below 10.7 mc. The procedure is identical to the one discussed with Foster-Seeley discriminators.

After this has been done, the two 68,000-ohm resistors are removed from the circuit.

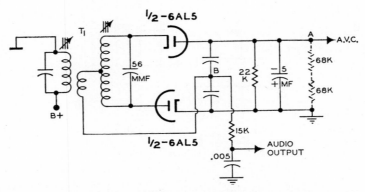

Fig. 11.18. Two 68,000-ohm resistors are connected as shown for the purpose of balancing the detector. See text.

To align the I.F. system, shift the A-M signal generator to the grid of the converter or mixed tube. Set the generator to the I.F. frequency. The vacuum-tube voltmeter is connected between point A and ground of the ratio detector. Now adjust the primary and secondary trimmers or cores of all I.F. transformers for maximum meter indication. If the transformers are overcoupled, use a loading network as previously outlined.

To align the R.F. sections of the receiver, shift the signal generator to the antenna terminals of the set (using an appropriate matching network as indicated by the manufacturer). The vacuum-tube voltmeter remains connected between point A and ground. Set the generator and the receiver dial to 108 mc and adjust the proper R.F. trimmers or cores for maximum meter reading. Next, change the generator frequency and the receiver dial to 88 mc (or thereabouts) and adjust the proper trimmers or cores (as indicated in the manufacturer's service manual) for maximum indication on the meter.   The set alignment is now complete.

In reading through the service literature that is put out by manufacturers, variations of the foregoing method will be found.   Thus, some manufacturers suggest that an output meter be placed across the speaker voice coil instead of the vacuum-tube voltmeter mentioned previously.   Since the signal must now pass through the audio amplifiers in order to reach the output meter, the I.F. signal from the generator must be amplitude-modulated.   Practically all A-M signal generators contain provisions for modulating their outputs with a 400-cycle audio note, hence this stipulation presents no difficulty.   However, since a well-aligned ratio detector will not permit an amplitude-modulated signal to pass through, complete alignment of the detector is left for the last.   Here is the sequence of alignment.

Connect an output meter across the voice coil of the speaker and connect the signal generator to the grid of the tube just preceding the detector.   Set the generator to the I.F. value (10.7 mc) and switch on the modulation.   Now, with the secondary trimmer or core of the discriminator coil tuned as far out as it will go, adjust the transformer primary for maximum meter reading.   This brings the primary winding into alignment.   The secondary, however, is still far out of alignment and this is done purposely in order to permit the detector to respond to A-M signals.

The I.F. and then the R.F. sections of the receiver are aligned next, at all times modulating the carrier signal with the 400-cycle (or whatever other low frequency note the generator contains). All adjustments in these two sections of the set are made for maximum meter indication.

After these circuits have been adjusted, the signal generator is moved back to the control grid of the tube preceding the ratio detector and set at the I.F. value.   The secondary of the detector transformer is now adjusted for minimum reading on the output meter.   At this point the A-M rejection properties of the detector are best, and the circuit is in alignment.

Balanced Ratio Detectors. When a balanced ratio detector (Fig. 11.19) is encountered, the alignment procedure is modified only when the detector circuit itself is being adjusted. To adjust the detector, we proceed as follows: Connect the A-M signal generator to the control grid of the last I.F. amplifier. Set it to the I.F. value (say 10.7 mc). Connect one lead from a vacuum-tube voltmeter to point B, Fig. 11.19. Attach the common lead to the receiver chassis. Back out the secondary iron-core adjustment of T_1 as far as it will go and then adjust the primary iron core for maximum meter deflection. Return to the secondary and adjust

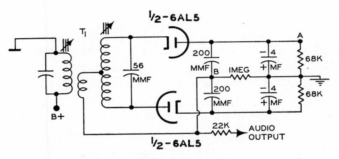

Fig. 11.19. A balanced ratio detector.

it for zero deflection. Check the linearity of the detector response as discussed with the unbalanced ratio detector.

Visual Alignment. Visual alignment of receivers employing the ratio detector is best accomplished by first adjusting the ratio detector and then adjusting the I.F. and R.F. circuits. The ungrounded vertical input terminal of the oscilloscope is connected, through a 10,000-ohm resistor, to point B. (Point B, Fig. 11.20, represents the audio output terminal of the detector.) The other terminal (ground) connects to the receiver chassis. The initial position of the sweep signal generator is between control grid and ground of the 6AU6 I.F. amplifier tube. A .05-mf condenser is inserted in the output lead of the generator. Set the generator to 10.7 mc, with a sweep of ± 300 kc. On the oscilloscope screen, the S-curve characteristic of ratio detectors should be visible. Adjust the primary iron core of T_1 for maximum linearity of the S-curve. Next, adjust the secondary iron core until the S-curve is symmetrical, with as much linear section above the 10.7-mc marker point as below. A marker signal, obtained from an A-M generator, can be used to determine the frequency extent of the linear section of the S-curve. The curve should be straight for at least ±100 kc.

The sweep generator and the marker generator are now shifted to the converter signal grid. The ungrounded vertical input lead of the oscilloscope is connected, through a 10,000-ohm resistor, to

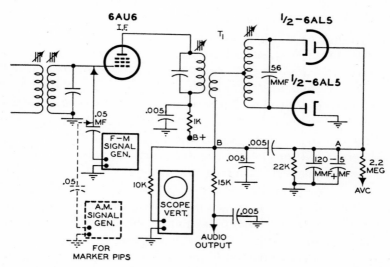

FIG. 11.20. Connection of test equipment to adjust visually the ratio detector.

point A, Fig. 11.20. The ground terminal connects to the receiver chassis. Remove temporarily the 5-mf condenser connected from point A to ground. Keep the signal generators at the same frequency used previously, and adjust the primary and secondary windings of each I.F. transformer for maximum amplitude and balance of the response curve. (See Fig. 11.15A.) Note that loading networks are not required with the visual alignment methods. The I.F. system is now adjusted. Reconnect the 5-mf condenser.

The purpose in removing the 5-mf electrolytic condenser, as indicated in the foregoing paragraph, is to permit the voltage variations caused by the F-M signal passing through the I.F. system to appear at point A. When viewed on the oscilloscope screen, these variations represent the response curve of the I.F. system.

Sweep alignment of the R.F. stages of an F-M receiver is seldom required. Simple peaking using an A-M generator, as previously described, is the method generally recommended by receiver manufacturers. However, if sweep alignment of the R.F. stages is desired, it is carried out as follows:

Connect the sweep generator to the antenna terminals of the receiver. The oscilloscope is connected to point B, Fig. 11.20. The sweeping range of the generator is set for approximately 1 mc, and the center output frequency is adjusted to 108 mc. Set the dial of the receiver to the same frequency. Now adjust the oscillator and input trimmer condensers (as specified by the manufacturer) until the ratio detector response curve (the S-curve) is symmetrical and possesses maximum amplitude. Since the oscilloscope is placed across the ratio detector output, the curve obtained on the oscilloscope screen will be that of the detector. However, if the R.F. stages are not properly adjusted, the response pattern will become distorted. The R.F. stages are correctly adjusted when the response curve possesses its proper form with a maximum amplitude.

The same procedure is repeated at 88 mc, completing the front-end alignment of the set.

Alignment Procedure for Beam-Gated Tubes. The alignment procedure for F-M receivers using the 6BN6 (or 12BN6) beam-gated tube differs in many respects from the alignment procedure employed for sets having one of the other detectors. The first difference occurs in the alignment of the I.F. stages themselves. Since the 6BN6 removes amplitude variations, and therefore cannot be transformed into an A-M detector, it becomes impossible to place either a vacuum-tube voltmeter or an oscilloscope at any point in this circuit and obtain the proper indications for peaking the I.F. coils. Hence, to align the I.F. system, a special probe detector must be constructed. A suggested circuit of a probe is shown in Fig. 11.21, using a 1N34 germanium crystal. When constructing this probe, be careful to keep the length of all connecting leads between components as short as possible.

To align the I.F. system, connect the input lead of the probe to grid 1 of the 6BN6.   (See Fig. 11.22.)   The output lead connects to the d-c scale of a vacuum-tube voltmeter, while the other output lead connects to the ground or common terminal of the meter. This same lead also connects to the receiver chassis.   An A-M signal is connected, in turn, to each of the control grids of the I.F. amplifier tubes, and the transformer associated with that stage is adjusted for maximum meter indication.   This is done for each I.F. amplifier in exactly

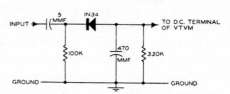

Fig. 11.21.   Circuit of the probe required in the alignment of F-M receivers employing the beam-gated tube.

the same manner that it is done in sets using the ratio or Foster-Seeley detectors.

After the I.F. system is aligned, the signal generator is moved to the input terminals of the receiver, and the R.F. section is

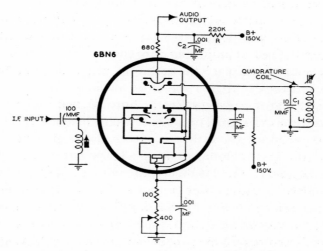

Fig. 11.22.   The beam-gated tube connected as a limiter-discriminator.

adjusted for maximum indication on the probe meter.   If visual alignment is desired for either the R.F. or I.F. sections of the receiver, the output of the probe detector connects to the vertical input terminal of the oscilloscope, and an F-M sweep generator is used.

To adjust the discriminator, the probe detector with its meter is left connected to grid 1 of the 6BN6. The signal generator, however, is removed, and the regular set antenna is now connected to the receiver and a station tuned in. The set should be tuned for maximum deflection on the probe meter, thereby indicating that the station is properly tuned in. As an added precaution, the dial should be rocked back and forth until the serviceman is certain that the meter deflection is maximum. The volume control should be turned completely counterclockwise so that no sound is heard from the speaker.

When the serviceman is satisfied that the station is correctly tuned in, the volume control is advanced until speech or music is heard, and the quadrature coil of the 6BN6 is adjusted for best sound from the speaker.

There still remains the adjustment of the variable resistor in the cathode leg of the tube. The function of this resistor, it will be recalled, is to provide the proper grid bias for the limiter, in order that the best limiting action (for A-M rejection) be obtained. A method of adjusting this control which is both simple and satisfactory is to place the set in operation just as it normally would be and then tune in a signal of medium strength. Insert a resistive attenuator pad between the antenna and the receiver and reduce the received signal to a level where hiss is heard with the sound. Now adjust the cathode control of the 6BN6 for clearest sound and the least amount of hiss. During the adjustment, the hiss may disappear. If this occurs, the input signal must be further reduced so that the hiss never disappears during alignment.

In order for this method to work properly, the resistive attenuator should be continuously variable. If such a pad is not available, then construct a loop antenna of several turns and connect it to the receiver input terminals. Connect a similar loop to the transmission line from the regular antenna. Now vary the spacing between these two loops until the received signal is reduced to a level where hiss is heard with the sound, and adjust the cathode control.

Alignment of a receiver employing the Philco locked-in detector is given in detail in Chapter 12.

PROBLEMS

1. What two methods can be employed to align F-M receivers? Can the same methods be used with A-M receivers? Explain.

2. What similarities exist between the basic alignment procedure for A-M and F-M receivers?

3. How is a Foster-Seeley discriminator aligned, using an A-M signal generator and a voltmeter?

4. Describe the alignment of a two-stage transformer-coupled limiter. What precautions must be observed when limiters are aligned?

5. Can improper alignment of the I.F. and limiter stages affect the operation of the discriminator? Explain.

6. What effect does the type of F-M detector used have on the method of alignment?

7. What effect will a strong signal have on the alignment of the I.F. and limiter stages? Assume the indicating meter is placed in the grid circuit of the limiter.

8. What is the purpose of an overall alignment check on the I.F. and detector stages? Describe how this check is carried out.

9. How are over-coupled I.F. transformers aligned?

10. Why is the I.F. system aligned before the R.F. section of the receiver? Would it be possible to reverse the process? Explain.

11. Describe the alignment of the R.F. section of an F-M receiver.

12. What equipment is needed to run a visual check on a receiver? Explain how each piece of equipment is used.

13. Explain the difference between sine-wave deflection and saw-tooth deflection of the electron beam in the oscilloscope.

14. What would happen if a sweep generator using sine-wave modulation was used in conjunction with an oscilloscope in which the electron beam was deflected by a saw-tooth voltage? How would the response pattern appear on the scope screen?

15. Why is a phase control incorporated in sweep signal generators?

16. What are marker frequencies? Why are they used?

17. Describe the alignment of the I.F. system and the discriminator by the visual method.

18. How are marker signals developed?

CHAPTER 12

COMMERCIAL F-M RECEIVERS

We have studied the various sections of an F-M receiver in considerable detail. In this chapter we shall observe how these principles are applied to a complete receiver. It will be found, after examination of the many receivers which are available, that they differ markedly in essentially two respects — the type of R.F. tuner employed and the F-M detector or discriminator. The remaining sections of the circuit, which include the I.F. stages, the audio amplifiers, and the power supply, are designed along closely similar lines. Although each of these stages are not exact duplicates of each other, complete understanding of one circuit will readily lead to the same comprehension of other models.

In regard to discriminators, all of the currently available receivers employ a conventional discriminator, a ratio detector, or a synchronized oscillator, the last exemplified by the Philco circuit. For complete coverage, one commercial model of each type is included in the chapter and each is analyzed in detail, both as to the circuit content and alignment procedure.

The Conventional Discriminator. The schematic diagram of a Stromberg-Carlson A-M–F-M receiver is shown in Fig. 12.1. It is an eleven-tube receiver covering the broadcast range (540–1620 kc), the short-wave bands (8.8–10.2 mc), and the frequency modulation frequencies (88–108 mc). The dial plate of the receiver would contain suitable calibrations for all three bands to enable the set user to note the exact location of all received stations. For the F-M band, most manufacturers list the frequencies while a few use the channel numbers into which the band has been divided. The latter method is the one followed in this receiver.

Band Switches: In examining a schematic diagram, the serviceman will generally find that, because more than one band is covered by the receiver, selector switches are employed. Furthermore, since many of the input circuits are fully connected only through these switches, there is a maze of wires going to or leading from each section of the switch.   For the sake of compactness, the various switches are mounted on one shaft to form one composite unit. As a distinguishing characteristic, however, each separate unit of the switch is generally labeled as a section, for example, section 2, section 3, etc.   In the circuit of Fig. 12.1, there are six separate sections, all mounted on the same shaft, and, in addition, each section has a front (F) and rear (R) plate.

Each switch contains a movable, circular metallic strip which, when rotated, contacts different switch terminals.   In Fig. 12.1, all the switches are shown in the short-wave position.   If we trace from the short-wave input coil to terminal 1 at the rear of section 1, we find that the movable strip of this section is also contacting terminal 3.   A wire from terminal 3 goes to the grid of the R.F. amplifier tube, a 6SG7.   Thus, through the switch, connection is made between the short-wave antenna coil and the 6SG7 tube. Note that the arrow (denoting contact arm) from terminal 3 to the movable strip is longer than the arrows from the other terminals of the same section.   This indicates that as long as the movable contact is not rotated completely past terminal 3, there will be electrical contact between the terminal and the movable strip. Other terminals — those which are drawn with short arrows (denoting shorter contact arms) — do not always touch the movable metallic strip.   If an indentation or groove in the movable strip is facing one of these other terminals, no contact is made. Thus, for example, terminal 2 of section 1-R does not contact the center strip when the switch is in the short-wave position.

Curved arrows at each section indicate that the switch is to be rotated in a clockwise direction.   In Fig. 12.1, when the switch is rotated once in a clockwise direction, the broadcast (B.C.) band is switched in.   Beyond this we have the frequency modulation band (88–108 mc), and a phonograph.   To aid in following the schematic readily, the active or connecting terminals at each switch position have been tabulated in Table 1.   In each block of the table, the numbers which are separated by a comma are electrically connected when the switch is at the position indicated at the left-hand side of the table.   If two sets of numbers are given, such as 3,4 and 5,6, then 3 and 4 connect together and 5 and 6 connect together, but there is no connection at that switch between each set.   However, it is entirely possible that some connection is made at some other portion of the receiver.

TABLE 1

Band	Switch Section										
	1R	1F	2R	2F	3R	3F	4R	4F	5R	5F	6R
Short wave	1,3	1,3	1,3	1,2	1,3	1,3	1,3 5,6	1,3	1,4 5,6	1,4	1,5
Broad-cast	2,3	2,3	2,3	. . .	2,3	2,3	2,3 5,6	2,3	2,4 5,6	2,4	1,5
F-M	3,4 5,6	3,4	3,4	2,3,4	3,4	3,4	3,4 5,6	3,4	3,4	3,4 5,6	2,3,5

A careful inspection of the connections at each switch section is important.   Unless this is carefully and systematically done, it will be extremely difficult to trace the various circuits.

Receiver Analysis: The schematic diagram of the receiver in Fig. 12.1 indicates that the stage arrangement is as follows:

1 — 6SG7 . . . .   R.F. amplifier
1 — 6SB7Y . . . . . .   Converter
1 — 6SG7 . . . .   First I.F. amplifier
1 — 6SH7 . . . .   Second I.F. amplifier
1 — 6SH7 . . . .   Limiter
1 — 6H6 . . . .   Discriminator
1 — 6SQ7 . . . .   A.V.C. demodulator and first audio
1 — 6SC7 . . . .   Driver and inverter
2 — 6V6GT . . . . .   Output
1 — 5U4G . . . . . .   Rectifier

The input circuits, three in number corresponding to the three bands of the receiver, are all condenser-tuned.   C-9, C-4 tune the antenna input coil, C-13 and C-16 are for the converter input, and C-24 with C-23 resonate the various oscillator coils.   All six condensers are ganged in accordance with conventional design.   A simple, single-wire antenna is provided on the S.W. and B.C. bands. For the F-M stations, a dipole antenna using a balanced transmission line is required.

The R.F. amplifier, a 6SG7, operates with A.V.C. on the B.C. and S.W. bands, and with essentially zero bias on the F-M channel. No A.V.C. is active when the receiver is set for F-M, the A.V.C. line being grounded by the contacts on the section I-R switch. Coupling between the R.F. amplifier plate circuit and the converter grid is accomplished by means of a modified impedance-coupled network (see Fig. 12.2). The R.F. voltage developed

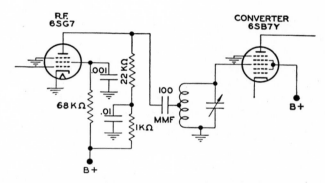

FIG. 12.2. A simplified diagram of the coupling network between the R.F. amplifier and the converter tube.

across the 22,000-ohm plate resistor is capacitively coupled to the proper tuned circuit which, in turn, connects to the grid of the 6SB7Y converter. The 100-mmf condenser from the R.F. amplifier is tapped down on the tuned circuit in order to reduce the capacitance shunted across this coil by the R.F. amplifier circuit. By maintaining the capacitance small, the coil inductance can be made larger, thereby improving the Q of the tuned circuit and providing more gain for the signal. The proper converter coil is selected with section 3 switch.

The 6SB7Y converter tube is one which has been especially designed for converter operation at the higher frequencies. Ordinarily, it is not recommended that a single tube both mix and generate the oscillator voltage at the higher frequencies. The reasons for this were previously noted. However, because of special construction, it is entirely feasible to use the 6SB7Y in this manner. Each band possesses a separate oscillator coil, each connected to a Hartley oscillator. Switch sections 4 and 5 control the connections within the oscillator coils. Two terminals which, when connected, supply the screen-grid voltage to the 6SB7Y are included in the section 4-R switch. When the switch is at the extreme right position, bringing in the phonograph, the screen-grid B+ voltage is disconnected and the front section of the receiver becomes inoperative. This eliminates all possibility of interference from outside sources while the phonograph is in use.

In the plate circuit of the converter, we have the 10.7-mc I.F. for the F-M bands and the 455-kc I.F. for the S.W. and B.C. channels. If the circuit is examined at this point, it will be seen that the windings are switched according to the band. In the stages following the converter, switching is not employed and either I.F. signal passes through both windings. Switching is employed in the first I.F. transformer to eliminate undesired beat-frequencies that have been found to appear if both windings are kept in the plate of the converter at the same time. However, beyond this section of the receiver, the large difference between intermediate frequencies make further switching and separation unnecessary. The I.F. stages are conventional in design, with the A.V.C. voltage applied only to the first I.F. amplifier. This, however, is only for the S.W. and B.C. bands. All the coils are permeability-tuned. Adjustment consists in properly positioning the iron cores with a small screwdriver.

At the output of the second I.F. amplifier, the S.W. and B.C. signals are fed to a diode detector where they are detected and applied to the triode section of a 6SQ7. A.V.C. is also developed in this circuit and used to control the gain of the first I.F. amplifier and the R.F. amplifier on the S.W. and B.C. bands only. Both circuits follow conventional design and require no special attention. For F-M signals, the second I.F. amplifier is followed by a 6SH7 limiter and a 6H6 discriminator. The limiter operates with grid-leak bias and lowered electrode potentials, producing complete saturation for a 2-volt signal. In the grid circuit of the limiter, a portion of the grid resistor, 4700 ohms, is by-passed with a

1000-mmf condenser.   During F-M alignment, it is the d-c voltage
appearing across this resistor which serves as an indication.   The
by-pass condenser prevents the I.F. voltage from passing through
the indicating meter and possibly injuring the movement.   The
discriminator has already been fully described in a previous chapter.
The audio output of the unit is connected through section 6-R switch
to the 1-megohm volume control.   A 1000-ohm resistor and series
0.5-mf condenser are placed across the lower portion of the volume
control and provide automatic tone compensation at low audio
volume.   The compensation is fixed, although an adjustable tone
control is available in the plate circuit of the 6SQ7 tube.

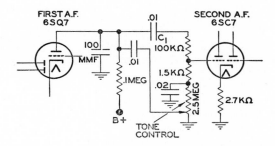

FIG. 12.3.   The arrangement of the tone control network when the low frequencies
are desired.

The adjustable tone control is a refinement of a simple bass-
boost control circuit previously analyzed.   In most receivers employing this form of control, the 0.01-mf condenser and series
2.5-megohm resistor are shunted from the plate of an audio amplifier to ground.   Here, however, we find that the grid return lead
of the following tube is also made a part of the circuit.   As a
result, the accentuation of the highs and lows becomes more pro-
nounced.   Two equivalent circuits of this network are shown in
Figs. 12.3 and 12.4.   Fig. 12.3 is the equivalent circuit when the
lows are at their maximum; Fig. 12.4, when the highs predominate.
In the bass position, the high audio frequencies are completely
by-passed to ground by the 0.01-mf condenser.   In addition, the
full 2.5 megohms of the tone control are in the grid network of the
6SC7.   Because of the added resistance, the 0.01-mf coupling con-

denser (C_1) becomes less effective in reducing the low frequencies that are applied to the circuit $(X_c = 1/2\pi fC)$, and more lows reach the grid of the 6SC7. At the other extreme, when the full 2.5 megohms are in the plate by-passing network, only 15,000 ohms is present at the grid of the 6SC7. Now the 0.01-mf coupling condenser substantially reduces the lows reaching the 6SC7 and indirectly aids the high or treble frequency response.

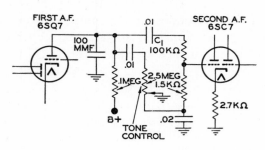

FIG. 12.4. The tone control network of Fig. 12.3 accentuating the treble frequencies.

The remainder of the audio amplifier network is conventional, providing push-pull output. Stability is aided by the negative feedback network from the plate of one 6V6GT amplifier, through a 0.01-mf condenser and 1.5-megohm resistor, to the grid of the same tube. B+ power is provided for the set and a wire recorder (not shown) by a 5U4G full-wave rectifier.

The placement of the radio components on the receiver chassis can be studied from the photographs of Fig. 12.5.

Alignment Procedure. A modern commercial receiver is a delicately adjusted mechanism and should never be aligned unless it is absolutely necessary. The procedure to be given here is the procedure which has been recommended by the manufacturer. However, it can be employed for almost all receivers having the same type of discriminator. In other sets, the condenser and transformer identification numbers will naturally be different, but the adjustment that is made at each stage will be identical in each receiver.

Allow the set to warm up for 15 to 20 minutes before beginning the alignment. Always align a receiver using the smallest signal

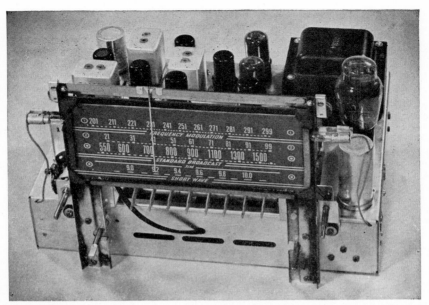

FIG. 12.5A & B. Views of the parts placement and circuit-wiring of the Stromberg-Carlson A-M–F-M receiver.

amplitude from the signal generator which will give a readable indication.   The volume control should be set to maximum position. The manufacturer recommends alignment of the A-M circuits first.

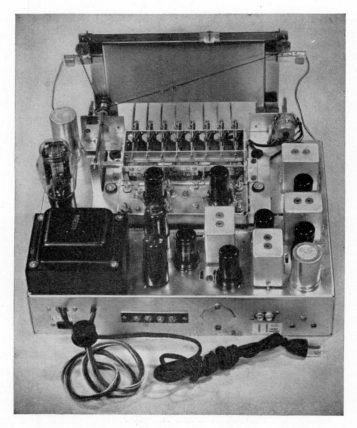

FIG. 12.5C.   Another view of the parts placement of the Stromberg-Carlson A-M–F-M receiver.   (Courtesy of Stromberg-Carlson.)

A-M–I.F. Adjustment: Unless there is reason to believe that the entire I.F. system is out of alignment, it is perfectly permissible to insert the test signal at the converter tube and adjust the entire system at one time.   The first step is to connect the signal generator to the converter signal grid.   This is terminal 8 of the 6SB7Y tube. The ground of the signal generator is connected directly to the receiver ground.   The output lead of the generator is connected to pin 8 (and other points to be specified later) through a 0.05-mf condenser.   Next, place an output meter across the voice coil of the speaker.   Most signal generators use a 400-cycle note for modulation and this should be turned to the on-position.   If there is control of the degree of modulation, set it at 30 per cent.   The tone control is set at the maximum high position.   If a separate bass knob is available, it is set to the lowest (counterclockwise) position.   Adjust the signal generator to the proper I.F. value (for this receiver, 455 kc) and adjust each of the I.F. cores for maximum output using as low a test signal as possible.   During this operation, the tuning dial is set to approximately 600 kc.

I.F. transformers which are slug-tuned must be adjusted slowly and without undue force, otherwise the threads within the coil form may be stripped.   The adjustment is made for maximum indication on the output meter.   In the receiver shown in Fig. 12.1, the I.F. cores adjusted are:

Stage	*Coils Adjusted*
Converter output	L-32, L-33
First I.F.	L-36, L-37
Second I.F.	L-41, L-42

A-M–R.F. Adjustment: We will consider the B.C. band first, then the S.W. band.   If the receiver contains a loop antenna, it should *not* be disconnected during the alignment.   The signal from the generator, in this instance, is coupled to the loop by means of another loop.   Construct a 6-turn, 6-inch diameter loop using ordinary hook-up wire.   Connect the loop to the terminals of the signal generator and place it near the radio loop.   If the receiver does not contain a built-in loop, connect the generator to the antenna post, using a 200-mmf condenser.   The modulation is again 30 per cent.   The output meter remains connected across the voice coil of the speaker.   The procedure, then, is as follows:

1. Set the signal generator at 1600 kc.
2. Set the station selector at 1600 kc.
3. Range switch should be at A-M.
4. Adjust the oscillator, R.F. and antenna trimmers for maxi-

mum indication on the output meter.   The trimmers in Fig. 12.1 are C-3, C-15, and C-22, each marked with the letter " T."

5. Reduce the input signal and readjust the trimmers until the maximum output is obtained for the least input voltage.

6. Rotate the station selector dial to 600 kc.

7. Set the signal generator to 600 kc.

8. Adjust the iron cores in oscillator, R.F. and antenna coils for maximum output.   Note that the low frequency response of an iron-core coil is governed by the iron cores, while a trimmer adjusts the high frequency end.   If the coils are air-core units, only the high frequency adjustment is possible.

9. Repeat the 1600-kc and the 600-kc alignments until no further change is necessary.

For the short-wave band the following steps apply.   Do not remove any built-in loop antennas.

1. Connect the signal generator to the antenna and ground terminals of the receiver using a 400-ohm series resistor.

2. Place range switch to short-wave.

3. Adjust the signal generator to 9.5 mc.

4. Set the dial pointer to 9.5 mc.

5. Adjust oscillator, R.F. and antenna trimmer for maximum output.   The trimmer condensers are: C-21 (osc.), C-14 (R.F.), and C-1 (antenna).

This completes the alignment of the A-M section of the receiver. Next, we turn to the F-M section.

F-M–I.F. Adjustment: The F-M–I.F. value is 10.7 mc in this receiver.   It is possible to align the entire F-M system at one time, just as was done on A-M, but because this system is more critical, it is best to align each stage separately.   The indicator, preferably an electronic voltmeter, is connected across the 4700-ohm resistor in the limiter grid circuit.   The voltmeter, in order to be most sensitive, is used on its lowest scale, and the signal is always adjusted so that it does not cause the needle to swing to the extreme right-hand side of the scale.   The sequence of steps is as follows:

1. Connect the signal generator to the grid of the 6SH7, second I.F. amplifier tube.   This is pin 4.

2. Set the signal generator to 10.7 mc.   No modulation is required since the signal itself produces a d-c voltage across the 4700-ohm resistor.

3. Adjust the cores (L-39 and L-40) of the third F-M–I.F. transformer for maximum output of the voltmeter.   At all times keep the signal amplitude at the lowest possible value needed to give an indication on the meter.

4. Transfer the signal generator to the grid of the first I.F. amplifier tube, 6SG7.   (Pin 4.)

5. Adjust the cores of L-34, L-35 for maximum indication of the meter.

6. Finally, transfer the generator to pin 8 (and ground) of the 6SB7 converter tube.

7. Turn the range switch to the low F-M band.

8. Adjust the cores of L-30 and L-31 for maximum indication of the meter.

Many manufacturers purposely overcouple one (or two) of the F-M–I.F. transformers in order to obtain a wide-band characteristic.   When an overcoupled stage is to be aligned with a single signal generator it is necessary to use loading networks.   The network loads the circuit so that the transformer is effectively below critical coupling.   In this condition, the transformer can be peaked.   The loading network to be used will be specified by the manufacturer and may consist of a single resistor or a resistor and condenser in series. When aligning a loaded stage, a greater signal is required from the signal generator and the stage will tune broadly.   If it is found that the generator does not possess sufficient strength, it will be necessary to increase the size of the loading resistor in order to reduce the effect of the loading.

To align an overcoupled transformer, place the loading network across one of the windings, and peak the unloaded winding at the intermediate frequency.   After this has been done, the loading network is switched to the other side of the transformer, and the winding, which is now unloaded, is peaked.   After adjustment of all the windings in this manner, the load is removed.

Discriminator Alignment (F-M) : 1. Connect output lead of the generator either to the grid of the 6SH7 (second I.F. amplifier) or to the grid of the limiter. The other generator lead is connected to the receiver chassis.

2. Connect the voltmeter between the center of the diode load resistors (R-23, R-24) and ground.

3. Adjust the primary of the discriminator transformer, L-43, for maximum meter indication.

4. Place the indicator across both diode load resistors.

5. Adjust the secondary of the discriminator, L-45, for zero output.

6. Swing the generator frequency 75 kc above and below 10.7 mc. Note the linearity of the discriminator. If not sufficiently linear, then the primary and secondary will have to be readjusted.

The only remaining adjustments are the alignment of the R.F. stages at the F-M band.

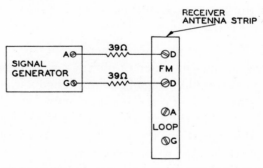

Fig. 12.6. The manufacturer's recommended method of connecting an A-M signal generator to a balanced input coil. (Courtesy of Stromberg-Carlson.)

R.F. Alignment–F-M : In the alignment of the R.F. end of the receiver, the two terminals to which a dipole is connected are used. However, in the alignment all antennas connected to these terminals are disconnected. Note that we have a balanced input here and the signal generator must be connected accordingly. The manufacturer recommends two 39-ohm resistors as shown in Fig. 12.6. Other manufacturers may specify different values, the most usual one being 270 ohms. In any event, check the receiver service manual. For the F-M band (88–108 mc) set the signal generator to 100.1 mc.

In each instance the range switch and the dial setting should be positioned at the proper point.   Place a voltmeter across the 4700-ohm resistor in the limiter grid circuit.   Adjust the oscillator, R.F. and antenna trimmers for maximum meter indication.

Alignment with Oscilloscope: It is preferable, when possible, to align F-M circuits with an F-M sweep generator and an oscilloscope.   The oscilloscope is placed across the 4700-ohm resistor of the limiter grid circuit when the I.F. stages are being adjusted.   The F-M sweep generator is moved from stage to stage toward the converter or mixer while the proper set of I.F. transformer cores is adjusted.   For the discriminator adjustment, the oscilloscope is placed across the full output of this stage.   Note that loading networks are not required with this method since the entire circuit response characteristic appears on the oscilloscope screen.   The circuits are then adjusted until the proper waveform and bandpass are achieved.

F-M Receiver with Philco Detector.   The synchronized oscillator type of F-M detector was recently developed by Philco and its principle of operation was described in Chapter 9.   A complete A-M–F-M receiver incorporating this detector is shown in Fig. 12.7. Many sections of the receiver contain essentially the same type of circuits analyzed in the previous receiver, and for these very little additional information is necessary.   Those circuits which do differ will be examined in detail.

The switching arrangement of the receiver is conducted chiefly by push buttons.   There are ten push buttons : six for instant tuning of stations in the standard broadcast band, one for selecting standard broadcast for manual tuning, one for short wave, one for the F-M band, one for power OFF (any one of the other nine buttons turns on the radio power).   In examining the schematic, the power OFF push button and the six buttons used for instant tuning of the standard broadcast stations are shown at the lower left.   (The buttons are shown in the OFF position — that is, not depressed and therefore inactive in the circuit.)

Push buttons 8, 9, and 10 are scattered throughout the circuit, but wherever they appear they are indicated as PB8, PB9, or PB10. These three push buttons are concerned with switching the set either to standard broadcast (manual tuning), short wave, or F-M. In the diagram, as it now stands, the circuit is set for manual tuning on standard broadcast.   This means that PB8 is depressed and active.   If, now, PB10 is depressed, PB8 will be brought out of its depressed position and all contacts of PB8, shown in groups of two, will switch from the position shown in Fig. 12.7 to their second position.   At the same time, contacts labeled PB10 will shift from their present position to the other contact of the set.

At each pair of contacts of PB8, PB9, or PB10, the letters P, B, S, and F appear.   These denote:

P = Push Button Standard A-M Broadcast
B = Manual A-M Standard Broadcast
S = Short Wave
F = F-M

Finally, there is another set of three rotary switches (labeled FS-1, FS-2, and FS-3) which are actuated only by the F-M push button.   When the F-M button is depressed, each of these rotary switches changes contact from that shown in Fig. 12.7.   More on this later.

Receiver Circuits: The front end of the receiver contains an R.F. amplifier (a 7W7 pentode) which is used solely for the amplification of F-M signals.   The F-M antenna, in this instance, is actually the a-c line that brings the power into the house.   Since the length of the a-c wiring throughout a house is quite extensive, it will, in all probability, pick up a considerable amount of F-M signal.   When the receiver plug is inserted into the a-c socket, this F-M signal will be brought right into the receiver.   If, now, a wire connected to the F-M input coil is capacitively coupled to the a-c line, it will receive the F-M signals.   This is the course followed in this receiver.

For the standard broadcast band, a loop antenna inside the cabinet is employed.   For the reception of short-wave signals, an external antenna may be connected.   On both these bands, signals received are applied directly to the grid of the converter triode (one half of a 7F8).   The other half of the 7F8 functions as an oscillator on all bands, with appropriate switching in coils.   Oscillator voltage is injected into the mixer by way of its cathode, a 750-mmf condenser serving as the coupling agent by bridging across both cathodes of the 7F8.

The oscillator circuit, a Hartley, is unique in that the grid is placed at R.F. (not d-c) ground potential while the cathode and plate assume R.F. potentials. In the more normal arrangement, the cathode is placed at ground potential, while the grid and plate are tapped up along the coil. The shift in the ground connection, however, does not alter the oscillator operation. A tube will function whether the grid is kept at R.F. ground potential and the cathode R.F. voltage is varied or whether the cathode is connected to ground and the grid voltage is varied. Grid-leak bias is developed across the 22,000-ohm grid resistor and the 100-$\mu\mu$f grid condenser.

The reason for this unique oscillator arrangement is due to a desire on the part of the set engineers to keep at a minimum the tube capacitance shunted across the oscillator tuned circuit. The oscillator coil already has a variable tuning condenser in shunt with it. To achieve a large oscillator voltage, with good selectivity, requires a high L to C ratio, and adding capacitance across the coil will lower this ratio. Furthermore, cathode injection of the oscillator voltage to the mixer requires less oscillator voltage than if the injection had been attempted from grid to grid.

The mixer output is applied to the first I.F. transformer. Note that in this receiver, in common with the previous set, a switch short-circuits the primary winding of the I.F. transformer not in use. The contacts of the switch are controlled by the F-M push button. Hence, on all but the F-M band, the contacts are in one position while, when the F-M push button is operated, the contacts shift to the other position. At the first I.F. transformer, terminals 6 and 7 make contact on all bands except F-M. On F-M, connection is between terminals 5 and 6.

In the I.F. system, the first, third, and fourth I.F. transformers have two sets of windings each. The second I.F. transformer has a single primary winding, a secondary winding tuned to 9.1 mc, and another secondary tuned to 455 kc. The reason for employing an untuned primary is to prevent instability on the A-M bands. In the second I.F. amplifier, the screen-grid voltage is increased when the set is switched to F-M. This is accomplished by removing the ground connection on the 100,000-ohm resistor (R_1). On all other bands, one end of the resistor is grounded, producing a volt-age-divider arrangement and lowering the voltage applied to the screen grid. The increased voltage at the screen grid results in greater gain.

The A-M detector, using one diode plate of the 6SQ7 tube, is quite conventional (see Fig. 12.8). The same diode section also supplies A.V.C. action for A-M reception. This A.V.C. voltage

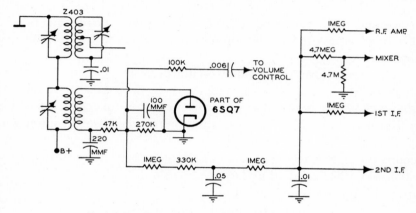

Fig. 12.8.   The A-M detector and A.V.C. circuits.

is applied to the triode mixer, the first I.F. amplifier, and the second I.F. amplifier. The A.V.C. line also connects to the R.F. ampli-fier, but this stage operates only on F-M signals. A.V.C. action is also obtained with F-M signals, the regulating voltage now being obtained from the other diode section of the 6SQ7. (See Fig. 12.9.) Since no I.F. stages function as limiters in this system, A.V.C. voltage on the F-M band can be obtained by the same method used on the A-M bands. This A.V.C. voltage is applied to the R.F. amplifier and the first and second I.F. stages. It is not fed to the mixer.

The Philco F-M type of detector, using the specially designed F-M 1000 tube, follows the third I.F. amplifier. It is the same detector which was described in Chapter 9. Plate-current variations, due to the fluctuations in oscillator frequency, produce the demodulated audio voltage across the 47,000-ohm resistor in the plate circuit of the F-M 1000 tube. The output is taken through a 0.03-mf condenser and 100,000-ohm resistor to the F-M push button and from here to the 2-megohm volume control. B+ voltage is applied to the various electrodes through the F-M push button and is active only when the switch is on.

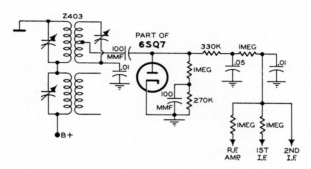

Fig. 12.9. The F-M A.V.C. circuit.

In the audio system, inverse feedback voltage is taken from the secondary of the output transformer and fed to the volume control. A bass control is connected to a tap on the volume control that is ordinarily used for the tone compensation network. A separate treble control is inserted in the plate circuit of the first audio amplifier. The audio voltage is taken from the volume control and fed to the grid of the triode portion of the 6SQ7 tube. A small amount of negative bias is obtained for this tube from the power supply. The 6SQ7 is resistance-coupled to a 6V6 beam-pentode output tube, the latter also receiving a negative biasing voltage from the power supply. The output stage is transformer coupled to a 5-by-7-inch oval electrodynamic speaker. Power output is 3 watts.

Receiver Alignment. The alignment of the broadcast and short-wave sections of the receiver follows identically the directions given for the preceding receiver. Consequently, we need examine only the F-M alignment procedure. This differs from what was previously given because of the Philco F-M detector circuit.

To set up the receiver for the alignment of the F-M bands, we use an A-M signal generator, connecting its ground lead to the radio chassis and the output lead through a small condenser (0.05 mf) to the points specified. Most manufacturers specify an A-M generator because it is the one most commonly found in repair shops. However, an F-M generator may be used if it is available. The use of the F-M sweep generator will be discussed after the alignment procedure, using the A-M signal generator, has been explained.

An output meter, serving as the indicator, is connected across the voice coil winding of the speaker. It remains in this position throughout the entire receiver alignment. The panel controls, as well as the treble tone and volume controls, are turned fully clockwise; but the bass tone control is turned completely counterclockwise. Finally, the F-M push button is depressed bringing in the proper circuits.

The Philco F-M detector is a synchronized oscillator which is forced to follow the frequency variations of the input signal. To align the I.F. stages, it is necessary to alter temporarily the F-M detector so that the output meter will indicate when each of the I.F. stages is properly peaked. By grounding pin 2 of the F-M 1000 tube or connecting it to the radio chassis, the Philco F-M detector is converted to an A-M detector. In this form, the voltage from an A-M generator can be used to align each of the F-M–I.F. amplifiers. The generator is adjusted for 400-cycle audio modulation so that the detected signal will pass through the audio amplifier stages and energize the output meter.

Before we start on the alignment of the I.F. stages, it is necessary to construct a loading network, since each I.F. transformer is overcoupled. The manufacturer specifies a loading network consisting of a 4700-ohm resistor and a 0.1-mf condenser in series. The network loads down one winding of a transformer while the other winding is being peaked. Set the generator to the I.F. value of 9.1 mc. Then, starting with the third I.F. amplifier, every transformer winding is adjusted for maximum indication on the output meter. There is no special discriminator transformer in this receiver, the final I.F. transformer (Z403, Fig. 12.7) being aligned as a normal I.F. transformer.

To align the F-M detector, remove the grounding lead at pin 2 of the F-M 1000 tube. This permits the oscillator to function again. However, in order to align the oscillator exactly to the center I.F., 9.1 mc, we short out the quadrature feedback network (see Chapter 9) by placing a jumper from pin 4 of the F-M 1000 tube to the top of the 47,000-ohm resistor in the plate circuit of the same tube. When this has been done, the signal generator, with the audio modulation off, is connected to the grid of the third I.F. amplifier tube. The frequency of the generator signal is 9.1 mc. The frequency of the oscillator is adjusted, using the trimmer across the oscillator coil (C300B in Fig. 12.7), until zero beat is obtained, as indicated by a zero reading of the output meter.

The indication on the output meter is the result of the formation of difference frequencies caused by the beating of the 9.1-mc signal voltage with the detector oscillator voltage inside the F-M 1000 tube. When the oscillator frequency is the same as the signal frequency, the difference frequency is zero and, consequently, the output meter indicates nothing. On either side of this zero frequency point, the two mixing frequencies produce a difference frequency which can extend up to 15,000 cycles. Note, however, that if the difference is greater than 15,000 cycles, the meter will again record no deflection because the intervening audio amplifiers will not pass higher frequency signals.

The jumper is now removed, and the iron core of the quadrature coil TC300A is adjusted for zero beat. With this final adjustment, the F-M detector is completely aligned. When making the last adjustment, it is necessary that the output from the generator be kept below the level where the oscillator locks-in. If this precaution is not observed, a false zero-beat indication is obtained. The proper adjustment is a single, very sharp zero-beat point.

After the alignment of the F-M detector, there remain only the R.F. coils to adjust. Using the A-M signal generator, we must again convert the F-M 1000 tube to an A-M detector; hence, ground pin 2 of the F-M 1000 tube. The signal generator is then connected, through a 0.05-mf condenser, to the ungrounded dipole input terminal. The ground of the generator is attached to the radio chassis. Set the signal generator (with the 400-cycle modulation on) to some frequency at the upper end of the F-M band, say 106 mc.   Set the receiver dial to the same frequency.   Adjust the F-M oscillator trimmer condenser (C501C in Fig. 12.7) for maximum deflection of the output meter.

Next, lower the signal frequency and set the receiver dial to a point at the low end of the band, say 90 mc.   Adjust the oscillator coil itself for maximum response by physically adjusting the spacing of the turns.   To determine whether the turns should be moved closer together or spread apart, take a tuning wand and insert the brass end in or near the oscillator coil (L501C in Fig. 12.7).   If the output meter reading increases when this is done, spread the turns apart slightly.   If, however, the powdered-iron end of the wand, when inserted into the coil, produces an increase in meter reading, compress the turns slightly.   The coil adjustments must be handled carefully since only a slight change is necessary at these high frequencies.   The coil is properly set if either metal causes a decrease in output-meter reading.   The adjustments at the high and low ends of the F-M band are repeated until no further improvement is noted.

Adjust each of the other coils and trimmer condensers in the R.F. section (C501B, C501A, L501B, and L501A) similarly until the best possible readings are obtained.

Oscilloscope Alignment.   Although the manufacturer outlined the foregoing receiver alignment with an A-M signal generator, the job could have been accomplished with an oscilloscope and an F-M signal generator.

To start the alignment of the I.F. stages, pin 2 of the F-M 1000 tube is grounded.   The vertical plates of the oscilloscope are then connected across the 47,000-ohm resistor in the plate circuit of this tube.   Connect the F-M signal generator to the input grid of each I.F. stage and adjust the proper trimmer condenser until the best response is obtained.   With this method, the full bandpass characteristics of the I.F. system is visible on the oscilloscope screen. Note that *no* loading networks are required in this method because the entire bandpass characteristic appears on the oscilloscope screen.

To adjust the F-M detector, the oscilloscope remains in the same position.   However, the grounding lead to pin 2 is removed.

With the F-M sweep generator at some intermediate stage, the detector-oscillator adjustments are made, while observing the F-M detector response to the full range of frequencies. The desired characteristic is a straight line, as shown in Chapter 9.

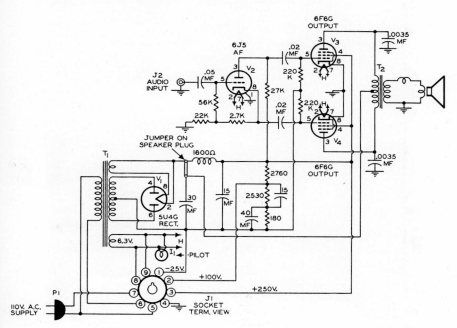

FIG. 12.11.   The audio amplifier section and power supply of the R.C.A. model 612V3 receiver.   (Courtesy of R.C.A.)

If the F-M sweep generator covers the 88 to 108 mc range, then the R.F. section of the receiver can also be aligned. Again ground pin 2 of F-M 1000 tube. Connect the signal generator to the dipole input terminals. Set both the generator and the receiver dial to the same frequency (say, first at 106 mc and then at 90 mc). Adjust all R.F. trimmers and coils for maximum response and desired bandwidth at eact point.

The Ratio Detector.   The ratio detector is a product of the research of the Radio Corporation of America and is used in their model 612V3 A-M–F-M receiver. A schematic diagram of this receiver is shown in Figs. 12.10 and 12.11. The schematic is

Fig. 12.12. The 612V3 A-M–F-M receiver described in the test. (Courtesy of R.C.A.)

divided into two sections, this being the manner in which the set is constructed. The main unit contains everything up to the first audio amplifier; the second, smaller chassis has the remaining audio amplifiers and the power supply. The entire receiver, including the cabinet, is shown in Fig. 12.12.

The twelve tubes of the receiver are divided, functionally, as follows:

6BA6	R.F. amplifier
6BA6	Mixer
6BE6	H.F. oscillator
6BA6	First I.F. stage

6AU6 ..... Second I.F. stage and phonograph amplifier
6AU6 ..... Driver for ratio detector
6AL5 ..... Ratio detector
6AT6 ..... A-M detector, A.V.C.
6J5 .... Second audio amplifier
6F6G (2) .. Output power amplifiers
5U4G ..... Power supply rectifier

This receiver contains many circuits which are similar to those already analyzed. As before, these will be omitted and the description confined to the circuits which differ from what has already been given. The switches are shown in their maximum clockwise position, in the F-M position. According to the system by which these switches are wired, the first position, in a counterclockwise rotation, is for the short-wave band. The next one, farther counterclockwise, is the broadcast band. The final position, beyond this, is for the phonograph.

The 6BE6 tube functions as an electron-coupled Hartley oscillator on the F-M band and as an electron-coupled Colpitts oscillator for the two lower bands. Simplified diagrams of the oscillator connections under both conditions are shown in Fig. 12.13. Note that the filaments of the tube, at the F-M band, are connected to the source of power by means of a short section of transmission line. The purpose of the line is to bring the heater wires (both of them) within the tube to R.F. ground potential. It has been found that if this is not done, the oscillator will not develop the fullest possible output and will be fairly unstable in operation. At the lower frequencies, the short length of this line is negligible and can be disregarded, placing the cathode and one side of the filament at ground potential.

The A-M section of the I.F. system uses only the 6BA6 tube for amplification. The F-M signal, however, is amplified by two stages of I.F. and one driver stage (also at the I.F. value) before reaching the 6AL5 ratio detector. The reason, of course, is the lower amplification that each stage is capable of providing for the 10.7-mc F-M signal.

In order to avoid the use of another tube, the 6AU6 second I.F.

amplifier also serves as the first amplifier for the phonograph attachment.   The output of the phonograph is fed to the grid of the 6AU6, and the amplified signal is taken from the screen grid, with the 22,000-ohm resistor serving as the grid load for the tube when it is being used as an audio amplifier.   The signal is tapped off by means of a 0.1-mf condenser and brought to the volume control,

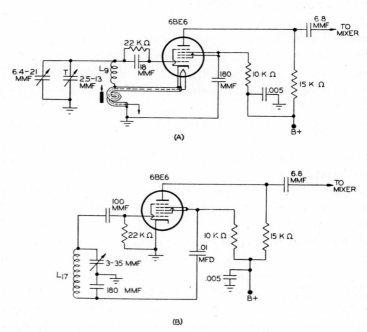

Fig. 12.13.   Simplified diagrams of the oscillator circuit (A) for the F-M band (B) for the A-M bands. L_{18} replaces L_{17} on short-waves.

after which it follows the same path taken by all the other audio signals.   As a means of preventing interference from incoming signals, when the phonograph is in operation, the switches are connected so that they ground the grid of the R.F. amplifier and open the grid circuit of the mixer tube and the first I.F. amplifier.   Still another precaution is the removal of the B+ voltage from the plate of the 6AU6 driver tube when the set is not in the F-M position.

Automatic volume control is developed and applied to the R.F. amplifier and first I.F. stage on all three broadcast bands.   When the set is switched to the F-M position, the A.V.C. is obtained from the ratio detector. On the two remaining bands, it is obtained in the conventional manner, using a diode. No A.V.C. is available in the phonograph position.

In the path of the F-M signal, between the second I.F. amplifier and the ratio detector, we find a tube labeled " driver." This is the 6AU6. Upon closer examination, it is found to be operating as a partial limiter, employing a modified form of grid-leak bias provided by a 15,000-ohm resistor in parallel with a 5-mf condenser. The inclusion of a driver stage may appear to contradict the basic advantage of a ratio detector — namely, the ability to function without the use of limiters. It is possible to omit the driver stage and obtain satisfactory operation, and indeed many commercial sets utilizing this type

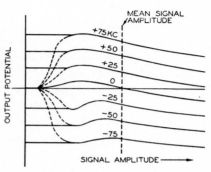

Fig. 12.14. The characteristics of the ratio detector as the signal amplitude varies. A perfect unit would give a constant output or, graphically, a series of straight lines.

of detector do so. However, through the use of a driver, or partial limiter, the fidelity of the unit can be improved.

The characteristic response curves of the ratio detector are shown in Fig. 12.14. These reveal that the output voltage of the detector decreases after the amplitude of the incoming signal has increased beyond a certain point. This behavior is due to the fact that the optimum coupling for the mean signal strength is such that the primary impedance increases as the signal-rise produces more secondary damping because of the presence of the diode tubes. When a diode conducts, its internal resistance depends upon the amplitude of the applied voltage. The greater the voltage, the lower the tube's resistance. It is this decrease in resistance that produces the damping of the secondary winding. The lowered secondary impedance and increased primary impedance alter to some extent the phase relations between the primary and secondary circuits and account for the behavior of the characteristic curves.

The convergence of the response curves at high signal amplitudes means proportionately less audio output. The inclusion of a stage preceding the detector to limit the maximum strength of strong signals would minimize this form of distortion. Hence, a driver stage is used which functions as a partial limiter and is effective actually only with strong signals.

Instead of coupling the driver output directly into the ratio detector, link-coupling is employed. The use of this type of coupling at this point is closely related to the distortion which is produced in the driver stage and the effect of this distortion on the detector characteristic. It was discovered, upon investigation, that the reason the zero deviation curve (marked 0 in Fig. 12.14) is not a straight line at different signal amplitudes is due chiefly to the formation of I.F. harmonics in the stages preceding the detector. By removing the harmonics, we can straighten out, to a great extent, all of the curves.

To minimize the transfer of harmonics to the ratio detector, link-coupling is employed. Between any two inductively coupled circuits, there also exists capacitive-coupling. The capacitive-coupling is due to the incidental capacitance that exists between any two conductors. The transfer of harmonics occurs chiefly through this incidental capacitance. The usefulness of link-coupling is that it is accomplished with a turn or two closely coupled to the driver plate circuit at a point where the R.F. potential is near zero. Link-coupling also reduces the effect of the secondary load variations on the driver plate circuit and thereby maintains a higher Q in the latter circuit. This further aids in the suppression of harmonics.

In the present circuit, the link-coupling coil serves yet another purpose. It functions as the " sense " or reference voltage for the phase detection of F-M signals. This was previously discussed. The ratio detector circuit is rearranged in Fig. 12.15 in order that the secondary purpose of the link coil, L_1, can be more readily seen. Point A of the link coil connects to the center of the secondary coil. From this point, we can follow the path through L_1 to point C, between the two 0.005-mf condensers. The demodulated audio variations which appear across the lower 0.005-mf condenser is passed through a de-emphasis network and then applied to the volume control at the entrance of the audio amplifier system. The link coil connects to point B on the secondary coil in order that the signal in L_p appears in L_s also.

The regulating voltage for the detector operation is developed across the 22,000-ohm resistor and the 5-mf condenser. This latter condenser is shunted by a 1000-mmf condenser in order to neutralize the inductance existing in the relatively large 5-mf condenser at 10.7 mc. The negative voltage at point D is useful for A.V.C. purposes

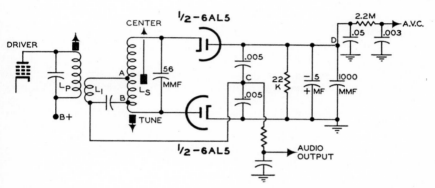

FIG. 12.15. The ratio detector of the RCA receiver of Fig. 12.10.

and is used as such. A filter, composed of a 2.2-megohm resistor and 0.05-mf and 0.003-mf condensers, prevents any of the I.F. voltages from reaching the A.V.C. line and the rest of the circuit.

Receiver Alignment. The step-by-step procedure for aligning an F-M receiver has already been noted. For the present RCA set, the reader should encounter no difficulty if the alignment procedure is tabulated in chart form. The first chart outlines the adjustment of the ratio detector, the second chart is for the remainder of the F-M circuits, and the third chart is for the A-M bands. The notes included with each chart tend to clarify the procedure and to indicate special precautions.[1]

Midget A-M, F-M Receiver. The receiver circuits just analyzed were F-M receivers that were in the console or quality class. Each could receive the short-wave bands as well as the broadcast

[1] The diagrams of the receiver and the alignment procedure are used through the courtesy of the Radio Corporation of America.

F-M RATIO DETECTOR ALIGNMENT

Set range switch to F-M position

Steps	Connect High Side of Osc. To	Tune Osc. To	Turn Vol. Cont. To	Adjust
1	Connect a 680-ohm resistor between pins 5 and 7 of the ratio detector tube 6AL5, (V7). Connect d-c probe of a voltohmyst to the negative lead of the 5-mf electrolytic capacitor C_1, and the common lead of the meter to chassis.			
2	Driver grid pin 1 of 6AU6 (V6) in series with a 0.01-mf capacitor.	10.7 mc 30% modulated at 400 cycles A-M.	Maximum volume.	Driver transformer T_6 for maximum d-c voltage across C_1 (approx. 14.5 volts).
3	Remove meter leads and disconnect the 680-ohm resistor from the tube 6AL5, (V7). Connect two 68,000-ohm resistors (within 1% of each other) in series across the 22,000-ohm, ratio-detector load resistor R_1. Connect the common lead of the voltohmyst to the center point of the 68,000-ohm resistors and the d-c probe to terminal A of the ratio-detector transformer T_7. Use the 30-volt scale.			
4	Same as Step 2.	Same as Step 2. (Approx. .25 volts output.)	Average volume level.	T_7 bottom core for zero d-c balance* T_7 top core for min. audio output (output meter across voice coil).**
5	Reconnect voltohmyst as in Step 1, omitting the 680-ohm resistor.			
6	Repeat Step 2 omitting 680 ohms.			
7	Remove all connections.			

* Near the correct core position the zero point is approached rapidly and continued adjustment causes the indicated polarity to reverse. A slow approach to the zero point is an indication of severe detuning, and the bottom core should be turned in the opposite direction.

**The zero d-c balance and the minimum A.F. output should occur at the same point: If such is not the case, the two cores should be adjusted until both occur with no further adjustment of either core. It may be advantageous to adjust both cores simultaneously, watching the voltohmyst and an output meter connected across the voice coil for the point at which both zero d-c and minimum output occurs.

NOTE: Two or more points may be found which will satisfy the condition required in Step 4. T_7 top core should be correctly adjusted when approximately $\frac{1}{8}$ inch of threads extend above the can. Therefore, it is desirable to start adjustment with the top core in its furthest "in" position and turn out, while adjusting the bottom core, until the first point of minimum A.F. and minimum d-c is reached.

F-M ALIGNMENT
Range switch in F-M position

Steps	Connect the High Side of the Test Osc. To	Connect Ground Side of the Test Osc.	Tune the Osc. To	Radio Dial Tuned To	Adjust
1	Connect the d-c probe of a voltohmyst to the negative lead of the 5-mf electrolytic capacitor C_1, and the common lead of the meter to chassis ground.				
2	Mixer grid pin 1 of 6BA6 (V2) in series with a 0.01-mf capacitor.	To chassis ground.	*10.7 mc unmodulated	Maximum capacitance (fully meshed).	**T_5, T_3, T_1 top and bottom cores alternately loading primary and secondary of each transformer with 680 ohms while the opposite side of the same transformer is being adjusted. Adjust all transformers for maximum voltage across C_1.
***3	F-M antenna terminals 1 in series with a 120-ohm resistor.	To F-M antenna terminal 2 in series with a 120-ohm resistor.	106 mc	106 mc	Osc., C_2 for max. voltage across C_1.
4			88 mc	88 mc	Osc., L_9 for max. voltage across C_1.
5	Repeat Steps 3 and 4 for exact calibration.				
6	Same as Step 3	Same as Step 3	106 mc	106 mc	R.F., C_3 for max. voltage across C_1.
7	Same as Step 3	Same as Step 3	90 mc	90 mc	R.F., L_{11} for max. voltage across C_1.
8	Repeat Steps 6 and 7 for maximum output.				
9	Same as Step 3	Same as Step 3	106 mc	106 mc	Ant., C_4 for max. voltage across C_1.
10	Same as Step 3	Same as Step 3	90 mc	90 mc	Ant., L_3 for max. voltage across C_1.
11	Repeat Steps 9 and 10 for maximum output.				

* When the windings are loaded, it is necessary to increase the 10.7-mc input since the gain will decrease and the voltage across C_1 will be less.

** This method is known as alternate loading which involves the use of a 680-ohm resistor to load the plate winding while the grid winding of the same transformer is being peaked. Then the grid winding is loaded with the 680-ohm resistor while the plate winding is being peaked.

*** Before proceeding with Step 3, set the pointer on MECHANICAL MAXIMUM CALIBRATION point at the low end of the band when the gang capacitor is fully meshed.

A-M ALIGNMENT*

Signal-Generator. For all alignment operations, connect the low side of the signal generator to the receiver chassis, and keep the generator output as low as possible to avoid A.V.C. action.

Output Meter Alignment. If this method is used, connect the meter across the voice coil, and turn the receiver volume control to maximum.

Steps	Connect the high side of the Test Osc. To	Tune Test Osc. to	Range Switch	Turn Radio Dial To	Adjust the following for maximum output
1	Mixer grid pin 1 of 6BA6 (V2)	455 kc	"A" band	High frequency end of dial.	**Top and bottom cores of T_2 and T_4.
2	High side of loop primary.	1400 kc		1400 kc	Osc. — C_5 R.F. — C_6 Ant. — C_7
3	Through a dummy antenna comprising a 200-mmf capacitor.	600 kc		600 kc	Osc. — L_{18} R.F. — L_{13} Ant. — L_6
4	Repeat Steps 2 and 3 for maximum output.				
5	Disconnect dummy antenna and adjust antenna trimmer C_7 on loop when set is installed in cabinet.				
6	"C" band antenna terminal 3.	15.2 mc	"C" band	15.2 mc	Osc. — C_8*** R.F. — C_9*** Ant. — C_{10}
7	Through a dummy antenna comprising a 150-ohm resistor in series with a 25-to 30-mmf capacitor.	9.5 mc		9.5 mc	Osc. — L_{17} R.F. — L_{12} Ant. — L_5
8	Repeat Steps 6 and 7 for accurate alignment.				

* It is absolutely necessary to adjust the 10.7-mc transformers before adjusting the 455-kc transformers.

** It is necessary to alternately load the primary and secondary of each 455-kc I.F. transformer with 10,000 ohms while the opposite side of the same transformer is being adjusted.

*** To guard against the possibility of alignment of L_{17} and C_8 to image frequencies, tune the test oscillator to 15.2 mc and turn the radio-dial to 15.2 mc. Then adjust the test oscillator to 16.11 mc (image frequency). By increasing the test oscillator output, a signal should be heard.

Tune the test oscillator to 9.5 mc and turn the radio dial to 9.5 mc; then adjust the test oscillator to 10.41 mc (image frequency). By increasing the test oscillator output, a signal should be heard. (If these image frequencies cannot be heard, the set is incorrectly aligned, therefore, repeat steps 6 and 7.)

A-M and F-M bands and each contained extensive audio systems including push-pull output amplifiers, tone controls, and large speakers. Lest the reader obtain the impression that all F-M sets are similarly built, Fig. 12.16 shows the schematic of an A-M, F-M receiver designed to fit into a small, table-model cabinet. It may be instructive to examine this circuit in order to see how these smaller sets differ from the more extensive sets previously analyzed.

The front end of the receiver contains two separate inputs, one for F-M signals and one for A-M signals. F-M signals are received at antenna terminals 1 and 2, generally from a dipole antenna. The incoming signals are fed to a 6BA6 R.F. amplifier through an untuned network consisting of a coupling condenser, C_1, and an R.F. choke, L_1. The bottom end of L_1 connects to a 5000-mmf condenser which serves to filter the A.V.C. voltage fed in at this point to the R.F. amplifier.

In the plate circuit of V_1, another R.F. choke, L_2, acts as the plate load for the amplifier. This, too, is untuned. The first tuned circuit we encounter is in the grid circuit of V_{2A}, the F-M mixer tube. V_{2A} is one triode section of the 12AT7. The other triode section, V_{2B}, is the F-M oscillator, in this instance an ultraudion oscillator. (Ultraudion oscillators are modifications of the well-known Colpitts oscillator.) The local oscillator voltage is fed from V_{2B} to the grid of V_{2A} by means of small 1.5-mmf coupling condenser. The incoming signal and the oscillator voltage mix in V_{2A}, and the difference or I.F. voltage thus produced is fed into the primary winding of T_1. The F-M, I.F. value in this receiver is 10.7 mc.

The circuit, thus far, is fairly straightforward. L_4 in the plate lead of V_{2A} is a small coil of 2 or 3 turns designed to prevent parasitic oscillations from developing in the mixer. The output circuit of V_{2A} is tuned and so is the input circuit. Furthermore, V_{2A}, being a triode, possesses a relatively large grid-to-plate capacitance. Thus, we have here all the basic ingredients for a tuned-grid, tuned-plate oscillator and if the lead inductance plus the stray wiring capacitance in the plate circuit should somehow combine to form a resonant circuit having a frequency close to the frequency formed by a similar combination of components in the grid circuit, then

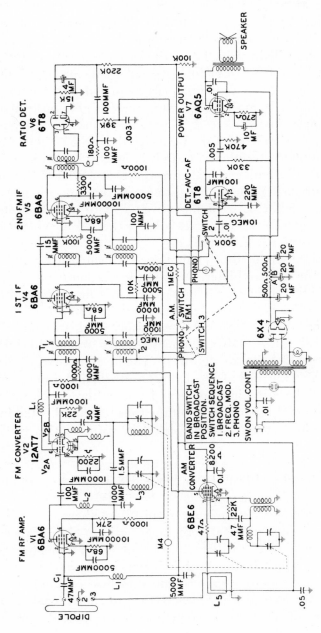

Fig. 12.16. A table model A–M–F–M receiver. (Courtesy Howard W. Sams & Co.)

parasitic (or undesirable) oscillations would result.   The presence of L_4 is designed to prevent this from occurring by offsetting the balance between grid and plate circuits.   Furthermore, by having this particular coil in the plate circuit of the mixer, an impedance is reflected into the grid circuit which tends to sustain a high input impedance.

Before we proceed into the I.F. system of the receiver, let us return to the antenna and trace the path taken by the incoming A-M signals.   A loop antenna, L_5, will receive all local broadcasts.   If reception of distant stations is desired, an outside antenna may be attached to antenna terminal 3.   A wire from this post runs close to the loop, and any signals picked up by the outside antenna are inductively coupled to the loop and fed to grid 3 of a 6BE6 converter tube.   The A-M converter circuit is conventional with the cathode and grids 1 and 2 functioning as the local oscillator while grid 3 receives the input signal.   The I.F. signal (455 kc) developed from the mixing of these voltages within the tube are fed to the A-M, I.F. transformer, T_2.

Because separate converters are used for the A-M and F-M signals, there is no need to employ a switching circuit for the primary windings of T_1 and T_2.   The secondary windings of these two transformers are placed in series and inject their respective signals into V_4.   This first I.F. amplifier also receives an A.V.C. voltage.

For F-M signals there are two I.F. amplifiers and a ratio detector.   The second I.F. amplifier operates as an amplifier for essentially all levels of input voltage.   Some manufacturers of midget sets operate their F-M circuits in this manner in order to obtain as much amplification as possible; other manufacturers design the second (this usually being the final) I.F. amplifier to function as a partial limiter, losing some gain this way but providing better noise-free reception on moderate signals.   In both types of receivers, weak signals will be noisy.   However, manufacturers feel that many set owners are interested solely in local stations and these can be received with sufficient strength to provide noise-free reception.

The A-M signal is amplified by only one I.F. stage (V_4) and then detected by one diode section of a 6T8.   This is in accordance with current practice in A-M midget sets. A.V.C. voltage is also produced in this detector circuit and applied to the first I.F. amplifier and the A-M converter. This, too, is conventional. By means of the contacts on switch 1, the A-M, A.V.C. voltage is effective only when the set is operating on the A-M band. On the F-M band, the contacts on this switch make connection with the A.V.C. voltage from the F-M ratio detector. This latter voltage is applied to the R.F. amplifier and the first I.F. amplifier. (Actually the A-M converter also receives this F-M, A.V.C. voltage because this tube is connected into the common A.V.C. line. However, screen and plate voltages are removed from V_3 during reception of F-M signals, and the A.V.C. voltage is without effect on V_3. By the same token, the R.F. amplifier receives the A-M, A.V.C. voltage when A-M signals are being received, but here, too, the operating voltages are removed. Switch 3 is mechanically attached to switches 1 and 2 and all rotate simultaneously.)

The A-M and F-M signals, after they have been converted into audio voltages, are fed to the grid of the triode section of the 6T8 through switch 2. A volume control permits setting of the volume control desired. A second audio amplifier, a 6AQ5 beam power tube, completes the audio section of this receiver. The speaker is a 5-inch P.M. unit. B+ supply voltage is supplied by a simple conventional full-wave rectifier and an r-c filter. Voltages obtained range about 170 volts.

PROBLEMS

1. Why are band switches employed in modern receivers? What are their disadvantages, especially in high frequency receivers?

2. What are the average gains per stage that can be expected in F-M receivers? Start at the antenna and work toward the F-M detector.

3. Why are pentagrid converters used sparingly in high frequency receivers?

4. How can one I.F. system be made to serve both F-M and A-M signals? Draw the schematic diagram of a 2-stage I.F. amplifier suitable for serving 10.7-mc F-M signals and 455-kc A-M signals.

5. In A-M–F-M combination receivers, the first I.F. coil not in use is shorted out. Explain. Why is the same procedure unnecessary in subsequent stages?

6. How is a de-emphasis filter added to an F-M discriminator?

7. How many actual audio amplifiers are there in Fig. 12.1?

8. List the recommended order of alignment in the Stromberg-Carlson A-M–F-M receiver.

9. Describe in detail the alignment of the F-M–I.F. system of the Stromberg-Carlson receiver shown in Fig. 12.5.

10. How are overcoupled I.F. transformers aligned? What effect does the type of indicator used have on the method of alignment? Explain.

11. How can the output of a signal generator be loosely coupled to the input terminals of a receiver?

12. Draw the F-M detector network used in the Philco A-M, F-M receiver of Fig. 12.7.

13. Draw the A-M detector network of the same receiver.

14. How is the A.V.C. voltage of this receiver obtained? On what bands does it function?

15. What similarities exist between the Philco and Stromberg-Carlson sets?

16. Draw the R.F. section of the Philco receiver when the receiver is set for A-M. For F-M.

17. When an A-M signal generator is used to align the F-M circuits of the Philco receiver, what changes must be made in the circuit?

18. Describe the alignment of the Philco F-M detector using an A-M signal generator and an indicating meter.

19. In what respects does the I.F. system of the Philco receiver differ from the I.F. system of the Stromberg-Carlson set?

20. What is the exact procedure for aligning the R.F. stages of the Philco receiver?

21. Draw the schematic diagram of the ratio detector used in the RCA model 612V3 receiver.

22. Illustrate how one of the I.F. amplifiers also serves as a phono amplifier.

23. Through which stages must all F-M signals pass? All A-M signals?

24. What is the purpose of the driver stage?

25. Explain, in detail, the alignment of the ratio detector.

26. Where is the indicator placed when the F-M–I.F. stages are being adjusted? Why is this position chosen?

27. Describe the alignment of the A-M sections of any one of the receivers discussed in this chapter.

28. How would we align the A-M stages of the RCA receiver, given a sweep signal generator and an oscilloscope?

29. Trace out and draw the circuits used to receive the short-wave band. Only the R.F. amplifier, mixer and oscillator circuits need be drawn.

30. Compare all receivers as to the number of similar stages and dissimilar stages.

CHAPTER 13

SERVICING F-M RECEIVERS

Extension of A-M Servicing Methods. The servicing of F-M receivers conforms essentially to the basic procedures currently in use for A-M sets but has been modified sufficiently to meet the altered construction of the F-M receiver. A comparison of the corresponding stages in both types of receivers shows that, except for the second detectors and limiters (if any), there is no *functional* difference between them. Remember that we are concerned at the moment only with the function of each stage and not its design. From the serviceman's point of view, function is all-important and design is secondary. The serviceman, called upon to repair a set, is interested only in what each stage does in order that he may properly apply his servicing instruments.

The F.C.C. has assigned F-M to the higher frequencies, 88 to 108 mc. When the serviceman, who has long been accustomed to working with receivers at the considerably lower A-M broadcast frequencies, is confronted with an F-M receiver, he will find himself considerably handicapped, unless he is familiar with the modified operation of radio components at frequencies of 100 mc. Let us, therefore, examine the behavior of each of the most common radio components as the signal frequency rises to the region of 100 mc.

Resistance: At the low frequencies, the resistance of a conductor is given by

$$R = \rho \frac{l}{A}$$

where R = resistance of wire, in ohms
  ρ = specific resistivity
  l = length of conductor
  A = cross-sectional area of conductor

As the frequency of the current through the wire increases, it will be found that the resistance offered by the same length of wire will also increase.   To understand the reason for the increase, let us consider what occurs within a length of wire when a current flows through it.   It is fundamental knowledge that current flow has associated with it a magnetic field or, what is the same thing in this instance, circular magnetic lines of flux.   These are everywhere encircling the current.   The definition of inductance depends upon these flux linkages and is governed by the formula

Inductance (henries) =

$$\frac{\text{Flux linkages encircling conductor}}{\text{Current producing these linkages (in amps)}} \times 10^{-8}$$

Consider now the end view of a small, round section of wire that has a current flowing through it (see Fig. 13.1).   Each small section

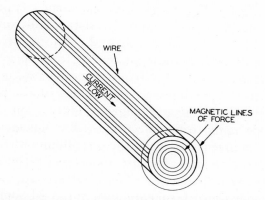

FIG. 13.1.   Current flow through a wire and the magnetic lines of force encircling the wire.

of current flowing through the wire has magnetic lines of flux encircling it, but the sections of current at the outer edges of the wire obviously have fewer lines of flux around them than the currents at the center of the wire.   This is because the flux produced inside the wire by the central currents does not encircle the outer currents and hence does not influence their flow.   The flux produced by the currents flowing at the surface of the wire does, however, encircle the currents at the center and, consequently, exerts an influence upon them. From the definition just noted for inductance, it is seen that, since more flux linkages encircle the center of the wire, the inductance of the wire at the center will be greater than that at the surface. As the frequency of the currents increases, the inductance at the center of the wire offers more opposition (reactance) than the outer sections of the wire where there is less inductance. Hence, the current, seeking the path of " least resistance " will tend to concentrate more at the surface (or skin) of the conductor as the frequency rises. This concentration has, in effect, reduced the useful cross-sectional area of the conductor. The resistance, due to this decrease in effective area, will rise, a phenomenon generally known as " skin effect."

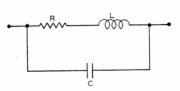

Fig. 13.2. The equivalent circuit of an ordinary resistor at higher frequencies.

Another fact of interest to the serviceman is that, at the high frequencies, the equivalent circuit of so-called " pure " resistances becomes as shown in Fig. 13.2. The resistive and inductive affects of a resistor are due, of course, to the previous explanation. The capacitance arises from the capacitance between the terminals and the capacitance between parts of the resistor itself.

Inductance: Inductance changes slightly from low to high frequencies, due again to the effect of the flux linkages and the currents. As the frequency goes up, the distribution of the currents in the wire will change and, because inductance depends upon this distribution, it too will change. The result is a slight decrease.

At low frequencies, those employed for A-M sound broadcasting, the inductance of the tuning coils is comparatively high. Hence, a wire several inches long that might be used to connect the coil to a tube or condenser would not add any significant amount of inductance. This is evident from an examination of the expression governing the inductance of a straight length of copper wire:

$$L = 0.0051s \left(2.303 \log_{10} \frac{4s}{d} - 0.75 \right) \text{ microhenries}$$

where $s =$ length of wire in inches
$d =$ diameter of wire in inches

So long as the coil inductance is in the henry or millihenry range, no ordinary length of connecting wire will add sufficient inductance to alter the coil characteristics appreciably. As the signal frequencies reach 100 mc, however, the inductance of the tuning coils approaches the point where even the small connecting link of wire can become important.

Note, then, that connecting wires become important at the higher frequencies, not because their inductance changes to any appreciable extent, because the important components in the circuit become smaller. Even such things as the plates of condensers introduce inductance into the circuit, and we find that trouble arises because of the interaction of the magnetic fields set up between ganged condensers connecting to different circuits. It is common practice to shunt paper and electrolytic condensers with small mica condensers in order to neutralize the inductance existing in these units.

Capacitance: The increased importance of stray capacitance in a high frequency circuit can be attributed to the same reasons as the importance of connecting wires. The stray capacitance does not increase, but rather the desired capacitance decreases, hence, assigning a more prominent role to any stray capacitance. In addition, there is leakage conductance which must be considered together with capacitance. Condensers and insulators may, because of certain conditions, allow small amounts of currents to flow through them. They act then as high resistances, or poor conductors. The conductance is low and is labeled " leakage conductance." This has a direct influence on the type of insulating material which can be used successfully in high frequency circuits, especially for tube sockets. Moisture and other atmospheric conditions may reduce considerably the effectiveness of these insulators at the higher frequencies and the result is poor operation of the set.

Tube Operation at the Higher Frequencies: Not only resistors, coils, and condensers but also the conventional vacuum tube is subject to modification with frequency. At the low frequencies, the time it takes an electron to travel the interelectrode distance is negligible, because this time represents a very small portion of the interval necessary to complete one cycle of the grid or input a-c wave. As the frequency of the input wave is increased, however, the time for one complete cycle of the a-c wave becomes less and less, and soon the electron transit time becomes comparable to the period of the alternating wave.   An example will make this clearer. Suppose that it takes an electron 0.000,000,001 sec to travel from the filament to the plate.   This may be ignored when the frequency of the input wave to the grid is, say, 1000 cps, for then one complete cycle requires 0.001 sec.   This is a very long interval compared to the electron transit time given just above.   But suppose that the frequency of the a-c wave is raised to 100 mc.   Now, one cycle is completed in 0.000,000,01 sec, which is not far from the time that it takes the electron to travel from filament to plate.   When this happens, something occurs in the grid circuit that causes the grid-to-filament (or cathode, as the case may be) impedance to drop from its low frequency value (which is so high it can be considered as infinite).   This affects the whole grid tuning circuit because the grid-to-cathode impedance is really in parallel with this tuner. Thus, if this high resistance is lowered in value, the same result is obtained as though a low resistance were placed in parallel with the resonant circuit.   The Q is lowered, and with it goes the efficiency of the circuit.

Electron Flow — Revised: In order to help visualize the entire process, some ideas on electron flow will be revised or, rather, extended.   Ordinarily, it is unusual to think of current flow in either the plate or grid circuits until the electrons from the cathode hit these elements.   Actually, however, this is the point that completes a cycle begun when the electron first left the cathode.   The charge of the electron is negative, and at the moment it leaves the cathode the conditions shown in Fig. 13.3A prevail.   Here it can be seen that on leaving the cathode the electron left an equal and opposite (positive) charge on the cathode.   At the same time a very small positive charge is induced on the plate.   This is because the cathode electron is slightly closer to the plate and an electron on the plate has been repelled a small distance from the anode surface.   As the cathode electron gets closer and closer to the plate, the positive charge of this anode will correspondingly increase, and the electron that was originally at the plate will be farther and farther repelled from the anode toward the cathode through the wire (see Fig.

13.3B).   When the cathode electron finally reaches the plate, it neutralizes the positive charge there, and likewise the anode electron by this time has reached the cathode.   The positive charge on the cathode is now also neutralized.   The circuit is then in equilibrium and the current flow has ceased (see Fig. 13.3C).   Multiply this electron by the billions that actually flow and there are the comparatively large plate currents observed in tubes. Some theorists may insist that it be explained that the electron that left the plate be shown as only going a small distance and pushing other electrons in the plate lead until one finally goes to the cathode and neutralizes the positive charge left there by the cathode electron that left for the plate.   The plate electron has been described as going the full distance from plate to cathode.   Be that as it may, the fact still remains that, when the cathode electron reaches the plate, the current stops.   This is the important thought to keep in mind.

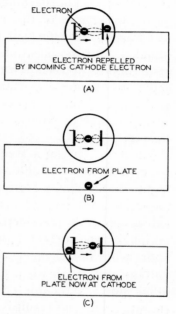

ELECTRON REPELLED
BY INCOMING CATHODE ELECTRON

(A)

ELECTRON FROM PLATE

(B)

ELECTRON FROM
PLATE NOW AT CATHODE

(C)

FIG. 13.3.   A simplified illustration of the modified conception of current flow in a tube at the higher frequencies.

The foregoing concepts are not new but are seldom mentioned because, at the low frequencies, results obtained agree with the ordinary ideas of electron flow in tubes.   With increase of frequency, however, the transit-time effects require that this more general idea be used.   Now the effect on the grid will be determined.

When an electron approaches the grid, there is induced in the grid a small charge, with the result that a small current starts to flow.   This is due to the displacement of the electrons in the grid wires caused by the oncoming electron.   If the time it takes any oncoming signal voltage to change is slow compared to the speed of the electron, the current induced in the grid by the approaching electron will be equal and opposite to the induced current when the

electron passes the grid and goes on to the plate. The two currents — that due to the approaching electron and that due to the
same electron when it is on the other side of the grid — will thus
cancel. As the frequency of the a-c grid voltage is increased, however, the signal voltage will change appreciably between the time
the electron is approaching the grid and the time when it is receding
on the other side of this element, and the induced currents due to
this moving electron will modify the phase and amplitude of the
signal. This modification, it has been found, causes losses in the
grid circuit. It is known as the transit-time effect in tubes and
begins to assume importance when the value of the signal voltage
at the grid changes appreciably in the time it takes the electrons to
move through the tube. A specific example might make this much
clearer.

A wave, having a frequency of 100 mc/sec, has one tenth of a
cycle occur in 0.000,000,001 sec. In ordinary tubes, the time of
flight of an electron from the cathode to the plate is approximately
0.000,000,001 sec. Thus an appreciable change in grid voltage
will occur while the electron moves from the cathode to the plate
region. Any current induced in the grid by this electron as it
approaches this element will occur at a different time in the a-c grid
voltage cycle than when the electron recedes from the grid on the
other side. It is this effect that gives rise to losses in the grid
circuit. The end result is a lowering of the usually high resistance
between the grid and cathode. If the grid-to-cathode resistance
drops, any tuned circuit placed between these elements will be
affected and the selectivity will drop.

Electron transit-time action in a tube is a complicated concept
to grasp and, yet, it is very important. Perhaps another impression, stated a little differently, might give rise to a mental picture of
what takes place. Consider Fig. 13.4A, where the cathode and grid
are considered as the plates of a small condenser equal in value to
the interelectrode capacitance. The a-c generator inserted across
this condenser is the input signal. Now, it is well known that, if
the current responds instantly to voltage changes across a condenser,
the current will lead the voltage by 90°. The curves in Fig. 13.4B
show this. But suppose, for one reason or another, that the
current cannot follow the voltage variations instantly. Then the

current will not be 90° out of phase with the voltage but will have some other angle, something less than 90°. This is equivalent to a condenser and resistor combination, such as shown in Fig. 13.4C.

For the first case (A) we can see that, if the current and voltage are 90° out of phase, the circuit is purely capacitive. But if the angle is something less than 90°, the equivalent circuit consists of a condenser with a resistor shunted across it. We have the same effect when the electron transit time modifies the signal phase and amplitude.

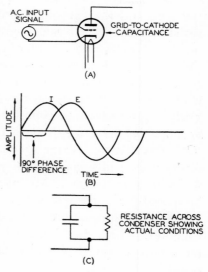

(A)

(B)

(C)

Fig. 13.4. Another method of illustrating the effect of transit time on the input impedance of a tube.

To carry the illustration one step farther, replace the a-c grid generator by a resonant circuit which can produce the same type of voltage. The resistance shown in Fig. 13.4C and mentioned just above will be in parallel with this tuned circuit, thus tending to lower its Q and selectivity and increase its losses. The tuning circuit may even stop functioning as such if the resistance becomes small enough. It is because of this last-mentioned effect that the transit time in a tube is important.

Several formulas have been derived to give the exact relationship between conductance of the grid and the frequency. One such relationship is given here and is due to W. R. Ferris:

$$G_g = K g_m f^2 T^2$$

where G_g = the input conductance between the grid and cathode (conductance is the reciprocal of resistance)

K = a constant of the tube

g_m = the mutual conductance of the tube

f = the frequency of the input signal

T = the time it takes an electron to move from the cathode to the plate

Inspection of the equation reveals that the conductance increases rapidly as the frequency rises due to the fact that the frequency termed is squared.

Minimizing Transit-time Effects: Since the resistance between the grid and the cathode decreases with frequency, and since this resistance shunts all tuned circuits placed between these two elements, it is desirable to attempt to minimize these adverse effects. One method which suggests itself is to increase the electron velocity until the time required to reach the plate from the cathode is made negligible in comparison with any alternating voltage applied to the grid. A means of accomplishing this consists in placing higher voltages on the plate to attract the electron more strongly, causing it to travel with greater speed. The electron, however, now that it has this additional speed, will hit the plate harder and cause it to become hotter. Means must be devised to cope with this increased plate dissipation.

As another possible method, we can move the electrodes closer together. This would again counteract transit-time effects of electrons because the electron has less distance to travel and any voltage

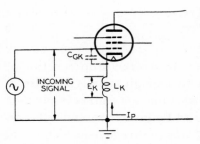

FIG. 13.5. Decrease of the input impedance of a tube is due, in part, to the inductance in the cathode lead of a tube.

placed on the plate will be more effective. There is, however, a limit to the spacing of the electrodes without having each affect the other adversely. Again, with elements closer together, less heat can be tolerated at the plate, and the amplification factor of the tube becomes less. Tubes which have been specifically designed for operation at 100 mc represent compromises of the foregoing conflicting factors.

The Effect of Cathode Inductance. Transit time of the electron is not the complete answer to the lowering of the input impedance of a tube at the higher frequencies. Of practically equal importance is the inductance existing in the cathode leads of the tube. The current of a tube must flow through the cathode lead wires and in the process develops a voltage across this inductance (see Fig. 13.5). The alternating component of this current, like the d-c component, is impressed between the grid and the cathode. As a result, the effective signal voltage is decreased because of the opposition of the cathode lead voltage to the input signal voltage. The situation is analogous to inverse feedback. However, this voltage is present even though the cathode of the tube is grounded at the tube socket. The lead inductance occurs in the wires within the tube itself. The input resistance resulting from the voltage developed across the cathode lead inductance is

$$\text{Input resistance due to cathode inductance} = \frac{1}{\omega^2 g_m L_k C_{gk}}$$

where $\omega = 2\pi \times$ frequency of the input signal
g_m = mutual conductance of tube
L_k = cathode lead inductance
C_{gk} = interelectrode capacitance between grid and cathode

Note that the voltage which is developed across this cathode lead inductance is due to the plate current. As far as the plate circuit is concerned, this voltage, E_k, is of little significance. It is at the grid, where the signal voltage is impressed, that the effect becomes important.

To eliminate the effect of the lead inductance voltage on the input grid circuit, tube manufacturers have designed tubes with two wires leading directly from the cathode structure inside the tube to the tube base. In this manner, one terminal is available for the grid circuit and one for the plate circuit, and its current and the two circuits are divorced from each other. In the circuit of Fig. 13.6, the 6AG5 R.F. amplifier tube possesses two cathode terminals. Even though both cathode terminals are grouded, pin 2 would be connected to the grid tuning condenser and coil. Pin 7 is the cathode connection for the plate circuit. To it would be connected the screen-grid and plate by-passing condensers. The d-c component of the plate current divides between both paths, but this is of no consequence since it does not contribute to the degenerative effect.

Servicemen should be cautious, in this respect, in accepting the connections of the two cathode terminals as shown on the manufacturer's schematic diagram. The diagram is not always an exact reproduction of the circuit, as laid out in the chassis, especially with regard to the separate connections of the same cathode.   In many schematics, the cathode is grounded, and the diagram indicates this fact without stating that separation exists as explained in Fig. 13.6. If someone, not familiar with the reason for the separate cathode terminals, connected them together, the result would be a decrease in receiver sensitivity due to a lower input resistance.

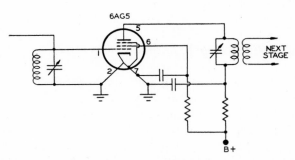

FIG. 13.6.   The use of two cathode wires to eliminate the adverse effect of cathode inductance.

Trouble Shooting Procedures.   The serviceman, when faced with the problem of trouble shooting or repairing an inoperative F-M set, will find that all his experience gained from servicing A-M receivers is applicable here, too.   Thus, for example, signal tracing, starting from the speaker and working forward is the best method of servicing an F-M receiver just as it is for any A-M circuit.   In addition, despite the fact that an F-M receiver is designed for the reception of F-M signals, A-M signal generators of the proper frequency range will serve for the signal tracing.   The alignment procedures for the commercial models described earlier included alignment with an A-M signal generator.   If a set can be aligned with an A-M signal generator, it most certainly can be tested with one.

Following recognized procedure, after the defect has been localized in a particular stage, voltage and — with the power off — resistance and continuity checks will lead the serviceman to the faulty component.   The only real difficulty which the serviceman will encounter and one which is due to lack of experience is the localizing of defects in the R.F. stages at the front end of the set. Component failure, here, especially if one of the coils or other R.F. components are faulty, will prove especially troublesome. However, if the serviceman is familiar with the basic operation of high frequency circuits, as outlined in the preceding section, and uses all special instructions issued by the manufacturer, he should be able to surmount successfully any difficulties that may arise. At all times, in replacing components and/or connecting wires, duplicate exactly what has been taken out. It is a common practice among present-day servicemen to replace faulty components with whatever part happens to be on hand. Although this procedure may work in the less critical A-M receivers, it will seldom be successful in F-M sets. This is also true of television receivers, which function at the same approximate band of frequencies.

Preliminary Tests: In receiving a set which is inoperative, there is seldom any reason for the serviceman to suspect that the tuned circuits are out of alignment. The more complicated receivers become — and the trend is in that direction — the less likely it is that someone owning a receiver will venture to meddle with it to the extent of adjusting the circuit alignments. Possibly the only meddling that is done nowadays is to remove the tubes to have them tested at a near-by radio store. Here, the possibility of improper replacement is quite likely and it may save the serviceman hours of work if he first checks the tubes and the sockets they are in. The standard octal socket can accommodate most tubes.

As a routine measure, the serviceman should replace all tubes in the set with test tubes known to be in good operating condition. Tube failure is one of the major reasons for sets becoming inoperative. It is also one of the easiest checks to make.

Many, if not all, of the present F-M receivers are combination A-M and F-M sets. This gives the serviceman another means of localizing trouble in the receiver. If it is found, for example, that the set is perfectly normal on the A-M bands, but completely inoperative when the switch is turned to F-M, then the trouble must be contained in some part of the receiver which is exclusively used for the F-M. It indicates, for example, that the audio amplifiers and the power supply may be eliminated immediately. Again, since most sets (for the sake of economy and compactness) have but one set of I.F. amplifiers, the chances are good that these are also in working order. It may be, of course, that one of the F-M–I.F. coils is shorted, but this is not a common occurrence and may, at first, be discounted. Thus, through the simple process of testing the set on A-M, we have eliminated anywhere from four to six tubes and as many stages. A glance at the circuit diagram of the set will show which circuits are common to both signals and which are not. Combination receivers are becoming increasingly numerous because of the many popular types of services available. The additional circuits may make the overall circuit more complex and yet, on the other hand, they can make the task of trouble shooting easier. A common defect will show up in all circuits, a special defect will be confined to one particular path.

Phonograph attachments are common in modern F-M receivers. These phonographs generally feed through the entire audio section of the set. As a simple test of the audio system, the serviceman has only to rub his finger back and forth across the phonograph needle and note whether any scraping noise is heard from the loudspeaker.

These are but a few of the little tricks and preliminary tests that the serviceman has at his disposal to simplify the process of repairing receivers.

General Servicing Procedure. For the purposes of testing a receiver to determine the cause and location of any defect, it is helpful to divide the set roughly into the following six categories:

1. Power supply.
2. Audio amplifiers.
3. F-M detector or discriminator.
4. I.F. system
5. H.F. oscillator and mixer.
6. R.F. section of receiver.

The foregoing classification is true for all superheterodyne receivers. Since no TRF types of commercial F-M sets are being manufactured at present, the analysis will apply to all receivers that the serviceman is called on to repair.

Power Supply: Trouble in the power supply produces either a completely inoperative set or else low volume in the receiver output. Under these conditions, the first place to test is the B+ terminal of the power supply. A partial short-circuit in any portion of the receiver may result in an excessive current drain on the power supply and lower the B+ voltage considerably. The audio output becomes weak and oftentimes noisy. A total short-circuit will burn out the rectifier tube and cause any protective fuses to blow. Never replace a blown fuse until the cause of the damage has been determined. A hoarse, raspy audio output is another indication of trouble in the power supply, this time a faulty, electrolytic filter condenser. This should not be confused with a scratchy output, which is a result of an incorrectly centered speaker cone.

Audio Amplifier System: The simplest and most rapid method of testing the audio amplifiers is by applying an audio signal and noting whether an output is obtained. With the same strength signal, the output should become louder as the test voltage is moved back away from the speaker. The output will be loudest when the signal is applied to the grid of the first audio amplifier. A more sensitive indicator is an output meter connected across the voice coil leads.

F-M Detector or Discriminator: The various types of commercial F-M detectors currently in use were analyzed in Chapter 9. To trace an A-M signal through the detector, we must connect the indicator (a voltmeter or ammeter) in such a way that response to an A-M signal is possible. In the diagram of the conventional discriminator, Fig. 13.7, connection of the meter across either load resistor will result in a deflection if the A-M signal voltage is being passed through the circuit. Each half of the discriminator is responsive to A-M and, when the circuit is functioning properly, the d-c voltmeter connected across either R_1 or R_2 will show a reading. It is usually most convenient to connect one end of the voltmeter to ground and the other end to the junction of the two load resistors, such as point A, Fig. 13.7. The ground terminal of the signal generator is connected to the receiver chassis. The output lead is connected through a 0.05-mf condenser to the plate or grid of the preceding limiter. If the frequency of the signal is varied, by rotating the knob of the signal generator, the meter deflections will increase and decrease.

The linearity of the detector to F-M signals can be determined by connecting the voltmeter across both load resistors and observing

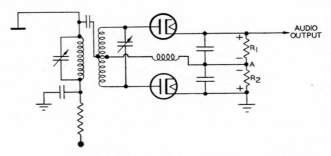

FIG. 13.7.   A conventional discriminator.

whether equal (and opposite polarity) deflections are obtained for frequencies located equal distances above and below the I.F. mid-value.   The linear response should extend ±75 kc from this I.F. point.

In the ratio detector, reproduced in Fig. 13.8, the voltmeter is connected between the point marked A.V.C. and ground.   Since

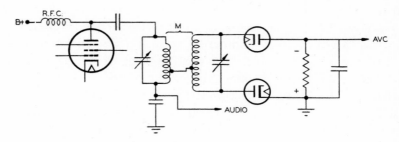

FIG. 13.8.   The ratio detector.

the A.V.C. point is negative, the negative lead of the d-c voltmeter is placed here.   The signal generator is then attached between the grid and ground of the last I.F. amplifier.   If the circuit is operating normally, the meter will show a deflection.   As the amplitude of the signal is slowly varied, the voltmeter will follow the changes in step.   In addition, if the signal generator is set at the mid I.F. value and then varied from 75 kc below this point to 75 kc above, the indicator will show only a small change.   This is true, providing the circuit is correctly aligned and the voltage output of the

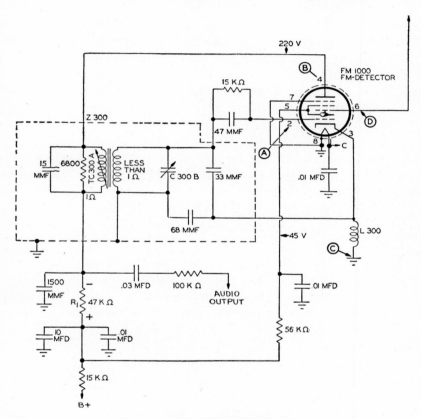

FIG. 13.9.   The Philco F-M detector.

signal generator does not change with frequency.   If either diode is inoperative, there will be no meter deflection.

The third F-M detector is the one developed by the Philco Corporation, shown in Fig. 13.9, together with several indicated test points for checking the circuit.   As a first step, the response of the circuit to F-M is tested.   This is done by observing the voltage drops across the audio-load resistor, R_1, as the frequency of the signal supplied by the generator is varied above and below the I.F. center value.

The signal generator is connected to point D, with a 0.05-mf condenser in series with the output lead of the generator. The ground terminal of the generator connects directly to the receiver chassis. For this test the output of the generator should be, at least, 0.5 volt. If it is not possible to obtain this much signal voltage, the signal generator will have to be connected to the grid of the last I.F. amplifier, or even the one previous to that. It is understood, of course, that these stages are functioning properly.

Connect the d-c voltmeter across R_1, observing the marked polarity. Use an unmodulated signal. Now swing the generator frequency approximately 80 kc above to 80 kc below the 9.1-mc I.F. The d-c voltage across R_1 is normally 15 volts, and this exists either in the absence of a signal or when the signal is at 9.1 mc (representing no modulation). At 80 kc above 9.1 mc, the reading becomes 8 volts; it is 23 volts at 80 kc below 9.1 mc. If these indications are not obtained, it is a sign that trouble exists within this portion of the receiver.

The next step, if the foregoing test indicates that further testing is necessary, is to connect an audio signal generator to point D, Fig. 13.9. A separate generator is not necessary if the R.F. signal generator can provide any audio note. It is customary to incorporate a 400-cycle audio note in most good R.F. signal generators. With the audio signal applied to point D, a loud, clear signal should be heard from the speaker. This indicates that any audio voltage appearing in the plate circuit of the F-M detector is able to reach the audio amplifiers. If an audio output is absent, check the plate voltage of the F-M detector tube. After the d-c potentials have been tested — and found to be correct — then the coupling condensers and resistors leading to the audio channel are next. Resistances are tested by means of continuity checks; condensers are best tested by direct substitution.

It is understood that each step in the procedure is given with the thought that the trouble exists at some point which has not yet been reached. In other words, if the second step just given reveals the source of trouble in the F-M detector there is obviously no need to continue. However, if the indications fail to reveal the defect, the next step in the testing of the detector must be taken.

For the third test, short-circuit pin 2 of the F-M 1000 tube to the chassis. The tube is now functioning as an A-M detector. Connect the R.F. generator to point D, Fig. 13.9, with the audio modulation in the " on " position. The incoming amplitude-modulated signal will be detected, and a loud, clear audio note will be heard from the speaker. The signal generator is set to 9.1 mc, and the signal voltage should be, at least, 0.5 volt. Absence of the audio output means that there is something defective in this circuit. Check tube, plate and screen voltages, condensers and resistors.

A final check, providing the receiver is still not working, is at the F-M oscillator. Possibly the simplest test to determine whether any oscillator is functioning, is to measure its grid-bias potential. Oscillators used in superheterodyne receivers are self-biasing, using a grid-leak bias form of circuit. A voltage will be present at this grid — with respect to ground — only when the oscillator is operating. The grid (pin 2) should be approximately 2.5 volts negative. Note, however, that presence of the negative voltage does not indicate that the oscillator is on frequency. It is merely an indication that the oscillator is functioning.

The proper indication, in all of these tests, means that the F-M detector is operating normally.

F-M Detector Checking with Sweep Generator. For those service shops that possess sweep generators, a good test of an F-M detector is to observe its response or S-curve. Connect a sweep signal generator to the grid of the tube preceding the F-M detector. Set it to sweep 200 kc above and below the I.F. Connect an oscilloscope across the output terminals of the detector. The appearance of the S-curve on the oscilloscope screen will tell the complete story concerning the operating condition of the detector. When the transformer coupling network connecting the F-M detector to the previous stage is not properly tuned or centered, the S-curve will appear either as shown in Fig. 13.10A or B. In either case, the sound output will be distorted. To correct this condition, adjust the trimmer condensers (or iron cores) of the F-M detector primary and secondary windings. The primary controls the linearity of the

S-curve, and the secondary adjustment governs the centering of the S-curve.

Another defect made evident by the S-curve occurs when the bandwidth of the tuning circuit is too narrow. (See Fig. 13.11.) When this happens, the output becomes distorted when the incoming

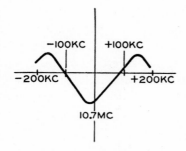

FIG. 13.10A. Secondary trimmer adjustment of discriminator transformer improperly set.

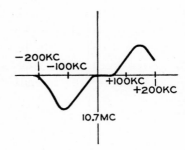

FIG. 13.10B. Primary trimmer adjustment of discriminator transformer improperly set.

signal is fully modulated. The sounds become "hissy" or "raspy." The solution for this, assuming that the circuits were not originally designed this way, is to realign them.

Whenever the complete response curves are viewed on the oscilloscope screen, marker signals obtained from a separate A-M signal generator should be used to identify the mid I.F. and the end frequencies of the linear section of the curve.

In the Foster-Seeley discriminator the two diodes should be matched fairly closely. If one discriminator diode has low emission, the S-shaped curve will now assume the appearance shown in Fig. 13.12. This condition results in poor noise rejection at low signal inputs and sound distortion at high signal inputs. When both discriminator diodes have low emission, the sensitivity of the receiver is poor.

Checking Limiters. When a receiver that has been operating normally suddenly becomes noisy, the discriminator tubes and alignment should be checked. If the receiver contains a limiter stage, this too should be checked. Limiters become noisy when their grid-leak circuits open, or the voltages applied to the electrodes rise above normal. In many circuits, the low voltages for the screen and plate are obtained by the voltage divider arrangement shown in Fig. 13.13. If R should open, the voltage applied to the screen

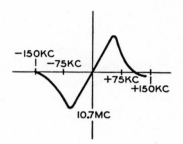

FIG. 13.11. Bandpass of discriminator too narrow.

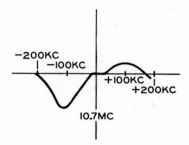

FIG. 13.12. The form of the S-curve when one diode of the discriminator circuit has low emission.

will rise. Under these conditions it will require considerably stronger signals to bring the tube to saturation, and the limiting action of the tube is impaired. Ordinarily, most limiter tubes will saturate with signal voltages of 2 volts or more. The best method of testing the limiter is to measure its grid, screen, and plate voltages and compare the values obtained with those specified by the manufacturer.

A noisy ratio detector can usually be traced to an open electrolytic condenser. This condenser, together with its shunting resistor, stabilizes the ratio detector against amplitude modulation of the received carrier. If the condenser becomes defective, noise will ride through and be heard. The serviceman will find that sets using the ratio detector will receive weaker signals with less background noise than the same signal in a set possessing the Foster-Seeley discriminator. In the latter receiver,

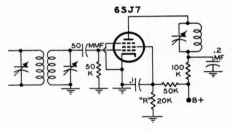

FIG. 13.13. If "R" should open up, the limiter may become noisy with moderate signals.

noise disappears only when the preceding limiter is driven to saturation, but no such "threshold" effect is apparent in the ratio detector. However, in all instances, when the noise or interference is stronger than the signal, the noise will prevail.

I.F. System: The placement of the indicator when the I.F. system is tested will depend upon the type of F-M detector used. For the conventional discriminator, which has one or two limiters preceding it, it is possible to place the indicating meter in the grid circuit of the last limiter, if there are two, and test the I.F. system. The signal generator is connected to the grid of the mixer tube, and the frequency of the signal set at the I.F. If all the intervening stages between the mixer and the limiter (where the meter is located) are in proper operating condition, the meter will deflect. If no indication is obtained, the signal generator will have to be brought back to the grid of the first tube preceding the limiter. In this way, only one stage is under test. If the meter deflects, indicating that the stage under test is functioning properly, the generator is moved back one stage and the signal applied again. In this manner, we gradually work back to the point where the trouble exists in the I.F. system. However, as a preliminary test, the signal is fed through the entire I.F. system, since if no trouble exists in this portion of the receiver, valuable time is not spent testing each stage.

While testing the I.F. system, it is possible also to determine whether the circuits are in alignment. Maximum deflection of the meter should be obtained when the test signal is at the I.F. value. Shifting the frequency an equal number of kilocycles above and below this point should produce equal readings on the meter.

Note that the foregoing procedure is followed only for F-M sets employing conventional discriminators with their attendant limiters. In receivers possessing the ratio detector and no limiter is employed, the voltmeter is connected to the point where the A.V.C. voltage is obtained from the detector. The positive lead of the meter is attached to the chassis. Any signal fed into a properly operating I.F. system will result in a voltage at this point in the detector.

In a Philco receiver, using their special detector circuit, it becomes necessary to convert the F-M detector to an A-M detector in order to be able to use an A-M signal for testing. When pin 2 of the F-M 1000 tube is connected to the chassis, the detector-oscillator becomes inoperative, and the circuit responds to A-M signals. As an indicator, we can place an output meter across the voice coil of the speaker or else listen for an audio note from the loud-speaker, providing, of course, that a modulated A-M signal is used.

The I.F. system of present F-M sets is generally a combination of A-M and F-M transformers with a single tube for each stage serving both A-M and F-M. With the exception of the I.F. switch and the F-M–I.F. transformers, parts giving normal indications on A-M will test normal on F-M. Hence, if the I.F. system is found to be in operating condition on A-M but not on F-M, it would be best to check these particular components first.

R.F. Section: To test the R.F. stages of the receiver, we still retain the A-M signal generator, provided its range extends to the necessary frequencies. Again, as before, the position of the indicating meter will depend upon the type of F-M detector in the circuit. The explanation given above will apply equally here. For the signal tests, use an R.F. signal generator with an amplitude-modulated output. The ground lead of the signal generator is connected to the chassis ground; the output lead is connected through a 0.05 mf-condenser to each of the test points, as explained below.

The input of the R.F. section of the receiver consists of an R.F. amplifier, a mixer, and an oscillator. In some sets, no R.F. stage is included; in others, such a stage is employed only for the F-M signals (see Philco diagram). A tube has recently become available, a 6SB7Y, which will function satisfactorily as a converter at frequencies of 100 mc. In the past, it has usually been necessary to have separate tubes for the mixing and oscillator functions, in order to avoid undesirable interaction between the two. However, with the appearance of special tubes, such as the 6SB7Y, it is likely that many companies will eventually use a single tube. At the present writing, they appear to be evenly divided between one tube and two tubes.

In the testing of an F-M receiver, the input circuits are tested last. Hence, if the foregoing step-by-step procedure has indicated that all of the other sections of the receiver are functioning properly, then in the testing of the R.F. circuits, it is best to start at the oscillator. The reason for this is that the oscillator is the one stage, in the front end of the receiver, which is most critical in operation and most likely to be at fault. By measuring the voltage between the control grid and cathode of the oscillator, we can determine whether or not the stage is functioning. Measure this voltage with a high-resistance voltmeter, otherwise the value read can be misleading. The voltage at the control grid (with respect to the cathode) may have any value between —2 volts and —10 volts. Consult the service manual issued by the manufacturer for the proper value. Too low a value may be due to a bad tube or lowered operating potentials. Measure the plate and screen voltages and if these are within the correct range, change the tube. The oscillator grid voltage should be measured on all bands since it is very possible that the oscillator will function on some frequencies and not on others. Reasons for this may be a defect in the switching system or the plain fact that a tube will oscillate readily at the low frequencies and yet fail to do so at the higher frequencies.

If the oscillator is operating satisfactorily, place the signal generator at the signal grid of the mixer tube. Adjust the front dial of the receiver and the signal generator for the same frequency setting. If the set, at this point, is operating satisfactorily, the indicator should show a deflection. If no response is obtained, change mixer or converter tubes, measure voltages at the electrodes and/or make resistance checks to locate the defective component. Once the defect has been traced to a single stage, a routine analysis will, in almost all instances, reveal the trouble.

In probing around the underside of the chassis, the serviceman must be careful not to rearrange any components — especially small coils. It is impossible to emphasize too strongly the criticalness of these high frequency circuits, a fact which is usually fully appreciated only after such a circuit has been built or rearranged and it becomes inoperative. Many of these circuits, especially the oscillator, contain compensating condensers. Their purpose is to compensate for changes in the electrical characteristics of other condensers and/or the coils. If one of these special condensers becomes defective, i.e., open, the circuit is detuned. If the serviceman is unaware of this situation, he may conclude that the circuits merely require alignment and rectify the situation by readjusting the circuits. For the moment, the set will function. However, after a short while it will be found that the set drifts during each warm-up period, and this drift may easily be sufficient to shift the circuits out of range of the signal. The station can be brought in by manually retuning the set — but this will have to be done at least once each time the set is turned on and possibly more.

Another defect, which is relatively new, is the howl that is heard on the F-M band. This howl is caused by the speaker vibrating the oscillator tuning slug. A fiber spacer placed between the oscillator and the mixer slug shafts will eliminate the vibration. This same effect may only become noticeable as the volume control is advanced, but the remedy remains the same. Howling may also be due to speaker vibrations reaching the oscillator sections of the gang condenser. Mounting the gang condenser on a rubber cushion or a felt strip will help to eliminate this howl. Also, floating the speaker on rubber grommets is helpful.

No special mention has been given to the testing of any R.F. amplifiers since the procedure is identical with what has already been given. Generally, instead of feeding the signal directly at the grid of the R.F. amplifier, the signal is fed in at the antenna terminals. The method for connecting the signal generator, especially with F-M receivers possessing balanced input, is identical with the methods outlined for the alignment of the receivers.

It may be instructive, before we end this chapter, to examine some typical troubles that have been encountered in F-M receivers, and which often baffle the inexperienced serviceman.

A set, in transit from the factory to the retailer and from the retailer to the customer, is often subjected to many jarring blows and knocks that can cause wires to short together, poorly soldered connections to break, trimmer condenser plates and iron core slugs to bend and stick, plus a host of other damaging mishaps which will render a set inoperative. Sometimes these happen to a set when it is moved about in the home, although generally sets are handled fairly carefully by their owners.

F-M CONVERSION CHART
(88 to 108 mc)

Fre-quency	Channel Number	Fre-quency	Channel Number	Fre-quency	Channel Number	Fre-quency	Channel Number
88.1	201	93.1	226	98.1	251	103.1	276
88.3	202	93.3	227	98.3	252	103.3	277
88.5	203	93.5	228	98.5	253	103.5	278
88.7	204	93.7	229	98.7	254	103.7	279
88.9	205	93.9	230	98.9	255	103.9	280
89.1	206	94.1	231	99.1	256	104.1	281
89.3	207	94.3	232	99.3	257	104.3	282
89.5	208	94.5	233	99.5	258	104.5	283
89.7	209	94.7	234	99.7	259	104.7	284
89.9	210	94.9	235	99.9	260	104.9	285
90.1	211	95.1	236	100.1	261	105.1	286
90.3	212	95.3	237	100.3	262	105.3	287
90.5	213	95.5	238	100.5	263	105.5	288
90.7	214	95.7	239	100.7	264	105.7	289
90.9	215	95.9	240	100.9	265	105.9	290
91.1	216	96.1	241	101.1	266	106.1	291
91.3	217	96.3	242	101.3	267	106.3	292
91.5	218	96.5	243	101.5	268	106.5	293
91.7	219	96.7	244	101.7	269	106.7	294
91.9	220	96.9	245	101.9	270	106.9	295
92.1	221	97.1	246	102.1	271	107.1	296
92.3	222	97.3	247	102.3	272	107.3	297
92.5	223	97.5	248	102.5	273	107.5	298
92.7	224	97.7	249	102.7	274	107.7	299
92.9	225	97.9	250	102.9	275	107.9	300

As examples of the type of troubles that can be expected from this source, consider the following case histories which were taken from actual servicing records.

Case 1. An A-M, F-M receiver was operating satisfactorily on A-M and phono, but was dead in the F-M position. This set used the same tubes for both A-M and F-M, and consequently the tubes, as a source of trouble, could be eliminated. The audio system was similarly eliminated since the phonograph fed its signal through this system. Checking the oscillator grid voltage disclosed that it was zero in the F-M position. Obviously, the F-M oscillator was not functioning.   In checking the various components in this circuit (coils, resistors, and condensers) it was found that the plates of the trimmer condenser used in this circuit were shorting together through a cracked mica sheet which served as the condenser dielectric.

By replacing the trimmer condenser and realigning the oscillator, the set returned to normal operation on F-M.

Case 2.   It should be fairly evident by this time that high frequency circuits such as we find in the front end and in the I.F. stages of an F-M receiver are more critical than low frequency circuits. Rough handling in shipment have been the cause of poor sensitivity of many an F-M set.   If the output of a set is weak, check the alignment of the circuits.   With a sweep signal generator and an oscilloscope, this job should not take more than 15 to 20 minutes and it may save hours of needless search for a nonexistent defective component.

Case 3.   A receiver operated normally on A-M and F-M, but was intermittent or hummed constantly on phono.   In A-M or F-M sets, the phono is usually connected into the circuit just ahead of the volume control.   This control, in turn, attaches to the control grid of the first audio amplifier.   Since the hum appeared only in the phono position of the selector switch, the trouble must have existed between the phono input and the volume control.

In the present instance it was found that the trouble was due to a poorly soldered ground connection on the phone jack.   With the ground lead off, the phono was floating, picking up some of the stray 60-cycle voltage present in nearly all sets.   These stray 60-cycle fields are due to poorly shielded power transformers or filament wires that extend into every section of a set wherever a tube is located.

Poorly soldered ground connections cause servicemen no end of grief.   Whenever a set is troubled with intermittent operation, hum pickup, or noisy operation, and the defect is difficult to locate, take 10 minutes or so to go over many of the soldered connections in the set with a hot soldering iron.   Check, too, at the same time to see whether any bare wires are accidentally touching each other or the sides of the chassis when they are not supposed to be grounded.   The time thus spent will be well worth your while.

To illustrate the foregoing remarks, here is a case that is periodically encountered.   The set becomes noisy, especially at the high frequency end of the dial and when the volume is turned up high.   The noise is somewhat like the sizzling sound obtained by frying butter in a pan.

The source of this noise can usually be traced to an ungrounded speaker when the latter unit is not attached directly to the receiver chassis.   To remedy this, run a wire from the speaker casing to the chassis, soldering the wires at both ends to insure proper electrical connection.

Case 4.   Some manufacturers of A-M, F-M sets place both I.F. coils within the same can.   Where the space is limited, it can readily happen that bare wires running from the various transformer windings to the connecting lugs may touch each other, shorting out one or both I.F. windings.   When this is the case, reception on either band (or both) will depend upon which winding is shorted out. Thus, if the A-M windings are shorted, there will be reception only on F-M; no A-M signals will be heard.   When the short occurs across the F-M winding, reception on this band may be either totally absent or weak.   In spite of the short, some reception may be obtained because the shorting wire may contain enough inductance at 10.7 mc to permit some signal to develop across it and be passed onto the next stage.   At the A-M, I.F. frequencies, however, the short effectively cuts out all signals.

Case 5.   A certain A-M, F-M receiver was found to develop an intermittent bad hum and sometimes the set became completely inoperative.   In this set, all filament and ground returns in the R.F. section are made through a single ground strap that connects the R.F. section to the chassis.   This is frequently broken in shipment or in moving the set around.   To remedy the condition, replace the strap with flexible copper braid.

Case 6.   Many F-M discriminators have a small condenser connected between the top of the primary winding of the discriminator transformer and the center tap on the secondary.   This was noted in the discussion on discriminators.   If this condenser should become shorted, B+ will be placed on the plates of the discriminator diodes.   The result may be either a completely dead set or the appearance of " motorboating." Since the condenser is generally not readily accessible, the only positive cure is replacement of the entire transformer.

Case 7. In almost every receiver, small 100- or 220-mmf by-pass condensers are connected from grid to ground or plate to ground of the first audio amplifier. The purpose of these condensers is to prevent any I.F. voltage from entering the audio amplifier system. When one of these condensers shorts out, no audio output will be obtained. When they open up, the set usually becomes noisy.

To localize this noise on a set just received, proceed as follows. Ground the grid of the final output amplifier. This will eliminate the noise. Next, ground the grid of the previous (generally the first audio) amplifier stage. The noise now will be heard, indicating that it is arising in the stage under test.

Case 8. Low volume and poor or fuzzy tone can usually be traced to insufficient voltage being applied to the audio amplifiers. Electrolytic condensers that have excessive leakage, rectifier tubes with poor emission, or weak selenium rectifiers will produce these symptoms. Especially sensitive to voltage drops is the local oscillator. Make certain when checking a dead set that the voltages are within 10 per cent of those specified by the manufacturer. Remember, too, that when an oscillator is operating properly, it will develop negative biasing voltages from 2 to 10 volts, depending upon the circuit. Check for this voltage.

Decrease in voltage has been noted quite frequently in sets using selenium rectifiers, and the best solution to this trouble is replacement of the unit.

In some districts, the a-c voltage of the local power lines is subject to fairly wide fluctuations during the 24-hour period of a day. If a set is sensitive to these variations, especially voltage reductions, it can (and will) happen that the oscillator within the set will cease to function when the line voltage is low. A complaint of set operation only during certain hours of the day can be checked for this cause in the shop by connecting a Variac between the set and the power line. Gradually lower the line voltage to the set and observe at what input voltage the set ceases to operate. Usually, most sets will continue to function down to line voltages of

100 volts. Some, however, will die out before this value is reached, and the foregoing complaints are heard with these latter sets. Larger filter condensers, lower-valued filter resistors, or a change in rectifier tubes are generally helpful in such cases.

Conditions will sometimes arise, when checking the various voltages in a set, which will lead to a false conclusion regarding the component at fault. A case that actually occurred concerned a certain receiver that developed considerable distortion when in operation 5 minutes or longer. A voltage check of the power tube (a 35A5) showed a positive voltage at the control grid. The first thought was a leaky or shorted coupling condenser between the plate of the preceding tube and the grid of the 35A5. However, replacement of this condenser did not correct the condition. The fault was found to lie with the tube itself and replacing the tube cleared up the trouble.

A similar instance involved a set which possessed a weak, distorted output followed, after several minutes, by a completely dead output amplifier. Checking the audio amplifier system revealed that the 6V6 output amplifier did not possess any cathode voltage, indicating that the tube itself was not conducting current. A further test showed continuity in the cathode circuit. Voltages on all the other elements were in order, yet the tube did not seem to be drawing current. It was found that the 500,000-ohm volume control across the control grid of this stage showed continuity only at certain positions of the movable arm.

What was happening here was this: With the grid circuit open, electrons collected on the grid and, having no path through which to escape, soon biased the tube to cut-off. When the set was turned off, the movable arm on the control moved down the resistor and, since the lower portion of the volume potentiometer did show continuity, the electrons which had collected on the grid were able to leak off. When the set was turned on again, some audio output was usually able to pass through the tube until it once again became blocked by the accumulation of electrons on the grid when the volume control arm was turned up.

Case 9. A series of troubles are encountered periodically that are due to the development of leakage paths between components that should normally be isolated from each other. These leakage paths permit voltages from one circuit to reach other circuits from which they would normally be excluded. The results in several instances are given below:

(A). A set was noisy, with the signals weak and fuzzy. Trouble was traced to leakage between the primary and secondary fixed condensers of an I.F. transformer, which were imbedded in wax, and enough dirt and moisture had collected to permit a leakage path to be formed between the two units. The faulty condition was remedied by cleaning off the wax.

(B). Receiver had a loud hum when a station was tuned in. The control grid of the R.F. amplifier was connected to a 3.9-megohm resistor through which it received A.V.C. voltage. Apparent corrosion between the wafers of the tube socket allowed a 500,000-ohm to one-megohm leakage resistance to form between the various pins and the center terminal which is grounded.

Cleaning off the corrosion may help although, if the corrosive action is well advanced, the only solution will be to change the socket. It is well to remember that this same thing can happen in almost any wafer socket.

(C). A set exhibited a severe a-c hum after it had been in operation for several months. Bridging the existing filter condensers with units known to be good had very little effect. Grounding the control grid of the audio output tube removed the hum; grounding the grid of the previous audio amplifier did not affect the hum. The trouble, then, was in this stage. It was discovered that leakage between the cathode by-pass condenser used here and one of the power-supply filter condensers was the cause of the trouble. Both units were contained in the same case.

(D). Hum due to electrical leakage between the heater (or filament) and cathode of a tube will be encountered occasionally. The minute current that flows between the heater and cathode develops enough voltage across the cathode resistor to introduce a 60-cycle variation in the tube's current flow.

A-c, d-c sets are particularly susceptible to this source of hum because of the series connections of the filaments.

The solution to hum developed in this manner is replacement of the faulty tube. Hum can also be reduced by operating the tubes at or slightly below their normal filament voltages. Operating a tube with more than rated voltage aggravates the problem. In high-gain audio systems, place the input tube as close as possible to the ground end of the filament chain. Also, if cathode self-biasing circuits are used, keep the value of the cathode resistor as low as possible. Keep the capacitance of the cathode by-pass condenser as large as possible because this reduces the impedance of the cathode circuit to 60-cycle voltages. In a well-designed amplifier, fixed bias is frequently used in the first audio amplifier, permitting the cathode to be grounded directly and thereby avoiding trouble from this source of annoyance.

Problems

1. What effect does increase in frequency have on the ordinary resistor? Why is this important in F-M circuits?

2. Why is stray capacitance more important at the high frequencies than at the low frequencies?

3. How can stray capacitance be kept at a minimum?

4. Why is the conventional concept of current flow in a vacuum tube unsuitable at the high frequencies?

5. What effect does a tube have on its associated network as we raise the frequency of the signal?

6. In what ways are the newer tubes better suited for high frequency operation than the older, conventional tube?

7. Define electron transit time. What is its effect on the operation of a tube?

8. Why are some tubes designed with two cathode terminals?

9. Illustrate how tubes possessing two cathode terminals should be connected into a circuit.

10. What preliminary tests should be made before any actual work of servicing is begun?

11. How is the audio system of a receiver tested?

12. Outline the method you would employ to check the Foster-Seeley discriminator, the ratio detector and Philco F-M detector.

13. Would a-c hum in the power supply affect an F-M receiver? Explain.

14. How does testing of the I.F. system depend upon the type of F-M detector used?

15. Must the indicating meter always be placed in the output of the F-M detector when the I.F. system is being tested? Explain.

16. List some of the defects which could possibly affect an I.F. system.

17. How is the R.F. section of an F-M receiver tested?

18. What indication do we obtain from a normally functioning oscillator?

19. In tuning over the F-M band, a hiss is heard in the speaker. At no point, however, are any stations heard although stations are known to be operating. What is probably wrong with the set?

20. Microphonic tubes produce what effect in a set?

CHAPTER 14

COMMERCIAL F-M TRANSMITTERS

(PART 1)

To generate F-M signals, two general methods are in use. One is the reactance method; the other, the phase-shift method. In the reactance method, the frequency of an oscillator is made to vary with modulation through the use of a vacuum tube. In the phase-shift method, frequency modulation is achieved by varying the phase of a signal obtained generally from a crystal oscillator. Chapters 14 and 15 describe commercial F-M transmitters employing reactance tubes whereas Chapter 16 is concerned with transmitters utilizing the phase-shift system.

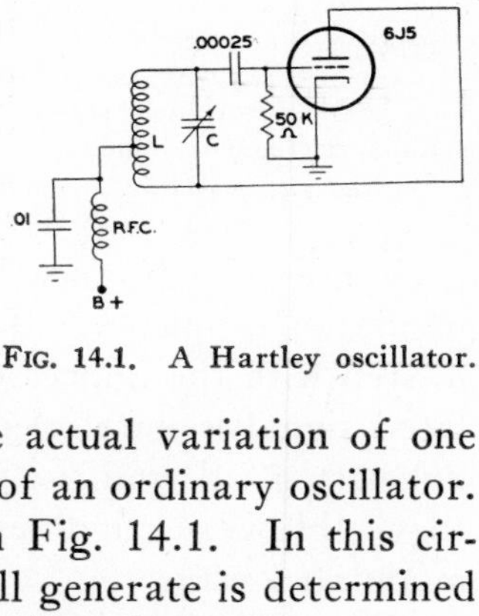

Fig. 14.1. A Hartley oscillator.

Reactance-Tube Circuit. Probably the most direct method of producing a frequency-modulated wave is through the actual variation of one of the frequency-determining components of an ordinary oscillator. Consider the Hartley oscillator shown in Fig. 14.1. In this circuit, the frequency which the oscillator will generate is determined primarily by L and C according to the familiar formula,

$$f = \frac{1}{2\pi\sqrt{LC}}$$

By varying either or both of these components, it is possible to alter the resonant frequency. For the production of a frequency-modulated signal, we would have to have either L or C vary in accordance with the spoken word or a musical selection.

One crude and elementary method of obtaining a variation in capacitance is by the attachment of a condenser microphone in parallel with the tuning condenser C. Such an arrangement is shown in Fig. 14.2.   As long as no sound reaches the microphone, the total capacitance across the coil remains constant.   The frequency due to this combination of L and C would represent the central or resting frequency. C, in this case, is the sum of the average capacitance of the microphone plus the capacitance of the tuning condenser.

When the microphone is actuated by sound, the movable condenser plate is forced to vibrate back and forth about its rest or center position.   At some time, under pressure of the moving air, the condenser plate approaches the fixed plate and the total capacitance increases. (Capacitance varies inversely with plate spacing.)   As a consequence, the frequency of the oscillator decreases.   Upon being released from this position, the movable condenser plate swings past its center position and comes to rest at a point farther away from the fixed plate.

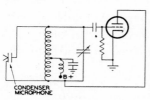

CONDENSER
MICROPHONE

FIG. 14.2.   An elementary method of frequency modulating an oscillator.

Under these circumstances, the total capacitance has decreased below its average value, increasing the oscillator frequency.   Thus the frequency of the oscillator varies in step with the impressed audio variations and a frequency-modulated signal is developed.   True, the linearity of this converter is not very good, and the results would not be commercially satisfactory.   However, it does illustrate the production of a frequency-modulated wave.

The attachment of a condenser microphone across the tank circuit is impractical, but we can obtain a variation in either inductance or capacitance by means of a vacuum tube.   As will be seen, the tube does not actually " add " or " subtract " a condenser or coil across the tank circuit.   However, because of its presence in the circuit, the effect produced is as though a variable inductance or capacitance were actually in the circuit.   Consequently, the frequency of the oscillator changes.   If the circuit is designed so that the frequency variations are governed directly by the audio sounds reaching the microphone, we have the desired frequency-modulated signal.

Reactive Impedance. Before we actually examine the circuit of a reactance tube, let us review briefly the ideas of resistive and reactive impedance. Consider pure resistance first. Any physics book will demonstrate that what is called resistance is merely the ratio of voltage across a conductor to the current flowing through it. We express this by Ohm's Law, $R = E/I$. If a given voltage produces a high current flow, then we say that the conductor possesses a small resistance or opposition. If a small current is produced, for the same voltage, then we say that the conductor has a high resistance. In any event, the resistance is never measured as such, but solely as the ratio of voltage to current. Recall any resistance measurements or experiments that you have performed or seen performed. Were any of these ever made without the use of voltage and current? The answer is no. In a limited sense, then, we may consider resistance as existing only when current is flowing through the circuit. Without current and voltage, resistance loses its significance.

What has all this to do with reactance-modulator tubes? We shall see in a moment. Now let us turn our attention to inductive and capacitive reactance. We learn early in our study of radio that for many common frequencies the opposition that a resistor offers is constant. But when we insert a condenser or an inductance into the circuit, we note that the opposition depends upon the frequency of the applied voltage. For the condenser, the opposition decreases with rise in frequency; for the inductance, it rises directly. Here, then, more so than in the case of the resistor, we see that the concept of opposition cannot be separated from the applied voltage and its ratio to the current flowing in the circuit.

From these few facts we can draw one simple, yet highly important, fact. A circuit may appear (to some other circuit, for example) either capacitive, inductive, or resistive depending upon the voltage and current conditions in that circuit and *not* upon whether capacitance, inductance, or resistance is actually present. In other words, if we can take a tube and so connect it that the voltage between its plate and cathode is 90° lagging the plate current, then it will appear as a condenser to any circuit connected to this tube. Why? Simply because it is the voltage-to-current ratio and their relative phase that are the determining factors and not the mere fact that certain components have been placed in the circuit. Remember these points, for they will greatly simplify the understanding of reactance tubes.

A Reactance-tube Modulator. The fundamental circuit of a reactance-tube modulator is shown in Fig. 14.3. Basically, its function is to vary the frequency of the oscillator in step with an applied audio voltage. For the moment, the audio voltage has been omitted. However, as soon as we understand how a tube can cause the frequency of an oscillator to vary, we will incorporate an audio signal.

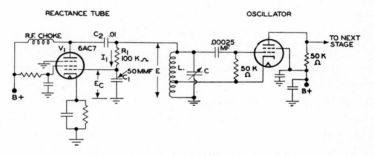

FIG. 14.3.   A reactance-tube modulator.

To begin, we note that, since the reactance tube is connected across the tank circuit of the oscillator, any voltage here will also be present across R_1 and C_1 (see Fig. 14.3). If we make the resistance of R_1 much higher than the opposition of C_1 (to this voltage E), then the current that flows through the R_1C_1 branch will be governed by the resistor and be practically in phase with the applied voltage E. Using vectors, we could show this condition as in Fig. 14.4A.

Examine the voltage that is developed across the condenser C_1. We know that with every condenser the current and the voltage (across that condenser) are out of phase (see Fig. 14.4B). In this instance, since the current through the series branch is practically in phase with the total applied voltage E, and, at the condenser, the current and E_c (the condenser voltage) are 90° out of phase, we can add E_c to the vector diagram of Fig. 14.4A to obtain the result shown in Fig. 14.4C. E_c lags the current and is placed behind it.

Returning to Fig. 14.3, let us investigate the position of E_c in the circuit. By its attachment between the grid and ground, it constitutes the grid voltage. Hence, whatever phase relationship E_c might have to the rest of the circuit, the same relationship will exist for the grid voltage of the 6AC7. And, since the grid voltage

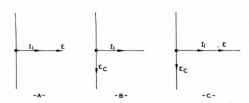

FIG. 14.4. (A) Phase relationship between oscillator tank voltage and current through R_1 and C_1. (B) Current and voltage phase for a condenser. (C) The phase of E_c with respect to E and I_1.

directly controls the plate current, we can derive a relationship between E_c, E_g (the grid voltage of V_1) and the plate current. C_2 serves only to prevent the $B+$ voltage of V_1 from being grounded by L. It is a relatively large capacitance and its imped-ance at the operating frequency is low.

Whenever the grid becomes positive, the plate current in-creases; whenever it goes negative, the current decreases. Both vary directly and both are in phase. Adding the plate current (I_p) to the vector diagram that has been developed already, we obtain the

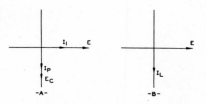

FIG. 14.5. (A) The phase angle be-tween E and I_p of the 6AC7. Its re-semblance to the phase relationship between E and I_L in the oscillator tank circuit (B) is evident.

diagram of Fig. 14.5A. The plate current, being in phase with E_c, is placed 90° behind voltage E. If we look carefully at this phase relationship between E and I_p, we are immediately aware of one fact.   Because of the phase relationship, I_p acts as if it is coming from an inductance.   Since I_p comes from the tube, then as far as voltage E is concerned the tube possesses inductance and presents inductive reactance to the outside circuit.   Thus, through the peculiar combination of R_1C_1 and the tube, we are able by a simple procedure to have the plate current of the tube lag the oscillator tank voltage E and appear inductive.

To progress one step further.   Voltage E is developed across L and C of the oscillator tank circuit.   If we plotted the relationship between the voltage to the current flowing through the inductance of the tank circuit, it would appear as shown by the vectors in Fig. 14.5B. E leads the inductive current of the tank circuit in

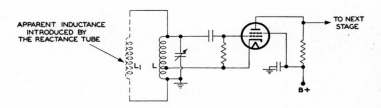

Fig. 14.6.   Equivalent circuit of Fig. 14.3.

exactly the same manner as it leads the plate current of V_1.   Again the similarity of the tube to an inductance is evident.

Because of the placement of the 6AC7 across the oscillator tank circuit, I_p must flow through the oscillator coil and add to the inductive current already flowing through the coil L.   That it will add is due to the voltage E.   This voltage is present across both the tube and the tank coil.   Since both inductive currents arise from the same voltage, they will be in phase.   The result, due to the presence of the tube, is the same as though another inductance had been placed across the tank circuit.   Actually, the tube represents this added inductance, arising from the plate-current phase relationship to the tank voltage.   An equivalent circuit is shown in Fig. 14.6.

When coils are placed in parallel, their total inductance becomes less than each individual inductance.   From the formula for frequency

$$f = \frac{1}{2\pi\sqrt{LC}}$$

it is evident that decreasing L will produce a higher frequency. Hence, by the addition of a tube across the tank circuit we have succeeded in shifting the oscillator frequency. The new frequency now represents the new resting point of the oscillator. No other change will occur as long as the operating voltages remain steady.

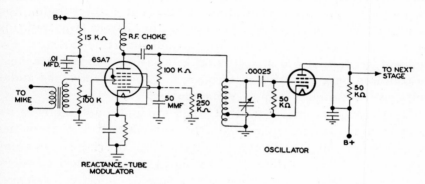

Fig. 14.7. A complete reactance-tube modulator. R may be connected across the 50-mmf condenser to provide a d-c path to ground for any stray electrons trapped on the grid.

Producing F-M. Thus far we have succeeded only in moving the frequency of our oscillator from one point to another. There has been no frequency modulation. This is to be expected since no audio voltages have been applied. This is done in Fig. 14.7, which is essentially the same as the diagram of Fig. 14.3. However, by employing a pentagrid tube we obtain a separate grid (grid 3) for the insertion of the audio voltage. Grid 1 causes the plate current to appear inductive to the oscillator tank voltage E.

When no audio voltage is being impressed on the tube, the plate current is steady. Upon the application of an audio voltage, the plate current is varied in step with the voltage. On positive half cycles, grid 3 becomes positive, allowing more electrons to flow. On the negative audio voltages, the plate current decreases below its normal value. The rapidity with which the current rises and falls is entirely governed by the frequency of the audio voltages. People with high-pitched voices will produce faster variations in the 6SA7 plate current than persons having low-pitched voices.

At the oscillator, these variations in plate current (I_p) will have the effect of changing the amount of inductive current flowing through the coil L. We know that the oscillator tank voltage remains constant. Nothing has been done to change it. Therefore, with the voltage constant and a variation appearing in the inductive current of the tank circuit, we can come to only one conclusion. The inductance must be fluctuating. By changing the inductance, we can alter its opposition to the current flow, and this could account satisfactorily for the various inductive currents. A moment's reflection will indicate that a variation in inductance must be followed by a variation in frequency. Consequently, the audio voltages will produce frequency modulation.

In passing, we may note that when the audio voltage is at its positive peak, the maximum inductive current will flow from the tube through coil L. At these moments, the overall or apparent value of L will be smallest (presenting the lowest inductive reactance and hence permitting the largest flow of inductive current). The frequency of the oscillator will be at its highest point. (See previous formula.) During the opposite half of the cycle, when the audio voltage is negative, the frequency is at its lowest point. Remember again that it is the varying effect of the tube across the tank circuit that is responsible for all this. The actual coil and condenser of the circuit never change.

We have been concerned thus far with a reactance tube that produced a varying inductive current. It is possible to achieve the same results by having the tube appear as a capacitance. This will be done in the next section when a balanced, reactance-tube frequency modulator is investigated.

Balanced Modulators. The degree of frequency shift can be increased and the linearity improved through the use of a balanced modulator, such as illustrated in Fig. 14.8. Two tubes act as reactance units, their grids connected across opposite ends of the audio-signal transformer, whereas their plates are attached to one common point. The purpose of this arrangement is to produce opposite effects in the tubes which will aid each other. Let us see how this is accomplished.

One tube, V_1, is connected as in the previous circuit. From this we know that the plate current produced by the tube will lag the

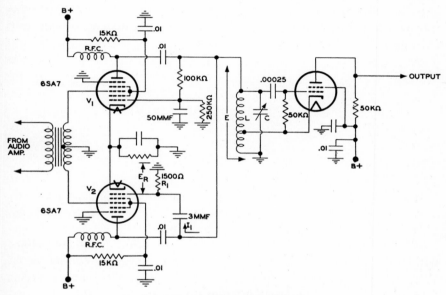

FIG. 14.8. A balanced modulator.

tank voltage E and appear inductive. For V_2, however, we find a slightly different arrangement. We still have a condenser (3 mmf) in series with a resistor, but their impedance values are reversed. The condenser, because of its very small capacity, presents a much greater opposition to the flow of current through this branch than the 1500-ohm resistor. Hence, the current will be almost entirely capacitive and will lead the applied voltage E by practically 90°. This is shown vectorially in Fig. 14.9A. The voltage that is developed across R_1 is in phase with the current because, at all resistors, current and voltage are in phase. We may add E_R to the vector diagram, as in Fig. 14.9B. Since the grid obtains its input voltage from the resistor, we see that E_g and E_R

are one and the same thing. In the vector diagram of Fig. 14.9B we can place E_g at the same point as E_R.

Proceeding with the analysis, we note that I_p of V_2, being governed directly by E_g, is also in phase with it. Hence, we arrive at a situation where, for V_2, the plate current is 90° ahead of the applied oscillator voltage E (see Fig. 14.9C). Thus, by rearranging the condenser-and-resistor combination and altering their relative values we obtain a plate current that leads instead of lags the voltage E. Then, V_2 appears capacitive.

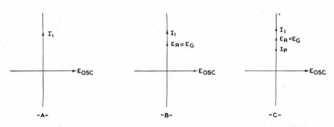

FIG. 14.9. The current and voltage phase relationship in the grid network of V_2 (Fig. 14.8).

Within the tank circuit, this capacitive current combines in phase with the capacitive current flowing through the tuning condenser C. Whether the effective capacitive effect across the entire circuit increases or decreases depends upon the variations in the plate current coming from V_2. If the capacitive current increases, this would have the same effect as a decrease in capacitive reactance. The reason is simple. The tank voltage E remains constant. Hence, the only way the current through C (or L) can change is through a change in the reactance in that branch. For an increase in capacitive current, we must have a corresponding decrease in capacitive reactance. In terms of capacitance this means a larger condenser because

$$X_c = \frac{1}{2\pi f C}$$

If X_c goes down, C must increase. The opposite current variation would mean a decrease in C.

Now let us apply an audio voltage to this reactance-tube modulator and determine how the frequency changes.

The grids of the 6SA7's are connected across opposite ends of the audio input transformer. When one grid goes positive, the other grid is driven negative. Suppose that the audio voltage applied to V_1 is positive, and that to V_2 is negative. Then the plate current I_{p1} will increase and I_{p2} will decrease. Across the oscillator tank circuit this will appear as an increased inductive current and a decreased capacitive current. We have seen that an increasing I_{p1} means a lower effective inductance across the tank circuit. We have also determined that a decreasing capacitive current has the apparent effect of a decrease in C. Hence, as a result of the application of the audio voltage, both the effective values of L and C have decreased. From

$$f = \frac{1}{2\pi\sqrt{LC}}$$

we note that the frequency rises. But since both L and C are effected, the overall frequency change is much greater than we could have obtained with the single-tube arrangement of Fig. 14.7.

We could go through the same analysis for the opposite situation when the audio input voltage reversed. However, from what has already been given there is no need for this. The frequency variation is now in the opposite direction, toward the lower frequencies. Between the positive and negative audio voltage peaks, intermediate frequency shifts take place, at each point directly proportional to the amplitude of the applied voltage.

The Complete Transmitter. Our progress, to this point, in the forming of an F-M signal has consisted solely in examining the action in a reactance tube and the associated oscillator. In practice, the oscillator frequency is somewhere in the neighborhood of 5 mc. Through the application of an audio signal to the reactance tube, we can vary the oscillator frequency about 4 kc. The output, then, from the oscillator will be 5 mc $\pm$ 4 kc. It is not practical to attempt to obtain a greater frequency deviation because of the non-linearity that rises. Hence, if we desire to reach the $\pm$75 kc authorized by the F.C.C., frequency multiplication must be achieved in the stages that follow the oscillator.

A block diagram of a complete reactance-tube F-M transmitter is shown in Fig. 14.10.   We are already familiar with the reactance tube and the oscillator.   Frequency multipliers are needed to develop the final, signal-frequency variation ±75 kc.   The power amplifier, of course, is used to raise the signal level to the rated power of the unit, be it 5 kw, 10 kw or even 50 kw.   Note that until we reach the power amplifier stages we have relatively low-

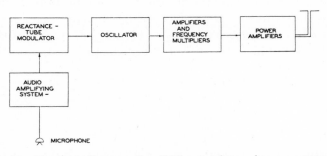

Fig. 14.10.   The block diagram of an F-M transmitter using a reactance-tube modulator.

power stages.   This permits the use of small, inexpensive receiving type tubes, with a substantial saving in cost.   In A-M transmitters, the modulation occurs at or near the final power amplifier. This necessitates large modulating voltages, with their attendant high-power tubes.   The cost of such an arrangement is usually considerable.

A second addition to each reactance-tube transmitter is a frequency-centering system.   The fundamental frequency that is received from the oscillator is the result of the normal resonant frequency of the oscillator tank circuit plus or minus whatever effect the reactance tube may cause by virtue of its attachment across the oscillator.   It is well to keep in mind that the simple attachment of the reactance tube (even when no audio signal is present) produces a frequency shift in the oscillator.   Of course, the change is fixed, not varying as when the audio is active.   As an example, the oscillator may have a frequency of 4.995 mc.   By attaching the reactance tube, we may raise the frequency to 5.000 mc. This now represents the normal oscillator output frequency and it is around this value that the audio signal will swing the frequency.

Once the normal or center oscillator frequency has been established, it is extremely important that it remain fixed. Every station is assigned to one frequency and thereafter it becomes their responsibility to maintain the center or normal frequency at this point.

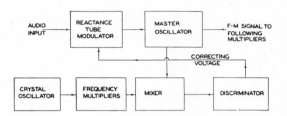

FIG. 14.11. A block diagram of a discriminator control system which keeps the master oscillator at its assigned center frequency.

Failure to do so will not only cause interference to stations on other bands, but undoubtedly result in revocation of their operating license by the F.C.C.

A simple method that has been successfully used to keep an oscillator on frequency is the system shown in Fig. 14.11. This network is arranged to produce an output voltage from the discriminator if the oscillator frequency shifts. By applying this voltage to the reactance tube, we can vary its plate current and, through this, its effect on the oscillator. If the discriminator voltage is properly applied, it will counteract any tendency on the part of either the oscillator or the reactance tube to change the center transmitter frequency. Note that the correction is applied only to maintain a fixed center frequency. It does not, in any way, interfere with the frequency-modulation excursions above and below the resting frequency.

Frequency Multipliers. The output from the modulated oscillator is usually within the frequency range of 4.7 to 6 mc. The frequency variation, due to the modulation, is generally near 4.2 kc. This is the initial maximum swing, destined to become ±75 kc at the output of the transmitter. Under present frequency allocations, the output carrier is confined to the range 88 to 108 mc. Hence, we must increase the relatively low oscillator frequency to some value between 88 and 108 mc. Suppose, as an illustration, we wish to broadcast on 90 mc. The most common arrangement is to utilize two triplers and a doubler, thus providing the minimum number of frequency multipliers with the proper amount of frequency multiplication. The total amount, then, by which the oscillator frequency is increased is 18 times. Since we require a 90-mc output, we find that an oscillator operating at 5 mc will do nicely. Again, with an eighteenfold multiplication, an initial frequency

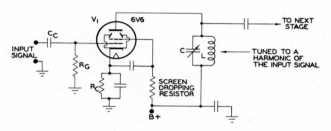

Fig. 14.12. A frequency multiplier. The main grid bias is developed by R_g; R_c is merely for protective bias.

swing of 4.1667 kc must be obtained for the loudest audio signal. Thus, ±4.167 kc, increased 18 times, gives the maximum ±75 kc permitted by the F.C.C.

A frequency multiplier is essentially nothing more than an ordinary amplifier with the output circuit tuned to a harmonic of the input frequency. In the circuit of Fig. 14.12, the resonant tank, L and C in the output of V_1, would be tuned to three times the input frequency. Any voltage that is developed across the tank and transferred to the next stage would be the third harmonic voltage. All other harmonics in the circuit would develop very little voltage across the tank impedance and only a negligible amount would reach the following stage. By successively choosing the desired harmonic, we can raise the original oscillator frequency to any desired value.

Grid-Leak Bias and Distortion.   In order to appreciate fully the operation of a frequency multiplier and its function in the F-M transmitter, there are several facts we must know. First, in any class C amplifier, such as we find in transmitters, the large grid-leak bias acting at the input of the tube produces a distorted wave in the plate circuit. Grid-leak bias is actually self-bias, where the amount of voltage developed across the grid-leak resistor, R_g, is directly dependent upon the strength of the incoming signal.

Initially, when no input voltage is applied, no bias is present on the grid. Upon the application of a signal voltage, the grid is driven positive on the positive half cycles and current flows in the grid circuit. The coupling condenser becomes charged. During the negative portions of the signal the condenser discharges, tend-

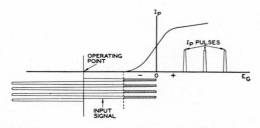

Fig. 14.13. The operating characteristics of a frequency multiplier. Only the shaded portion of the input signal is effective in producing plate current.

ing to maintain a voltage across R_g with the polarity as shown. As long as the strength of the incoming voltage is constant, the bias will keep the tube fixed at one operating point.

The amount of bias voltage developed across R_g will depend upon the size of this resistor (for any one value of input signal). In practice, the resistor is chosen to give a bias equal to approximately 2 or 3 times the cut-off voltage of the tube. If the latter voltage is given as 15 volts by the manufacturer, then the grid-leak bias will be between 30 and 45 volts. Its position is indicated in Fig. 14.13. With this as the operating point, the incoming voltage will vary above and below this value. At the positive peaks, the grid will be driven sufficiently positive to maintain the bias voltage across R_g fixed.

Plate current flows only for that portion of the input voltage when the total grid voltage is more positive than the plate-current cut-off value.   This region is shown shaded in Fig. 14.13.   The plate current, during those moments when it is permitted to flow, will do so in pulses.

The fact that the plate-current form, produced as a result of the action of the grid bias, is not an exact duplicate of the input signal immediately indicates that distortion has been introduced. It can be demonstrated mathematically that when a wave is dis-

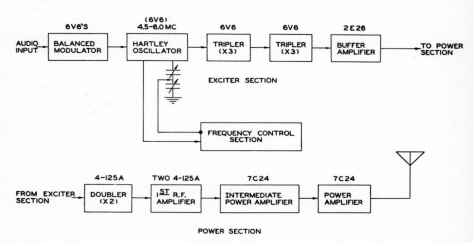

FIG. 14.14.   The outline of a modern RCA F-M transmitter.   The notation above each block designates the tubes used in that stage.

torted, odd and even harmonics of that wave are produced.   If the plate tank circuit is tuned to one of these harmonic frequencies, then the major portion of the voltage developed across the coil will be at this harmonic.   Transfer to a succeeding stage, also tuned to the same harmonic, will practically eliminate all the other frequencies.   Thus, in Fig. 14.12, tuning L and C to the third harmonic of the input will produce this component across the circuit.

It will be found that multiplication seldom exceeds the third harmonic in any one stage.   The reason is simply due to the fact that in any frequency multiplier, the voltage that can be obtained through the use of a harmonic is proportionately lower than if we used the fundamental.   For the third harmonic, the output voltage developed across L and C would be usually less than ½ of the fundamental if L and C were tuned to the fundamental frequency. Higher harmonics will give progressively less output.

Although the pulses that are fed into L and C do not resemble sine waves, the fly-wheel action of the tank redevelops them. The pulses keep the current circulating between the condenser and the coil and this action forms the necessary sine waves at whichever frequency the circuit is tuned.

The plate tank circuit of the frequency multiplier is tuned broadly enough to include any frequency variations of the carrier about its resting point. Thus, if the input frequency to the first tripler is 5 mc and is accompanied by a ±4.167-kc variation due to audio modulation, it will vary between the limits of 5.004167 mc and 4.995833 mc (4.167 kc has been changed to 0.004167 mc and added and subtracted from 5 mc). At each point in this range, the third harmonic will be produced and developed across the tank circuit. Hence, the output will fluctuate between 15.012501 mc and 14.987499 mc. This can be expressed as 15 mc ± 12.501 kc. Thus we see that both the carrier and the sidebands each receive the same frequency multiplication.

With one more tripler, the foregoing values would be converted to 45 mc ± 37.503 kc. Add a doubler, and we obtain the desired frequency, 90 mc, with ±75-kc deviation.

After these multipliers, power amplifiers are added in sufficient number until the desired output power is attained.

RCA F-M Transmitter. The present RCA F-M transmitter incorporates many of the preceding circuits and ideas in its design. It uses a slightly modified pair of push-pull modulators, a Hartley oscillator, two triplers, a buffer amplifier, a doubler, and several power amplifiers. A block diagram is shown in Fig. 14.14, and the corresponding schematic appears in Fig. 14.15.

The push-pull modulators differ from the previous push-pull modulator in that the grids receive their energy from the oscillator tank circuit by means of a link-coupling arrangement. Previously, it will be remembered, we obtained the R.F. voltage for each grid by means of a resistance-capacitance circuit coupled directly to the oscillator tank. Through this R-C arrangement, each grid received voltages that made them lead or lag the oscillator tank current by

90°.   If the plate current of one modulator tube was 90° leading, the current of the other tube was 90° lagging.

In the RCA transmitter, the R.F. voltage from the oscillator is transferred to L_1 inductively. The voltage developed across L_1 produces a current flow in the link-coupling circuit, establishing a similar voltage across L_2 at the other end.   The voltage from L_2 is then coupled to L_3 and L_4 inductively.

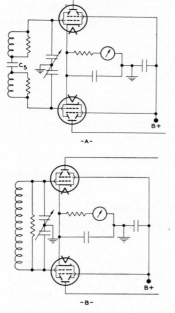

FIG. 14.16.   (A) R.F. input circuit of the RCA modulator. (B) An equivalent diagram.

If we examine the grid circuit of the two modulator tubes, we note that they form essentially a push-pull circuit. The two inner ends of L_3 and L_4 are placed at the same R.F. potential by means of C_5. C_5 offers only slight opposition to R.F. currents and thus we may consider L_3 and L_4 as being directly connected. C_3 and C_4 resonate L_3 and L_4 to the same frequency as the oscillator tank circuit.   A simplified illustration demonstrating the direct resemblance of this arrangement to a push-pull circuit is shown in Fig. 14.16. Since the grids are so connected, each receives R.F. voltages that are 180° out of phase with respect to each other. If one grid is, at one instant, positive, the other grid is negative.

To obtain the required reactance from each modulator, the designers have arranged the link-coupling network, L_1 and L_2, in conjunction with the other coils — L, L_3, and L_4 — so that the R.F. voltage transferred from the oscillator is shifted 90°.   Thus, the voltage is first shifted 90° and then applied to L_3 and L_4 to make each grid 180° out of phase with each other. As a result of this arrangement, each tube presents to the oscillator tank a different form of reactance.   However, with no audio input signal at V_1 and V_2, the push-pull connection of each modulator acts to cancel the reactance produced by each tube at the oscillator tank.

The audio voltage is applied through transformer T_1 to each grid of the modulator.   Since the grids are connected to opposite ends of the transformer, the audio voltage will be applied 180° out of phase to each grid.   Application of the modulating voltage will upset the balance of V_1 and V_2, causing one tube to draw more current and the other tube less current.   Across the oscillator tank circuit, the result is the same as if we had varied the reactance (inductive or capacitive), thereby producing a frequency shift. The two tubes, in push-pull, produce a greater frequency shift than if one tube alone had been used in the modulator.

From $L,$ the frequency variations are fed to V_4, the first tripler, by means of capacitive coupling through C_6.   The output coil of V_4 is tuned to the third harmonic of the input or oscillator frequency.   This, as we have already seen, will triple the input frequency and also the *frequency variation*, which is the F-M. V_5 is another tripler, whereas V_6 is merely an isolating or buffer amplifier.   The layout, to this point, represents the exciter unit and is completely contained within one cabinet (see Fig. 14.17).   Included also is a spare exciter assembly for emergency use, a power supply and a frequency control unit.

As a preventative measure, V_4 and V_5 have cathode resistors. These are used to protect the tubes in case something should cause the oscillator to cease operating.   The two tubes, in ordinary operation, obtain practically their full bias from the grid-leak input resistors, R_1 and R_2.   However, if the oscillator should fail, the voltages across R_1 and R_2 drop to zero.   If no other protection existed for the tubes, the zero-biased grids would permit sufficient current to flow and actually cause the plates to become red hot.   By inserting cathode resistors, a bias is automatically developed and serves to prevent excessive heating at the plate.

The cathode resistor of V_6 is actually used for operative bias, since this amplifier, being a buffer amplifier, is operated class A. V_4 and V_5 are biased for class C operation.

The center frequency, at the output of V_6, is somewhere between 44 and 54 mc.   This is now doubled to the final operating frequency by the first stage of the second unit of the transmitter (V_7 is the doubler, using an Eimac 4-125A tube).   Beyond this there are two tubes in parallel, V_8 and V_9, functioning as the first or intermediate power amplifiers. V_{10} (an RCA-7C24 tube) is the first or intermediate power amplifier and V_{11}, another RCA-7C24 tube, is the final power amplifier. From the latter stage, the signal is fed to the antenna system. The complete assembly of tubes will

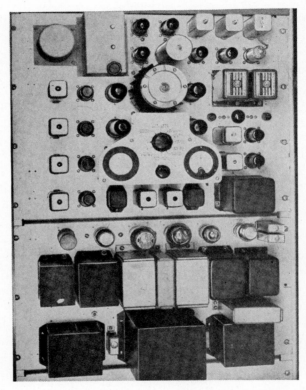

Fig. 14.17. A view of the exciter unit used in R.C.A. F-M transmitter.

produce a 3-kw signal. By removing the last RCA-7C24 tube and attaching the antenna directly to the output of the intermediate power amplifier, we reduce the output to 1 kw. This arrangement makes for greater flexibility since it permits a station using the lower-powered circuit to increase its output merely by the addition of one stage.

Grounded-grid Amplifiers. A close inspection of V_{10} and V_{11} will reveal that they are not connected as conventional amplifiers

(Fig. 14.18A) but as grounded-grid amplifiers (Fig. 14.18B). In a conventional amplifier, the input signal is fed to the grid of the tube, with the cathode kept at a fixed potential. In a grounded-grid amplifier, the grid is connected directly to ground (through condenser C_1), while the cathode receives the incoming signal. As far as the current flow through the tube is concerned, it makes no difference whether the grid is kept at zero R.F. potential and the cathode voltage is varied, or the cathode is placed at R.F. ground potential and the grid is varied. Tube current is, at all times, subject to the voltage difference between the grid and cathode.

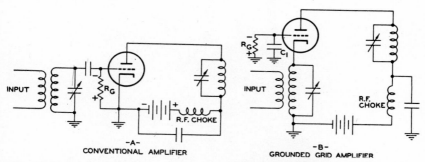

FIG. 14.18. A comparison between conventional and grounded grid amplifiers.

The distinct advantage of a grounded-grid amplifier arises from its excellent operation at high frequencies. By placing the grid at R.F. ground potential, we effectively shield the output and input circuits from each other and thereby minimize undesired feedback and oscillations. In the conventional amplifier, this can only be accomplished by special neutralizing precautions. It is only when the power of a grounded-grid amplifier is above 10 kw that any special neutralizing steps are required.

A disadvantage of a grounded-grid amplifier is the necessity for more driving power than we require with the usual amplifier. The reason for the increase is due to the fact that the input power is being applied to the cathode coil (or resistor), and the cathode of a tube is common to both input and output (or grid and plate) circuits. Hence part of the applied input power is used to drive the grid and part appears in the plate circuit. This differs from the conventional amplifier where all of the input power is effective at the grid. To make up for that portion of the input power which goes directly to the output circuit and therefore is not effective in driving the tube, a greater amount of input or driving power must be fed to a grounded-grid amplifier.

Fig. 14.19.   A recently developed tube (RCA-7C24) designed especially for grounded-grid operation.

Note carefully that the excess power required by the grounded-grid amplifier is not lost but combines in phase in the output circuit with the power developed by that portion of the input signal effective at the grid of the tube.   The greater amount of driving power sometimes works a hardship on the preceding amplifiers, since now they must be designed to provide more power.

The RCA-7C24 tube, shown in Fig. 14.19, is designed especially for use in high frequency, grounded-grid amplifiers.   It possesses a grid structure that presents a maximum of shielding between plate and filament electrodes. This results in a low plate-to-filament capacitance. The grid terminal is a disk-seal brought out through the glass completely around the tube. When used in connection with an external shield, the input and output circuits of the stage are well isolated from each other.

Frequency-Control Circuits. The F.C.C. specifies that each F-M broadcast station must be maintained within 2 kc of the assigned center frequency. To insure that this condition is maintained at all times, it has become customary to employ automatic frequency control. This is especially necessary in transmitters that employ reactance-tube modulators because in these units the main oscillator is usually some form of Hartley oscillator. Unless definite precautions are taken, frequency drift will occur because of the effect of heat, humidity, and aging of tubes and circuit components. With a properly designed,

FIG. 14.20. Two views of the frequency-determining capacitor mounted on the shaft of the motor. An oil dampening unit mounted on the front end of the motor shaft, prevents overshooting. (Courtesy of RCA.)

frequency-correcting network, the carrier will be confined to the regulation limits at all times.

In recent reactance-tube transmitters, two general types of frequency-control systems have been used. One utilizes motor control, in which a 2-phase motor is attached to one of the oscillator tuning condensers (see Fig. 14.20). Any center-frequency drifting causes the motor to rotate the tuning condenser in a direction to counteract the drift. In the second control system, a discriminator produces a voltage that is fed to the reactance tubes. By varying the grid-bias voltage of the reactance tube, we can also vary its effect on the oscillator and thereby produce a shift in frequency sufficient to recenter the wandering oscillator. Each system is explained in the following paragraphs.

Motor Control. In the RCA transmitter shown in Fig. 14.15, condensers C_1 and C_2 are motor-controlled. The condensers are connected across the oscillator tuning coil L and any rotation of C_1 and C_2 will result in a change in frequency. A block diagram of the frequency correction network and its place in the transmitter is shown in Fig. 14.21. A portion of the oscillator voltage is fed to

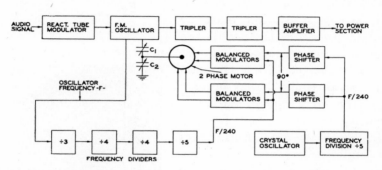

FIG. 14.21. An outline illustrating the several circuits of the frequency control section.

a series of frequency-divider stages, where a total frequency division of 240 times occurs. Thus, with the main oscillator frequency somewhere between 4.5 and 6.0 mc, the output of the final frequency divider stage will decrease to the 18.75–25 kc range. (It should be understood that, for any one station, the main oscillator has but one frequency. However, to cover the entire F-M band, 88 to 108 mc, it is necessary to provide the values of 4.5 to 6.0 mc for the oscillator.) The divider output is then fed to a balanced modulator.

The other input to the modulators is obtained from a highly accurate crystal oscillator. The crystal oscillator frequency is lowered by ⅕, at which value it will be exactly 1/240th of the correct main oscillator frequency. This frequency is then compared in the balanced modulator with the frequency obtained from the main oscillator. If any difference exists, the motor is actuated and the tuning condensers rotated until the oscillator is again centered at its assigned spot.

Since the motor control circuits are concerned only with any drifting of the carrier from its assigned center frequency, the signal they receive should consist solely of the carrier and none of its sidebands, since these sidebands have frequencies different from that of the carrier. In an A-M transmitter, the carrier is generated separately and feeding some of this energy to a frequency control system is easily achieved. But in reactance-tube transmitters, the point where the signal is generated is also the place where it is modulated, and it is impossible to obtain a sample of the unmodulated carrier.

The solution to this problem lies in the frequency divider networks. Whenever an F-M signal is passed through a frequency divider, not only is the carrier frequency reduced, but the spread of the sidebands about the carrier is also reduced. Thus, suppose an F-M signal has a center frequency of 5.0 mc with a spread of 8 kc, and this is fed to a divider where a division of 2 occurs. At the output, the signal will have a center frequency of 2.5 mc and a spread of only 4 kc. By this process, then, we have in effect concentrated the signal power closer to the carrier. With sufficient frequency division we can obtain a carrier having a substantially constant amplitude.

In the RCA F-M transmitter, a small portion of the modulated carrier at the master oscillator is divided by a factor of 240 before it is applied to the motor control circuits. If the F-M signal at the oscillator is 5.0 mc with a spread of 8 kc, then at the output of the frequency-divider chain, it is approximately 20.8 kc with a spread of 33 cycles. With a maximum frequency deviation limited to only 33 cycles, no less than 93 per cent of the power in the signal is concentrated in the carrier, and the motor control circuits receive a substantially constant carrier signal. Under these conditions, only carrier frequency drift will be instrumental in actuating the motor.

This is briefly the operation of the system. Before we consider the complete schematic, it would be advisable to review the operation of several of the units in order to gain a better appreciation of their function in this particular network.

Frequency Division. The frequency divider, shown in Fig. 14.22, is a combination mixer and oscillator. As an indication of how it functions as a frequency divider, consider the oscillator section first.   The oscillator, consisting of L_1 and C_1 in the plate circuit and L_2 in the grid circuit, is tuned to the desired output frequency. L_1 and C_1 determine the fundamental frequency at which the circuit will oscillate. As is usual in such oscillators, the tube operates on the nonlinear portion of its characteristic curve and the plate current contains

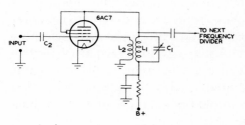

Fig. 14.22.   A frequency divider similar to those used in the RCA F-M transmitter.

many harmonics.   Although harmonics are generally not desirable, their presence is required here for the mixing action.

The frequency to be divided is fed to the oscillator through condenser C_2.   Let us say that its value is 6.0 mc.   An output one-fourth of this is desired, so the oscillator functions at 1.5 mc.   At the tube the 6.0 mc will mix with either the third harmonic (4.5 mc) or the fifth harmonic (7.5 mc) of the oscillator to produce a difference frequency of 1.5 mc.   Because of the harmonic relationship between the incoming signal and the oscillator voltage, a lock-in will occur, with the incoming signal acting to keep the oscillator at some sub-harmonic value.   If the incoming frequency should shift, then the lock-in will still remain, and the oscillator frequency will be shifted or " dragged along."   However, the incoming signal will be able to maintain control only within certain limits.   If these are exceeded, the oscillator breaks loose and returns to its natural frequency.   However, in this circuit, the frequency shift is seldom so great that the lock-in is broken.   The oscillator circuit is designed to enable it to follow the incoming frequency over fairly wide limits.

To recapitulate, the oscillator in the frequency divider is set at a sub-harmonic of the correct incoming frequency.   Then one of the harmonics of the oscillator mixes with the incoming signal to produce a difference frequency which is equal to the fundamental oscillator frequency.   Because of the harmonic relationship of the incoming signal and the oscillator frequency, the two lock-in.   Once locked-in, any small shift in the signal will produce a shift in the oscillator and thus indicate to the following frequency dividers that the main F-M oscillator is off the center-frequency.

Returning to the block diagram of Fig. 14.21, we see that the system contains four frequency dividers. Multiplying each of the frequency divisions together, we obtain a total of $3 \times 4 \times 4 \times 5 = 240$. Thus, if the main oscillator is at a frequency of 6.0 mc, the output of the final divider is 6.0 mc/240 mc or 0.025 mc or 25 kc. The reason we require this much frequency division is due to the 2-phase motor, as we shall presently see.

The overall purpose of the frequency divider is to bring to the balanced modulators immediate indication of any change in the main oscillator frequency. However, the sole fact that the frequency has shifted is not significant unless it is compared with a standard frequency, one that remains fixed. For this we include the crystal oscillator. After the output of the crystal oscillator is decreased by one-fifth, its frequency has the same value that the main oscillator frequency should possess after it had been divided 240 times. Hence, if the main oscillator frequency should shift even the slightest amount, this becomes immediately apparent by comparison. The comparison of the two frequencies takes place in the balanced modulator. Disregard, for the moment, the phase-shifting network between the crystal oscillator and the balanced modulator.

Balanced Modulators. In a balanced modulator we can feed two signals into the grids of the tubes and obtain only one of the input signals plus the sum and difference frequencies of the two signals at the output. The other input frequency does not appear at the output. In the circuit of Fig. 14.23, one signal is applied to terminals A and B, the other signal to terminals C and D, and the sum and difference frequencies appear across points E and F. It is customary to apply the higher frequency at terminals C and D and the lower frequency at A and B. However, in this case, both incoming signals have approximately the same frequency, and either set of terminals may be used.

The reason the signal at terminals C and D does not appear across E and F is due to its method of application. Both tubes, V_1 and V_2, are connected in push-pull, which means that their respective plate currents flow through the output coil or transformer in opposite directions. For V_1, the plate current flows down through its winding, whereas for V_2 the flow is up through the coil to the center point.   As long as the currents are equal, their opposite effect will cancel.

At the input circuit, any voltage across terminals C and D will be applied to both grids in like measure.   The voltage will drive both tubes positive or negative at the same time.   Both plate currents will thus be in phase, and the result is a complete cancellation of the magnetic effects in the output.

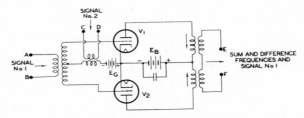

Fig. 14.23.   A balanced modulator.

When we apply another signal at terminals A and B, we upset the equal voltages that the signal at C and D is applying to the grids.   When A is positive, B is negative and these voltages, added to those already existing on the grids due to the signal at C and D, produce an unbalance.   First, one tube will conduct more current, then the other.   The result of this mixing of frequencies in V_1 and V_2 is the production of the sum and difference frequencies across terminals E, F.   We also find in the output, the frequency of the signal that is applied to terminals A, B.

Now let us see how these facts are useful in the F-M transmitter. Two balanced modulators are needed, the output of each connected to the windings of the 2-phase motor. The output from the fourth frequency divider (bringing the signal from the main oscillator) is applied to each balanced modulator. We could, for example, feed this signal into terminals, A, B of each modulator. The output of the frequency divider following the crystal oscillator is also fed to each modulator, say terminals C, D. However, there is introduced (through the phase-shift network) a phase difference between the two crystal oscillator voltages of 90°. The need for this is due to the use of a 2-phase motor. In order for the motor to rotate, the two currents flowing in its windings must differ by 90° — hence the phase-shift network.

In the modulators, the two signals mix, producing sum and difference frequencies. Of particular interest in this instance are the difference frequencies. When these currents flow through the two windings of the 2-phase motor, a torque is produced and the motor rotates the attached condensers. If both signals have the same frequency, the difference frequency is zero, or d-c. Since the motor requires alternating currents, no torque is produced and no rotation occurs. When signals entering the modulators have identical frequencies, the main oscillator is obviously at the proper operating point.

It may be wondered why the motor does not respond to the sum frequencies, or the frequency of the signal that is applied across terminals A, B. These are also present in the output. Sum frequencies are produced as long as two signals are present, whereas difference frequencies occur only when the two signals differ in frequency. The reason the motor responds only to difference frequencies is due to its operational characteristics. It will not respond to frequencies beyond 1000 cycles. Since either input signal or the sum frequencies (produced through the mixing of the signals) are always above 1000 cycles, they cause no motor rotation.

The schematic diagram of the control system is shown in Fig. 14.15. Included with the crystal oscillator is a heating unit to maintain a constant temperature. The power supply is presented in block form.

Discriminator Control. We have studied the operation of a motor-control network. Now, let us see how control of the main oscillator center frequency may be obtained with a discriminator. In Fig. 14.11, a block diagram illustrates the essential features of the system. As before, a crystal oscillator is the standard against which the main oscillator frequency is compared. As soon as deviations occur in the oscillator center frequency, an output (d-c) voltage is obtained from the discriminator. If the oscillator frequency drifts to a higher value, the output voltage of the discriminator is of one polarity. Should the frequency drift below its normal value, then the voltage from the discriminator reverses. The application of the d-c voltage from the discriminator to the control grid of the reactance tube controls the effect of the reactance tube on the main oscillator and, through this, the center frequency. The corrective voltage applied to the reactance tube is always of such polarity (either positive or negative) as to bring the main oscillator center frequency back to its assigned position.

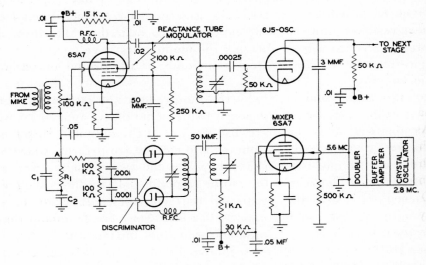

FIG. 14.24.   A discriminator frequency-stabilization circuit.

A frequency stabilization circuit is shown in Fig. 14.24. The resonant frequency of the crystal oscillator is at 2.8 mc. This voltage is passed through a buffer amplifier and then doubled in the frequency multiplier to 5.6 mc. From the output of the doubler, the 5.6-mc voltage is applied to grid 3 of a 6SA7 tube, connected as a mixer.

The 5.0-mc oscillator voltage is picked off by means of a small condenser and brought to grid 1 of the 6SA7. The two signals beat together in the tube, forming sum- and difference-frequency voltages across the plate tank circuit. Of particular interest is the difference frequency, 600 kc, since this is the center resonant point of the following discriminator. So long as this frequency is the difference frequency produced in the mixer, the output voltage from the discriminator is zero. The reason was shown previously in Chapter 9.

However, when a change occurs in the main oscillator frequency, the mixing will produce some other difference value. Consequently, an output voltage will appear at point *A*. If the input frequency to the discriminator is above 600 kc, the output voltage will be of one polarity. If it is below, the polarity will be opposite. From point *A* the voltage is fed to the grid of the reactance tube. At the tube it affects the plate-current flow and, with this, the shift in oscillator frequency caused by the modulator connection.

The drift of an oscillator is seldom a rapid or sudden affair. Rather, the shift is gradual. To produce a large controlling bias voltage from point *A*, for only small changes in frequency, the bandwidth response of the discriminator is made fairly narrow. As the selectivity of the discriminator tuning circuit becomes sharper, more output voltage is obtained for any given frequency shift. With additional grid bias, the reactance modulator and the entire system become very sensitive to slight frequency changes. Of course, if the main oscillator frequency should suddenly shift by a considerable amount, we would find that a narrow-band discriminator is useless. However, this almost never occurs.

There is one precaution that must be observed when using this network. The signal fed from the oscillator to grid 1 of the mixer contains frequency modulation. If the correcting voltage developed at the output of the discriminator is permitted to follow these frequency variations, all the frequency modulation produced by the audio signal would be nullified. What we desire to prevent are changes in the main oscillator frequency due to uncontrolled causes, such as heat, humidity or aging of the tubes. We do not want to prevent frequency shifting due to applied audio voltages. The oscillator must be kept at its proper resting point, or central frequency. From this position it will swing back and forth under the influence of the audio modulation.

A low-pass filter is used to eliminate all the frequency modulation from the correcting voltage obtained at the output of the discriminator. In Fig. 14.24, this filter consists of C_1, R_1, and C_2. It cuts off at approximately 10 cycles and effectively by-passes or eliminates all audio variations (caused by the reactance tube in modulating the oscillator) and permits only the very slow frequency drifts of the oscillator to be effective. The center frequency of the oscillator drifts very slowly, well within 10 cps.

Unlike the RCA motor control circuits, the signal fed from the master oscillator to the discriminator is not passed through a frequency-divider chain. Hence, most of the energy is not concentrated in the carrier but varies with the modulation between the carrier and the sidebands.

PROBLEMS

1. What two general methods are employed to develop F-M signals?

2. What is a reactance tube? Does this differ in physical characteristics from any other tube? Explain.

3. Draw the schematic circuit for a simple reactance-tube modulator.

4. Explain the operation of the modulator drawn in Question 3.

5. A simple series circuit containing a resistor and capacitor is connected to an R.F. generator. When will the voltage developed across the resistor be nearly in phase with the applied R.F. voltage? When will this resistor voltage be almost 90° out of phase with the R.F. voltage?

6. To the circuit of a Hartley oscillator add a vacuum tube which appears as a pure resistor to the oscillator tank circuit.

7. Explain what causes a tube to function as a resistor, capacitor, or inductor.

8. How does an applied audio voltage cause the reactance tube to alter the frequency of an oscillator?

9. What are the advantages of a balanced reactance-tube modulator?

10. Explain briefly the difference between balanced and single-ended reactance-tube modulators.

11. Is the F-M signal fully developed at the output of the modulated oscillator? Explain.

12. The signal obtained from the output of an oscillator had a frequency of 5.6 mc with an F-M swing of 4.0 kc. How could we obtain a carrier frequency of 100.8 mc? How much frequency swing would we produce in raising the original 5.6 mc to 100.8 mc?

13. What precautions can be observed to insure that the frequency of a reactance-tube modulated oscillator is kept on-frequency?

14. Explain the operation of a frequency multiplier.

15. What advantages do grounded-grid amplifiers possess?

16. Draw the circuit of a grounded-grid amplifier. Could such a unit be employed in an F-M receiver? Explain.

17. Explain briefly the operation of the frequency-control circuit in the RCA F-M transmitter. Illustrate by means of a block diagram.

18. How does a frequency divider function? What is its purpose in the RCA F-M transmitter?

19. Contrast a discriminator frequency control network with a motor-controlled circuit.

20. Draw the block diagram of a discriminator frequency-control network and explain how it functions.

21. Why are grounded-grid amplifiers used only in high-frequency circuits? Could they be used in standard broadcast A-M receivers? Explain.

22. Draw the block diagram of a complete F-M transmitter containing the following components.

     1. Reactance-tube modulator.

     2. A 3-stage audio-amplifier system.

     3. Two triplers and a doubler.

     4. An intermediate power amplifier.

     5. A power amplifier.

     6. A discriminator type of frequency control circuit.

CHAPTER 15

COMMERCIAL F-M TRANSMITTERS

(PART 2)

WESTINGHOUSE DIRECT F-M TRANSMITTER

The Westinghouse F-M Transmitter uses the direct method of achieving frequency modulation but employs a reactance modulator which differs substantially from the circuits shown in Chapter 14. A block diagram of the transmitter, without the frequency stabiliz-

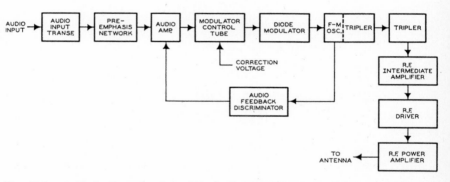

FIG. 15.1. A block diagram of the Westinghouse F-M Transmitter. The frequency stabilization system, which supplies the above correction voltage, is not shown.

ing circuit, is shown in Fig. 15.1. The audio circuits, to the point where their signal is applied to the modulator control tube, are conventional. An audio feedback discriminator, which is peculiar to this circuit, tends to stabilize the audio stages by applying a small amount of inverse feedback voltage. The operation of this circuit is simple and will be analyzed after the operation of the modulating system has been investigated.

The oscillator, using a 1614 beam-power tetrode, is connected as an electron-coupled Colpitts oscillator and tripler circuit. (See

Fig. 15.2.)   The grid circuit generates a frequency ⅑ that of the transmitted carrier frequency.   This frequency is tripled in the plate circuit of the oscillator tube to ⅓ the output frequency.   The grid circuit of V_4 is tuned by the grid inductance, L_2, by the coarse and fine variable condensers, C_1 and C_2, and by the capacitive reactance of the modulator tube, V_3.   In the plate circuit, L_5 in conjunction with L_6 forms a tuned coupling circuit having a very large

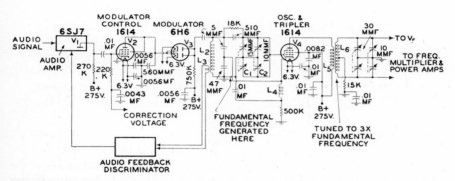

Fig. 15.2.   The modulator and oscillator circuits of the Westinghouse F-M Transmitter.

coefficient of coupling.   Tuning here is accomplished by the grid tuning condensers of the following R.F. tripler stage.   The final frequency multiplication (3 times) is achieved in the plate circuit of the following tube, V_5 (not shown).   The frequency, at this point, is equal to the carrier frequency authorized to that station.

Beyond V_5, intermediate and power amplifiers increase the power of the signal until it has attained the full value at which the station operates.

Modulating Circuits.   The modulator circuit consists of two tubes, a 1614 beam-power tetrode and a 6H6 diode.   The 1614 is connected as a triode and operates as a class A audio frequency amplifier.   The 6H6, with both sections connected in parallel, is placed in series with the plate of the 1614.   Hence the instantaneous current through the diode depends upon the current flowing through the 1614.   Since the 1614 is operating as a class A amplifier, its plate current and that of the diode will always be proportional to the applied audio signal.

The diode, in addition, is connected across the grid inductance of the oscillator. (See Fig. 15.3A.) This means that the inter-electrode capacitance existing between cathode and plate of the diode and the tube's internal plate resistance are also shunted across the oscillator tank circuit. (See Fig. 15.3B.) By varying the value of this plate resistance, we change the overall reactance of the network, which, in turn, causes the frequency of the oscillator to

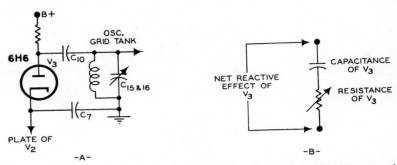

Fig. 15.3. (A) The diode modulator is connected across the grid inductance of the oscillator. (B) Equivalent circuit of diode showing its electrical effect on oscillation tank circuit.

change. Thus, the audio voltage at the grid of V_2, by varying the current flowing through this tube and the diode, will also vary the reactive effect of the diode on the oscillator.

To prevent amplitude modulation as well as frequency modulation, the 6H6 is operated at a point where the change in resistive current through the tube is very small in proportion to the change in capacitive current. A plot of the current through the 6H6 tube is shown in Fig. 15.4. It will be noted that, between the points A and B, a very small change in resistive current, I_R, occurs for a relatively large change in the resistive effect of the tube. At the same time, between these two points, the change in capacitive current, I_c, is quite large. Hence, by operating the diode between points A and B, we secure frequency modulation accompanied by only a negligible amount of amplitude modulation.

Audio Feedback Discriminator. The purpose of the audio feedback discriminator is to provide an inverse feedback voltage for the audio amplifier, V_1, in order to stabilize its operation and to reduce distortion. The discriminator circuit is, in essence, a Foster-Seeley F-M detector. The primary and secondary windings of the discriminator transformer are tuned to the frequency of the master oscillator, V_4. A small coupling link, L_3, transfers the signal from the oscillator grid coil to the discriminator transformer. When the oscillator is unmodulated, the output of the discriminator will be zero. This action, of course, is in accordance with the operation of a discriminator circuit. However, when an audio voltage is being applied to the circuit, the oscillator signal becomes frequency-modulated, and a similar audio voltage is obtained from

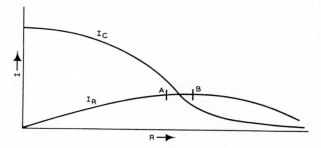

FIG. 15.4. Resistive and reactive current in diode modulator.

the discriminator. This voltage possesses the proper phase to be applied to the grid of V_1 as an inverse feedback voltage.

Frequency Stabilization Circuits. We come now to the frequency stabilization circuits, these being necessary in all reactance-modulated F-M transmitters. In the previous chapter, one system using motor control and one system employing a discriminator were described. The present system represents still another approach, using a series of pulses and a pulse-counting circuit to keep the transmitter on frequency. When the master oscillator drifts to one side of its assigned frequency, the output pulses of the circuit have one polarity; when the drift is to the other side of the assigned frequency, the pulse polarity reverses.

A block diagram of the entire frequency stabilizer section is shown in Fig. 15.5. The master oscillator feeds a portion of its signal to two separate mixers through a buffer amplifier. The same amount of voltage is applied, in phase, to each mixer. At the same time, a crystal oscillator, operating at the exact frequency to which the master oscillator should be set, also feeds its voltage to each of the mixers.   However, the crystal oscillator output must first pass through two resistance-capacitance phase shift networks so designed that the crystal oscillator voltage reaching mixer No. 1 is advanced 45° in phase while the voltage reaching mixer No. 2 is retarded by 45°.   The two voltages, then, are actually 90° out of phase.

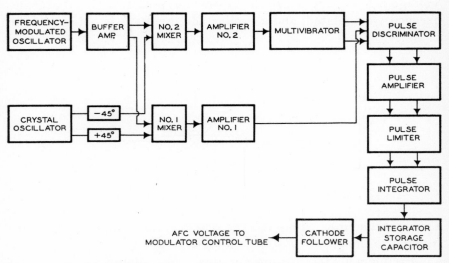

FIG. 15.5.   A block diagram of the frequency stabilization system employed in Westinghouse F-M Transmitters.

Within each mixer, the signals from the crystal and master oscillators mix, and if the two are not equal in frequency, the difference and sum of these frequencies will be generated.   Of interest in this discussion are the difference frequencies since the sum frequencies are by-passed to ground.

Any output frequencies developed in the mixers will be equal, but the phase of the voltage from mixer No. 2 will differ from that of mixer No. 1 by 90° because of the phase difference in the applied crystal oscillator voltages.

Let us examine this latter point in greater detail.   When the master oscillator is operating at its proper center frequency, then its frequency and that of the crystal oscillator will be equal. Under these conditions, no difference frequency voltage will be obtained at the output of either mixer. However, when the two oscillator frequencies do not agree, the following will happen.

1. When the oscillator frequency is higher than the crystal reference frequency, the output of mixer No. 2 will lead the output of mixer No. 1 by 90°.

2. When the oscillator frequency is lower than the crystal reference frequency, the output of mixer No. 2 will lag the output of mixer No. 1 by 90°.

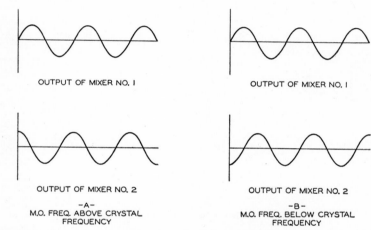

OUTPUT OF MIXER NO. 1   OUTPUT OF MIXER NO. 1

OUTPUT OF MIXER NO. 2   OUTPUT OF MIXER NO. 2

-A-   -B-
M.O. FREQ. ABOVE CRYSTAL   M.O. FREQ. BELOW CRYSTAL
FREQUENCY   FREQUENCY

FIG. 15.6. The phase relationship between the outputs of mixers 1 and 2 when the master oscillator is not operating at its assigned center frequency.

Fig. 15.6 illustrates these phase relationships, with the output of mixer No. 1 kept constant while the output of mixer No. 2 lags or leads by 90°. During modulation of the master oscillator, the applied audio-modulating voltage will swing the oscillator frequency above and below its operating point. This means that during the positive half of an audio frequency cycle, when the carrier shifts (in this circuit) in the low frequency direction, the output of mixer No. 1 will lead the voltage output of No. 2. During the negative half of the audio cycle, the output of mixer No. 1 will lag the output of mixer No. 2. If the center operating frequency of the master oscillator is properly set, no correction voltage will be developed by the frequency stabilization network. However, if the master oscillator is not properly centered and has instead drifted to one side, then a difference frequency will appear in the mixer plate circuits even when no audio voltage is being applied to the circuit. When, now, an audio voltage is applied, the outputs of the mixers will not lead and lag for an equal length of time as they did when the master oscillator was on frequency. This will

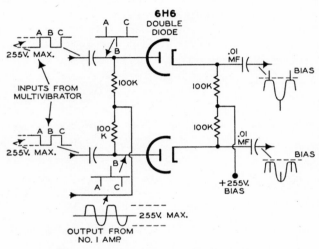

Fig. 15.7. The pulse discriminator circuit.

result in a correction voltage being developed by the stabilization system which will act to return the oscillator to its proper center frequency.

The output of each mixer is fed to a separate amplifier. The output of mixer No. 1 is fed to amplifier No. 1. This tube is biased practically to cut-off and acts to square off the applied sine wave, giving it the shape shown in Fig. 15.7. This wave is then applied to the center of the following pulse discriminator.

The output of mixer No. 2 is passed through amplifier No. 2 and then used to trigger a multivibrator. Although it is beyond the scope of this text to go into the operation of multivibrators, it can be said that this circuit, containing two tubes, transforms the sine-wave output of amplifier No. 2 into a series of square waves.

These square waves are then passed through a resistance-capacitance network which converts them into a series of positive and negative pulses. It is these pulses which are received by the same pulse discriminator to which the amplified output of mixer No. 1 is applied.

Note that the pulse discriminator receives equal and oppositely phased pulses from the multivibrator. This is required because of the manner in which these voltages are applied to the pulse discriminator.

Pulse Discriminator. The purpose of the pulse discriminator is to combine the output of the multivibrator with the amplified output from mixer No. 1 in such a manner that voltage pulses appear on one side of its output circuit when the master oscillator is above its correct center operating frequency and on the other side of the output circuit when the oscillator frequency is below its correct operating frequency. If the master oscillator is on frequency, then during audio modulation, the number of pulses appearing on one side of the discriminator during one half cycle of audio voltage will be exactly equal to the number of pulses appearing on the other side of the discriminator, during the next half cycle. However, this will not be true if the master oscillator has drifted.

The pulse discriminator consists of two diodes, the cathode of each being biased by a positive 255 volts. The maximum possible signal voltage available from amplifier No. 1 is also +255 volts, and therefore the voltage due solely to amplifier No. 1 cannot cause the discriminator to pass current. The same is true of the voltage pulses obtained from the multivibrator. However, when both voltages appear at the same time and add in the positive direction, current will flow. The voltage will add together on one side of the discriminator when one mixer voltage leads, and on the other side of the discriminator when the voltage from the other mixer leads.

Note that, whenever one of the diodes conduct, only the voltage pips riding atop the wave from amplifier No. 1 appear in the output. If the voltages oppose each other, nothing appears at that side of the discriminator.

The positive pulses appearing on either side of the discriminator are kept separate from each other and are passed through separate pulse amplifiers and a pulse limiter. These stages bring all pulses to the same amplitude, removing any variations that might possibly exist between them. The pulses are then applied to a pulse integrator circuit in such fashion that half of the integrator responds to the pulses appearing on the other side of the circuit and half of the integrator responds to the pulses appearing on the other side of the circuit. The currents flowing through the first half of the integrator charge a condenser in one direction while the currents flowing through the second half of the integrator charge the same condenser in the opposite direction. The voltage developed across the condenser is then applied through a cathode follower to the modulator control tube where it can alter the center or resting frequency of the modulated oscillator.

When the master oscillator is on frequency, the average voltage developed across the condenser over one audio cycle is zero. For all other conditions either a positive or negative resultant voltage will appear across the condenser which, when applied to the modulator control circuit, will act to bring the master oscillator back on frequency.

In spite of the apparent complexity of this circuit, it is simple to operate because it requires no adjustments once it has been placed in operation. There are no tuned circuits, frequency dividers, or locked-in oscillators. Most tubes operate from cut-off to saturation, reducing to a minimum the effect of any variation in tube characteristics. Actually, under these conditions, the only positive manner in which a tube can interfere with the proper circuit operation is by complete failure, and generally tubes are removed from the circuit, during periodic inspections, long before this occurs.

THE FEDERAL F-M TRANSMITTER

Still another approach to direct frequency modulation is utilized in the Federal F-M transmitter. This modulator relies upon the fact that the input capacitance of a tube is dependent upon its mutual conductance. The mutual conductance, in turn, will vary as the plate current varies and, going one step farther, this will depend upon the grid voltage. Thus, tying all these facts together, we have a direct connection between the grid voltage of the tube (in this instance, the modulator tube) and the input capacitance of the tube. If, therefore, we apply an audio voltage to the modulator grid, we can cause the input capacitance of the tube to vary at

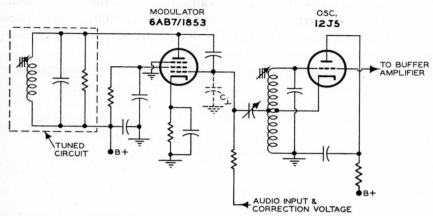

FIG. 15.8A. A simplified diagram of the modulator and oscillator used in the Federal F-M Transmitter.

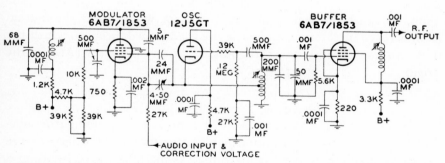

FIG. 15.8B. The complete schematic of the modulator and oscillator. Shown, too, is the buffer which follows the oscillator.

an audio rate. By connecting the tuned circuit of an oscillator across the grid of the modulator tube, we effectively shunt this input capacitance across the oscillator and cause the generated frequency to vary in step with the applied audio voltage. The result, of course, is frequency modulation.

The basic and actual circuits of the Federal modulator and oscillator are shown in Fig. 15.8. The oscillator uses a 12J5GT triode arranged to operate as a conventional Hartley. Connected across part of the oscillator tank inductance is the modulator tube, a 6AB7/1853 pentode. This particular tube was chosen because it possesses a high g_m value and because this g_m can be made to vary linearly with grid voltage. The latter qualification is necessary to insure that the frequency modulation produced is directly proportional to the applied audio-modulating signal.

It can be shown by a rather lengthy mathematical analysis that the input capacitance of an amplifier tube is given by

$$C_i = C_{gk} + C_{gp}(1 + A)$$

where C_i = input capacitance of amplifier tube
C_{gk} = grid-to-cathode capacitance of tube
C_{gp} = grid-to-plate capacitance of tube
A = gain of the tube

For all practical purposes, C_{gk} and C_{gp} are constant and will not change appreciably with tube current. The gain, on the other hand, will vary with tube current because, for a pentode, the gain, A, can be shown to be equal to $g_m Z_L$ where g_m is the mutual conductance of the tube and Z_L is the load impedance into which the tube works. Hence, the foregoing equation can be rewritten in the form

$$C_i = C_{gk} + C_{gp}(1 + g_m Z_L)$$

Note that C_i is not only affected by the g_m of the modulator tube, but also by Z_L, the load impedance of this tube. In order to have C_i affected solely by g_m, the plate load is made resistive by using a resonant circuit, which is resistive at its resonant frequency. A resistor is shunted across the resonant circuit in order to have it tune broadly and therefore remain in resonance over the range of frequencies covered by the oscillator when it is frequency-modulated. With this circuit modification, the equation for the input capacitance of the modulator becomes:

$$C_i = C_{gk} + C_{gp}(1 + g_m R_L)$$

where R_L now represents the load impedance.

Since the 6AB7/1853 modulator tube is a pentode, the C_{gp} of this tube is very small, on the order of .015 mmf, and its effect, in comparison to C_{gk} (which is 15 mmf) would be almost negligible. To overcome this, a 5-mmf capacitance is shunted across the tube, from plate to grid providing sufficient input capacitance variation with changes in audio signal. Another condenser, this one variable, connects the grid of the modulator tube to the tuning inductance of

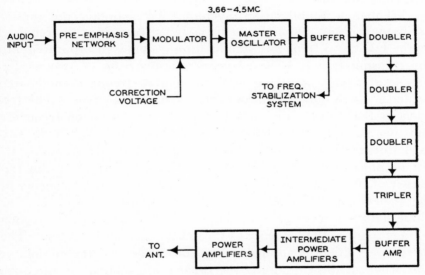

FIG. 15.9. A block diagram of the R.F. stages of the Federal F-M Transmitter.

the oscillator. Its purpose is to provide a fixed frequency swing for a given change in audio voltage. To prevent too much R.F. signal from appearing on the modulator grid, this variable capacitance is connected to a tap on the tank inductance.

The audio voltage is applied to the grid of the modulator tube, and as it varies the current through the tube the g_m will change and with it the value of the input capacitance. The center frequency of the oscillator is set at some value between 3.66 and 4.5 mc, so that with a frequency multiplication of 24 (3 doublers and a tripler) the transmitted carrier frequency ends up between 88 and 108 mc. The 75-kc deviation for 100 per cent modulation is 75/24 or 3.12 kc at the oscillator frequency.

The sequence of low-power stages beyond the modulated oscillator consists of a series of three doublers and a tripler, at which point the signal frequency is between 88 to 108 mc. (See Fig. 15.9.) The signal is now transferred to a buffer and an intermediate power amplifier where its power is increased to 250 watts. Beyond this point, power amplifiers raise the signal power to 1, 3, 10, 20, or 50 kw, depending upon the authorized power for the particular station.

Frequency Stabilization System. To maintain the master oscillator within 2000 cycles of its assigned frequency (as required by the F.C.C.) a frequency stabilization system is incorporated into the transmitter. It is based upon a comparison of two oscillators — a crystal oscillator and the master frequency-modulated oscillator — to obtain a mean center-frequency control. The frequencies from both units are each divided to a common frequency and then combined in a balanced phase detector. When the two oscillators are exactly in step, the two inputs to the detectors are 90° out of phase and the detector output is zero. If the mean frequency of the master oscillator tends to vary from the frequency of the crystal oscillator, the 90° phase relationship varies and the phase detector develops a d-c output which is used as a correction voltage to offset the tendency of the master oscillator to vary. The correction voltage is applied to the control grid of the modulator tube where it directly affects the capacitance shunted by this tube across the master oscillator tuning circuit.

A block diagram of the frequency stabilization system is shown in Fig. 15.10. The frequency output from a buffer immediately following the frequency-modulated oscillator is fed to a frequency-divider chain where the 3.66–4.5 mc frequency is divided 256 times to a frequency between 14.3–17.6 kc. (It is understood that only one center frequency will be obtained from the master oscillator and consequently only one frequency will appear at the end of the divider chain.)

At the same time, a crystal oscillator, operating at some frequency between 114.4 kc and 140.8 kc, has its signal pass through two frequency-divider stages where the initial frequency is lowered by a factor of 8 (2×4). This will produce a frequency between

14.3 and 17.6 kc, or the same frequency that the master oscillator should produce at the end of its frequency chain if it is exactly on frequency. The two divided signals are then passed through separate buffer amplifiers and low-pass filters and applied to the phase detectors.

The reason for the extensive frequency division which must be employed stems from the limitations of the phase detector. The

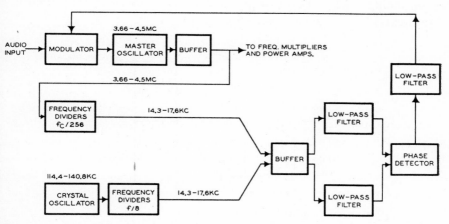

FIG. 15.10.   A block diagram of the frequency stabilization system employed in Federal F-M Transmitters.

crystal oscillator frequency is quite stable in value. However, the instantaneous frequency deviations of the carrier may extend for as much as 75 kc which, in terms of equivalent phase variations, will amount to thousands of degrees. The phase detector, on the other hand, operates only over a range of 180°. Hence, to employ this type of detector, the frequency deviation must be reduced, and this is achieved by the frequency-divider chain. Of course, not only are the frequency deviations reduced, but the carrier frequency as well. In fact, by the time the signal deviations from the master oscillator are reduced by a factor of 256, the instantaneous carrier variation at 100 per cent modulation produces a phase variation of approximately 23° when the modulating frequency is 30 cycles.

There is still another reason for using frequency division, and this concerns the varying amplitude of the center frequency component. It was shown in Chapter 1 that when a carrier is frequency-modulated, power for the sidebands is obtained from the carrier. At times, therefore, the carrier amplitude will decrease to zero, making accurate synchronization impossible. The frequency division, however, acts to concentrate the carrier power into a smaller and smaller bandwidth, resulting at the end of the frequency division chain in a signal of substantially constant amplitude (containing no less than 96 per cent of the power of the unmodulated carrier) for synchronization purposes.

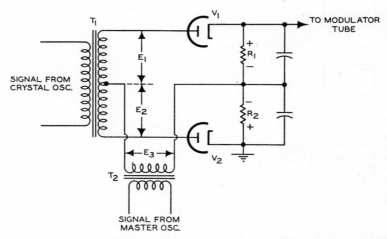

Fig. 15.11.   The phase detector used in the frequency stabilization system of the Federal F-M Transmitter.

Phase Detectors.   The phase detector compares the phase between the frequency-divided signals from the master oscillator and the crystal oscillator.   When the master oscillator is on frequency, the two signals at the detector will possess a phase difference of 90°.   The reason for this particular phase difference is that, under these conditions, the output of the phase detector is zero. The latter condition should occur when the master oscillator center frequency is correct, since at this moment no correction voltage is needed.

To demonstrate that the foregoing conditions exist, consider the circuit of the phase detector shown in Fig. 15.11.   The frequency-divided signal from the crystal oscillator is applied to transformer, T_1. Since the secondary is center-tapped, equal voltages appear across each half of the secondary winding. These are labeled E_1 and E_2. Since the voltage polarities at either end of the secondary windings are opposite to each other with respect to the center tap, E_1 and E_2 can be represented (by vectors) as shown in Fig. 15.12A. E_3 differs from E_1 and E_2 by 90°, as specified above. If now, E_1 and E_3 are added vectorially, and the same is done to E_2 and E_3,

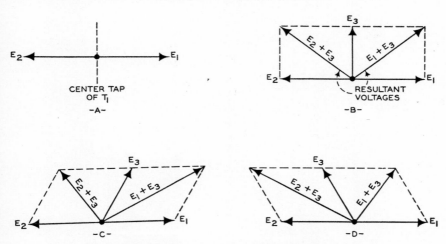

FIG. 15.12. Phase relationships between E_1, E_2, and E_3 of Figure 15.11.

we obtain the resultant vectors or voltages as shown in Fig. 15.12B. $E_1 + E_3$ is applied to tube, V_1, while $E_2 + E_3$ is applied to V_2. Since both resultant vectors are equal in amplitude, the same currents will flow through V_1, V_2, R_1, R_2, producing equal voltage drops across the two load resistors. Their combined voltage, which is fed to the control grid of the modulator tube, is zero because of the back-to-back placement of R_1 and R_2.

Consider, now, what happens when the frequency (and, consequently, the phase) of the master oscillator changes from the desired center value. E_3 will no longer be exactly 90° from E_1 and E_2. When the master oscillator frequency changes in one direction, E_3 will approach closer in phase to E_1 and hence cause $E_1 + E_3$ to be greater than $E_2 + E_3$. (See Fig. 15.12C.) V_1 will now conduct more strongly than V_2, developing a greater voltage drop across R_1 and feeding a positive voltage to the modulator tube. However, when the master oscillator drifts in the other direction, the conditions shown in Fig. 15.12D obtain. Now V_2 will conduct

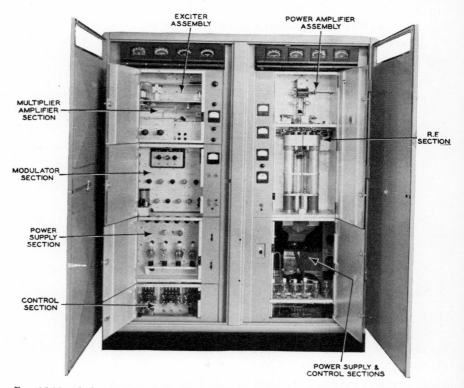

Fig. 15.13. A front view of the Federal F-M Transmitter Model 191-A with access doors open. This is the 1-kw unit. (Courtesy Federal.)

more strongly than V_1, giving rise to a greater voltage across R_2 and feeding a negative voltage to the modulator. In each instance, the modulator will tend to return the master oscillator to its proper center frequency.

A 10-cycle low-pass filter is inserted in the path of the correction voltage from phase detector to modulator. Since the lowest modulating frequency used is 30 cycles, the filter removes any residual modulation that may be left. The only changes that are permitted to reach the modulator are those caused by the drifting of the master oscillator, and these occur at a frequency less than 10 cps.

Fig. 15.13 shows the physical location of each of the transmitter sections.

WESTERN ELECTRIC F-M TRANSMITTER

The Western Electric F-M Transmitter contains circuits which are, in many respects, similar to circuits which have been analyzed in the preceding chapter (14) and in this chapter.   The master

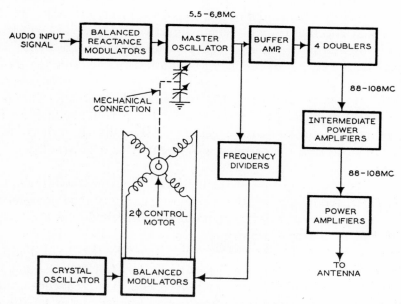

FIG. 15.14.   A block diagram of the Western Electric F-M Transmitter.

oscillator is frequency-modulated by reactance tubes in push-pull to produce a frequency deviation of ±4.7 kc about a mean frequency set somewhere between 5.5 to 6.8 mc.   Beyond the oscillator the signal is passed through a buffer and four doublers which raise its frequency to the assigned value in the 88 to 108 mc band.   Intermediate and power amplifiers then increase the signal power to whatever output power is authorized.   (See Fig. 15.14.)

Stabilization of the center frequency of the master oscillator is achieved by motor control in a manner similar to that employed in the RCA transmitter. A portion of the master oscillator signal (obtained at the buffer) is passed through a series of ten frequency-divider stages until a frequency division of 1024 has been achieved. This signal is then fed to two sets of balanced modulators where its frequency is compared to the frequency generated by a crystal oscillator. The latter is set to operate at precisely $f_c/1024$, where f_c is the correct frequency of the master oscillator. The two voltages are 90° out of phase with each other in order that they may be used to drive a 2-phase motor. When their frequencies are equal, there will be no difference frequency produced by the modulators and the motors will remain inactive. However, when the master oscillator drifts in frequency, a difference frequency will appear at the output of the balanced modulators, causing the motor shaft (with the attached condensers) to rotate. Since these condensers are electrically connected across the master oscillator tuning inductance, any changes in their capacitance will produce an immediate change in oscillator frequency. The direction of rotation is such as to bring the frequency of the master oscillator back into line again.

The precise operation of the modulated master oscillator differs sufficiently from any of the previous reactance-tube systems to warrant a separate brief explanation. The circuit of the modulator and oscillator is shown in Fig. 15.15. The oscillator is a balanced, push-pull arrangement, using two 6J5 triodes. The frequency of the oscillator is established by C_1, C_2, C_3, C_4, and L_1. C_1 and C_2 are hand-operated and serve as coarse frequency adjustments. C_3 and C_4 are connected to the 2-phase motor mentioned previously and provide the vernier adjustments.

Coupled to the oscillator tuning inductance, L_1, is a second coil, L_2, which transfers the voltage from the oscillator to two-points — a buffer amplifier and the grids of the two modulator tubes. For the latter application the voltage from L_2 is first passed through a 90° network. Thus the R.F. voltage which is applied in equal measure to the control grid of each modulator tube is 90° out of phase with the voltage existing across L_1. Let us call this voltage, E_g, and place it as indicated in Fig. 15.16A.

Further examination of the circuit reveals that the plate of one modulator tube, V_1, connects to the top end of L_1 while the plate of the other modulator tube, V_2, connects to the bottom end of L_1.

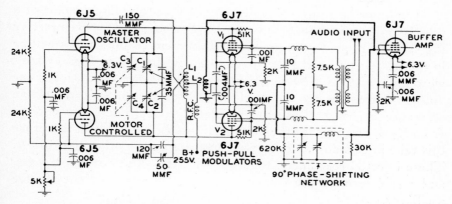

FIG. 15.15. The schematic diagram of the Western Electric modulator and oscillator.

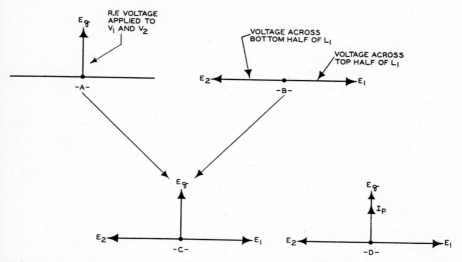

FIG. 15.16. Phase relationships in the modulator and oscillator circuits. (See text.)

Since the center tap of L_1 is effectively at R.F. ground potential, the voltage polarity between the two ends of L_1 will differ by 180°. Hence, the voltage developed across the top half of L_1, E_1, and the voltage developed across the bottom half of L_1, E_2, can be indicated by vectors pointing in opposite directions. (See Fig. 15.16B.) E_g can be added to this illustration as shown in Fig. 15.16C because E_g is 90° out of phase with both these voltages.

We know from previous discussions that the plate current of a tube is in phase with its grid voltage. Since V_1 and V_2 each receive the same R.F. grid voltage, the plate current of both tubes will be in phase. Let us call this current I_p. Adding I_p to Fig. 15.16C, we obtain Fig. 15.16D. We now note that for V_1, I_p leads the voltage across L_1 by 90° and therefore V_1 injects a capacitive reactance across half of the oscillator coil. The plate current from V_2, however, lags the voltage across L_1 by 90°, and therefore this tube injects an inductive reactance across the other half of L_1. These injected reactances, together with the values of L_1, C_1, C_3, and C_4, determine the center operating frequency of the master oscillator.

To produce frequency modulation, an audio voltage is applied in push-pull to the grids of V_1 and V_2. When one grid is driven positive by an audio voltage, the other is driven negative. Consider, for example, that the grid of V_1 is being driven in the positive direction. This causes the plate current through this tube to increase, effectively increasing the capacitance injected by V_1 across L_1. (The reasoning here is exactly the same used in the discussion of reactance modulators at the beginning of Chapter 14.) At the same time, the grid of V_2 is being driven negatively, reducing the plate current flow through V_2. This acts to increase the inductance injected across L_1 by V_2. (Again, see Chapter 14.) Thus, both L and C combine to produce a reduction in oscillator frequency. By following the same line of reasoning when the plate current through V_1 is reduced and the current through V_2 is increased, it will be found that both injected capacitance and inductance decrease, causing the oscillator frequency to rise. Thus, both modulator tubes work in step with each other.

PROBLEMS

1. Draw a block diagram of the Westinghouse F-M transmitter showing all circuits except the frequency stabilizing section.

2. Explain the function of each block in the diagram drawn for question No. 1.

3. How is modulation achieved in the Westinghouse F-M transmitter? Describe in detail, using simple schematic circuits.

4. What is the purpose of the audio feedback discriminator in the Westinghouse circuit?

5. Draw a block diagram of the frequency stabilization system used in this transmitter.

6. Explain briefly the operation of the frequency stabilization system.

7. In what way does the Federal F-M transmitter make use of the fact that the input capacitance of a tube is dependent upon the mutual conductance of that tube? Explain fully.

8. Draw a simple schematic circuit of the Federal modulator and master oscillator.

9. What type of frequency stabilization system does the Federal F-M transmitter employ? Illustrate with a block diagram.

10. Describe the operation of a phase detector.

11. Would it be possible to interchange the frequency stabilization system employed in the Westinghouse transmitter for the unit used in the Federal transmitter? Explain fully, indicating what changes might be required in the stabilization circuit frequencies or components, if any.

12. Explain the operation of the Western Electric Modulator and oscillator circuits. How does this differ from the modulator and oscillator circuits used in the RCA transmitter, Chapter 14?

CHAPTER 16

COMMERCIAL F-M TRANSMITTERS

(Part 3)

F-M Through Phase Modulation. It was previously seen that, indirectly, frequency modulation is produced when a carrier is phase-modulated. Major Armstrong employed this fact when he first produced frequency modulation. Since then, several large manufacturers have designed broadcast transmitters based fundamentally upon the same system. The advantages of the Armstrong system are derived from the control of the transmitter frequency by a crystal oscillator. This control provides a high degree of accuracy and eliminates the need for any frequency-controlling network, such as required in transmitters producing F-M by the reactance-tube method. In the latter system, it will be recalled, it is not possible to use a crystal in the main oscillator because the F-M is produced here. In the Armstrong system, as we shall presently see, the F-M is produced beyond the oscillator. Hence, crystal control is feasible.

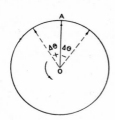

Fig. 16.1. Phase modulator represented by vectors. $\Delta\theta$ is the maximum phase shift of the carrier.

Before we investigate the operation of the Armstrong modulator, let us briefly review the production of F-M by phase shifting or phase modulation. Phase modulation is produced when the carrier wave, as represented by vector OA in Fig. 16.1, is made to shift back and forth as it spins around at its fixed frequency. As a result of this shifting, we obtain the same effect as if the frequency were instantaneously being varied. The variation, superimposed on the regular, fixed frequency of the carrier, represents the frequency modulation.

The indirect F-M produced depends (1) upon the maximum angle that the carrier wave is shifted, as shown in Fig. 16.1, and

(2) on the frequency at which the shifts take place.   Mathematically, we can say that

$$\Delta F \text{ (the frequency swing)} = f \cdot \Delta\theta$$

where $f =$ frequency at which the carrier wobbles or shifts back
              and forth
          $\Delta\theta =$ maximum angular shift of carrier

Through the use of vectors, we can readily demonstrate the formation of phase modulation.   From this, it requires only a simple transition to bridge the gap to the electrical apparatus. However, let us begin with something which is more familiar, namely, amplitude modulation.

A-M Versus P-M.   Fig. 16.2 illustrates the conventional and the vectorial representation of amplitude modulation.   In conventional notation, the low frequency audio signal at A varies slowly from 0° to 360°.   Directly beneath it, in B, we have the unmodulated carrier.   When the audio signal voltage is applied to the carrier, the result is a modulated signal containing all the intelligence (whatever it may be) of the audio voltage.   This is shown in C. In D, we have the vector equivalent of the modulated carrier. Note how the amplitude changes at each point, as a result of the addition or subtraction of the audio voltage.   Its frequency remains untouched, although, as we have seen, the sidebands formed in this process differ in frequency from the carrier by an amount equal to the audio-modulating voltage.

In direct contrast to this, we have the formation of a phase-modulated wave.   At each instant during modulation, we must apply the audio-modulating voltage so that it causes the phase of the carrier to advance or retard.   It is this shifting, first in one direction, then in another, that is illustrated by the vector in Fig. 16.1.   Now, it was noted in amplitude modulation, that the audio voltage increased or decreased the amplitude of the carrier vector. This meant that the audio voltage was being applied either in phase or 180° out of phase with the carrier voltage.

In phase modulation, we do not wish to alter the amplitude of the carrier, merely its relative phase from moment to moment.

This phase change can be accomplished by adding the audio voltage vectorially at right angles to the carrier voltage or, electrically, by combining them 90° out of phase with each other.

Let us examine this critically.   In Fig. 16.3A, the unmodulated carrier and the audio-modulating voltage are shown separately.

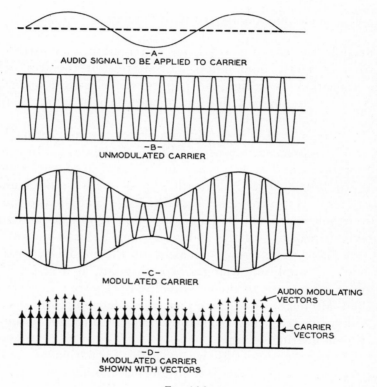

-A-
AUDIO SIGNAL TO BE APPLIED TO CARRIER

-B-
UNMODULATED CARRIER

-C-
MODULATED CARRIER

AUDIO MODULATING VECTORS

CARRIER VECTORS

-D-
MODULATED CARRIER SHOWN WITH VECTORS

Fig. 16.2.

If we combine them 90° out of phase as in Fig. 16.3B, then a resultant vector is formed which is displaced from the original position of the unmodulated carrier by some small angle.   In other words, by combining the two voltages as shown, we have produced a resultant carrier which is displaced slightly from OA.

As the audio signal goes through one complete cycle, its amplitude will vary and, with it, the angular shift of the resultant carrier vector from the position it would occupy if no modulation voltage were present. The variation of the angular shift or displacement at various points in the audio-modulating voltage cycle is shown in Fig. 16.4. Note that the resultant vector (which is the phase-modulated wave) first occupies a position to one side of the unmodulated carrier; then it moves to the other side. In this way it fluctuates back and forth, just as it was pictured in previous discussions. From the wobbling or shifting, an equivalent frequency modulation arises.

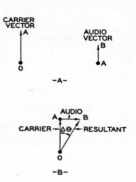

The formation of frequency modulation, or the variation in frequency in the phase-modulated wave, is clearly indicated in Fig. 16.4. The solid sine wave drawn at the center represents the unmodulated carrier. The other wave, drawn with dashes, is the resultant vector (or the modulated wave) at various instants during the application of the audio signal. At the left-hand side of the

FIG. 16.3. (A) The separate audio and carrier vector (*OA* and *OB*) and their vector addition to produce P-M. (B) $\Delta\theta$ is the phase difference between the unmodulated carrier and the modulated resultant.

diagram the resultant wave is shifted behind the unmodulated carrier's position. This means, in effect, a decrease in frequency.

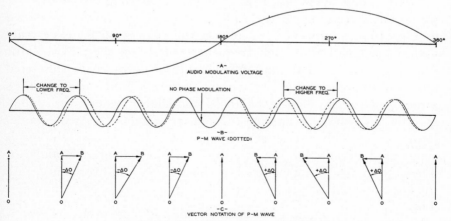

FIG. 16.4. Illustrations of phase modulation.

Therefore, the dotted wave, at this point, spreads out (lower frequency) and the maximum peaks are farther apart than those of the unmodulated carrier (shown by the solid lines).

When, immediately after this, the audio-modulating voltage drops to zero, the dotted line blends into the solid line, indicating both are of the same frequency. With no audio voltage, there is no modulation.

On the positive half of the modulating cycle, the resultant, or phase-modulated carrier, is shifted to the opposite side, indicating that the phase of the carrier has advanced. This is equivalent to a slight increase in frequency, demonstrated by a comparison of the dotted and the solid curves. We note that the modulated carrier

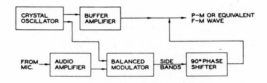

FIG. 16.5. The basic Armstrong system for generating F-M waves.

peaks move closer together, effectively increasing the frequency. Finally, at the zero point (360°), the modulation disappears and the phase-modulated carrier is again at its central value.

Armstrong System of F-M. In the Armstrong system of F-M we do not directly apply the audio voltage to the carrier as shown in Fig. 16.4. However, we obtain the same results. We start with a fixed source of high frequency voltage, a crystal oscillator (see Fig. 16.5). The output from the oscillator is then directed into two different paths. One path contains a buffer amplifier; the other path is through a balanced modulator where the audio-modulating voltage is applied to the carrier signal. At the modulator output, only the sidebands appear. The carrier voltage is suppressed because of the operation of the balanced modulator. The sidebands are then shifted in phase by 90° and combined with the unmodulated carrier present at the output of the buffer amplifier. The final result is a phase-modulated wave and, indirectly, also frequency-modulated.

The sideband frequencies obtained from the balanced modulator contain the intelligence of the audio voltage, much the same as though we had amplitude-modulated a carrier. The sidebands are then shifted in phase by 90° and combined with the carrier from the buffer amplifier.

Let us pause for a moment and compare the Armstrong method with the previous system for obtaining phase modulation. In one instance we apply the audio-modulating voltage directly to the carrier (maintaining 90° phase relationship) to obtain phase modulation whereas in Major Armstrong's system we use the sidebands produced by amplitude modulation and combine these with the carrier. In both methods, the results are seemingly the same and yet, obviously, both methods are not exactly alike. How does this happen?

The answer lies in the fact that Major Armstrong's system is definitely limited in application. First, we can produce phase modulation by applying the audio voltage directly to the carrier. This is entirely analogous to amplitude modulation, except for the manner in which the audio voltage and the carrier are combined. Here, the audio voltage is *directly* shifting the carrier's relative phase position and, if the system is properly designed, there will be no distortion produced for fairly wide angles of phase shift.

Major Armstrong's method will produce the desired phase and frequency modulation from the combination of a carrier and two sidebands *only* when the resulting carrier has a maximum phase shift 30° or less. Expressed in radians (one radian is equal to 57.3°) 30° is approximately 0.5 radians. If these voltages are combined so as to give a greater phase shift to the resultant, then along with the phase modulation we have amplitude modulation. This represents distortion and a waste of useful power. But, by keeping the phase shift within the above limits, pure phase modulation is obtained.

It can be shown mathematically that, when a carrier is phase-modulated at angles 30° or less, the resulting modulated wave will contain a total of only two sidebands, one above and one below the carrier. This is shown in Fig. 16.6. Furthermore, each sideband will be 90° out of phase with the carrier. Hence, in the Armstrong system, we take a carrier and separate it into two parts. One part is modulated by the audio signal to produce the necessary sidebands. These sidebands are then shifted 90° and combined with the remaining half of the carrier (which was fed into the buffer amplifier, Fig. 16.5) to produce the phase or frequency modulation.

To recapitulate, the Armstrong method can be used because:

FIG. 16.6. A low value of phase shift produces only two sidebands.

1. A carrier, phase-modulated at angles of 30° or less, will produce only two sidebands.

2. Each sideband is 90° displaced from the carrier.

In the Armstrong system we take (a) one carrier and (b) two sidebands and combine them 90° out of phase to obtain a phase-modulated wave. Note, however, that this method is valid only for small phase shifts.

The actual Armstrong unit has the block arrangement shown in Fig. 16.5. The equivalent schematic is shown in Fig. 16.7. The quartz-crystal oscillator operates near 200 kc (depending upon the assigned frequency of the transmitter), and its output is applied to a buffer amplifier and a balanced modulator. Since the control grids of the balanced modulator tubes are connected in parallel, both grids become positive and negative in step with each other. The modulator plates, however, are connected in push-pull, with the plate current from each tube passing through the load circuit coils (L_1 and L_2) in opposite directions. Thus, in the absence of an audio voltage, each field cancels the effect of the other and no voltage is obtained across L_3.

Upon the application of an audio-modulating voltage at the input terminals of T_1, a varying potential is applied to the screen grids of V_3 and V_4. Suppose, for example, that the screen grid of V_3 is going more positive. At the same time, the screen grid of V_4 is less positive since it is attached to the opposite side of the transformer secondary winding. Because of the increased positive voltage, the current in V_3 will increase while the current in V_4 is lowered by a corresponding amount. In a push-pull transformer arrangement, such as we have for L_1, L_2, and L_3, a decrease in one coil, say L_2, and an increase in L_1 combine to aid each other and to produce a fairly large voltage across L_3.

On the next audio half cycle, when the screen grid of V_3 becomes less positive and the screen grid of V_4 is driven more positive, the

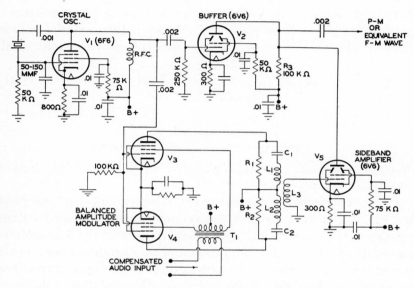

FIG. 16.7.   The schematic diagram of the basic Armstrong modulation.

opposite set of conditions prevails.   The voltage across L_3 is also of opposite polarity.   Thus, until the audio voltage is active, nothing appears across L_3.   The effect of the audio signal is to unbalance the circuit and produce the sideband voltages across L_3.

The arrangement of components in L_1 and L_2 also produces a 90° phase shift, which is accomplished through the insertion of condensers C_1 and C_2 in series with L_1 and L_2.   These condensers neutralize the inductive reactance of their respective coils (C_1 for L_1, C_2 for L_2) and present to the tube a purely resistive load. Under these conditions, the grid voltage of each modulator tube is in phase with its plate current.   The plate current, in flowing through the load, will develop a magnetic field about each coil. The variation of a magnetic field is directly dependent upon the current that produced it.   Hence, the control grid voltage of each tube, the plate current of that tube, and the magnetic field set up about the coil are all in phase.

The magnetic field, in cutting across L_3, will induce a voltage. From elementary a-c theory we know that an induced voltage is maximum when the magnetic flux lines are changing most rapidly. This rapid change occurs when the field is going from positive to negative (or negative to positive) values.   However, the induced voltage is minimum or zero when the flux is hardly changing at all.

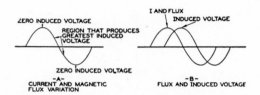

FIG. 16.8.   The relationship between a magnetic field and the induced voltage.

This absence of change occurs at the positive and negative peaks (see Fig. 16.8).   If we plot the relationships of induced voltage to magnetic flux variations, we immediately see that a phase difference of 90° is introduced.   In this manner we produce the necessary sidebands and shift them 90° with respect to the crystal oscillator carrier.

Tube V_5 amplifies the sidebands and combines them with the carrier.   Resistor R_3 is the common load for V_2 and V_5, and it is here that the combination of carrier and sidebands takes place.

Frequency Swing Compensation.   Before we turn our attention to the succeeding frequency multipliers, it is first necessary to ascertain how great a frequency shift we obtain from the combination of sidebands and carrier.   We know that the equivalent F-M derived from phase modulation is based on the equation

$$\Delta F = f \cdot \Delta \theta$$

where f = frequency of audio modulating voltage
  $\Delta \theta$ = maximum phase shift

Actually, in the foregoing equation, $\Delta \theta$ should be $\Delta \theta \sin 2\pi f t$ because the angle varies from instant to instant.   However, we are interested only in the maximum value of the phase swing; hence we use $\Delta\theta$. The maximum value of sin $2\pi ft$ is 1, and $\Delta\theta \times 1$ is $\Delta\theta$. $\Delta\theta$ should be expressed in radians, which is, as we have seen, equal to the angle in degree divided by $57.3°$; f is expressed in cycles.

The maximum phase swing is restricted to $30°$ in commercial equipment. At the highest audio frequency, utilizing the full phase swing of $30°$ (0.524 radian), the equivalent frequency swing or variation is:

$$\Delta F = 15{,}000 \times 0.524$$

$$\Delta F = 7860 \text{ cycles}$$

$$\Delta F = 7.86 \text{ kc}$$

Now, let us see what happens when low frequency audio signals are applied. The lowest audio frequency desirable is generally 50 cycles. Substituting this in the equation,

$$\Delta F = 50 \times 0.524$$

$$\Delta F = 26.2 \text{ cycles}$$

Note that both signals gave the same *phase* swing, yet the low frequency voltage produced a frequency variation of only 26.2 cycles whereas the highest audio frequency produced a frequency variation of 7.86 kc.

Suppose we transmitted the carrier with these frequency shifts. At your receiver, which would give the greatest output? The 7.86 kc, of course, since all F-M receivers develop a greater output for a wider frequency swing. But this does not represent the conditions at the transmitter. Here, both signals were equally strong. Something, then, must be done to place both signals, or all frequencies for that matter, on an equal footing. No matter what the frequency, signals of equal amplitude should produce equal frequency shifts.

To achieve this, a predistorter circuit is inserted in the audio amplifier stages (see Fig. 16.9). The resistor R is made very large in comparison to the reactance of condenser C at all audio frequencies. This means that for any voltage impressed across terminals A, B, the current will be determined by the resistor R. The effect of C is negligible. Thus, no matter what the audio frequency, the same voltage will produce the same current through R and C.

Across C, the voltage will depend upon the frequency. A higher frequency will develop less voltage across C than a lower frequency. This is because the condenser offers less opposition to higher frequencies. Hence, we obtain the desired inverse effect to counterbalance the rising f effect of phase modulation. The predistorter components of R and C apply less high frequency voltage to the grid of the tube.

Since the low frequencies produce the smallest equivalent F-M, the audio-correction network reduces the effect of all frequencies higher than the lowest audio frequency — say, 50 cycles — so that, in the end, all the frequencies of the same strength will produce the same frequency modulation. The amount of equivalent F-M, then, that a 50-cycle voltage produces (which is ±26.2 cycles) will determine how much multiplication is to be applied to obtain the final ±75 kc.

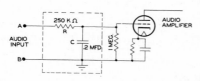

FIG. 16.9. A predistorter network.

Let us return to the circuit of Fig. 16.7. Utilizing the maximum phase shift of ±30°, we discovered that, at 50 cycles, the carrier has a frequency variation of ±26.2 cycles. The carrier frequency, at this point in the circuit, is the crystal oscillator frequency, or 200 kc. Hence, our F-M signal is 200 kc with a frequency swing of ±26.2 cycles. What we desire, at the antenna, is the assigned station frequency, say, 90 mc ± 75 kc. The problem is to increase the 200 kc ± 26.2 cycles to 90 mc ± 75 kc. In order to deal with round figures, let us change the 26.2 cycles to 25 cycles.

Frequency Multiplication. If we divide 75,000 cycles (the desired frequency swing) by 25 cycles (the swing we now have) we see that a frequency multiplication of 3000 (75,000/25) is necessary. Although it may be a trifle difficult to have exactly a 3000 increase using triplers and doublers, we can get very close, say, 2916. This frequency multiplication is possible if we use the following assortment of doublers and triplers: 2, 3, 3, 3, 3, 3, 3, 2.

The signal is passed through successive stages until the total multiplication of 2916 is obtained.

The frequency multiplication is applied not only to the frequency swing (the sidebands) but also to the carrier. This means that the original 200 kc of the crystal oscillator will be multiplied 2916 times — a final output frequency of 583,200 kc or 583.2 mc — resulting in a value considerably above the desired 90 mc. Something must be done to prevent the carrier from rising to a frequency higher than its assigned frequency, in this case, 90 mc, and, at the

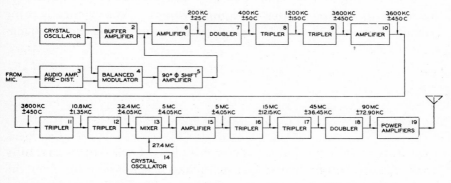

FIG. 16.10. A complete block diagram of the basic Armstrong F-M transmitter.

same time, to obtain the maximum frequency deviation of ±75 kc for the sidebands.

A method to accomplish this is shown in Fig. 16.10. The entire transmitter is arranged in block diagram, with each unit numbered for easy identification purposes. At the input to the amplifier in block No. 6, the equivalent frequency modulation has been achieved. Thereafter, the carrier and its sidebands are sent through a series of frequency multipliers until, by the time the mixer is reached (block No. 13), the carrier has been increased to 32.4 mc and the frequency variation to ±4.05 kc. Note that at the input to the mixer the carrier is 32.4 mc whereas at the output it has been reduced to 5 mc. The reason is the mixing action within the tube.

Whenever we mix two signals, the output consists of the original two mixing frequencies and the sum and difference frequencies. Of primary interest is the difference frequency, 5 mc. To accentuate this frequency and minimize or eliminate the others, we place a resonant circuit at the output of the mixer which is peaked at 5 mc. With this simple arrangement it is possible to reduce the original carrier to the point where it can be further increased to the desired 90-mc values.

But what of the sidebands during this process? The incoming signal to the mixer has a frequency variation of ±4.05 kc. The range, then, of the input signal is from 32.39595 mc (32.4 mc − 4.05 kc) to 32.40405 mc (32.4 mc + 4.05 kc). We change 4.05 kc to 0.00405 mc and then add and subtract this figure with 32.4 mc to arrive at the foregoing values. When the 27.4-mc mixing frequency is added, the following output difference frequencies are derived:

$$
\begin{array}{cc}
32.39595 & 32.40405 \\
-27.40000 & -27.40000 \\
\hline
4.99595 & 5.00405
\end{array}
$$

or, what is the same thing, 5 mc ± 4.05 kc. Look at this carefully for it demonstrates clearly that by mixing it is possible to lower the carrier frequency and, at the same time, retain the original frequency variation.

Hereafter, the tripling and doubling sequence is straightforward until we arrive at the 90 mc ± 72.9 kc. By assuming a starting frequency variation of 25 cycles, we obtain only a ±72.9-kc frequency shift at the output. However, with the 26.2 cycles proposed originally, we would come much closer to ±75 kc. In any event, we do not have to hit it exactly on the head. Anything slightly less is still quite satisfactory.

There is one more fact to be noted concerning the Armstrong transmitter. In addition to the audio predistorter, or audio-correction network, recently discussed, we also require a pre-accentuator. The pre-accentuator is used here as in the reactance-tube F-M transmitter, namely, to raise the level of the higher audio tones in order that they may be in a better position to combat the effect of noise at these frequencies. At the receiver, a de-accentuator or a de-emphasis circuit returns the higher frequencies to their proper level.   A commercial audio-amplifier network, containing both pre-emphasis and audio correction, is shown in Fig. 16.14.

Do not confuse the purpose of the two circuits.   The audio correction network is needed to counteract the tendency of the higher frequencies to produce more equivalent frequency modulation than the lower frequencies, assuming both signals are equal in strength.   This circuit is required only in phase-modulation systems.

The pre-emphasis network is placed in *all* F-M transmitters to produce a better signal-to-noise ratio at the receiver.

The Dual Channel Armstrong System.   An improvement over the preceding system with respect to frequency stability and distortion has been achieved through the design of a dual channel system of phase modulation.   Essentially, phase modulation is still used to produce frequency modulation.   The sidebands are generated in a balanced modulator and then combined 90° out of phase with the original carrier.   The method of combination and the subsequent process of mixing are, however, quite different from the preceding modulator.

The basic circuit of the Armstrong Dual Channel Modulator is shown in Fig. 16.11.   A crystal oscillator functions at a frequency near 200 kc, the same frequency as in the previous modulator.   A buffer stage follows the crystal to serve as an isolation amplifier, improving circuit stability.   If desired, the crystal oscillator can be placed in a temperature-controlled oven, although this is not necessary in this system.   As we shall see presently, any variations in this oscillator have no effect on the final transmitter frequency.

The output of the buffer amplifier is coupled to the modulator input coil, L_1 (see Fig. 16.11B).   The voltage appearing across L_1 is applied to the balanced modulator — consisting of tubes V_1 and V_2 — and to points C, D.   In the modulator stages, the carrier signal is shifted 90° and then audio-modulated to produce the upper and lower sidebands.   After this, the sidebands are recombined with the carrier at points C, D.   It is here that the phase modulation (and, with it, of course, the frequency modulation) appears.

Modulator Operation.   At the balanced modulator, the signal at L_1 is applied to the phase-shifting network, C_1R_1 and C_2R_2. Both condensers are equal in value, and the same is true of the

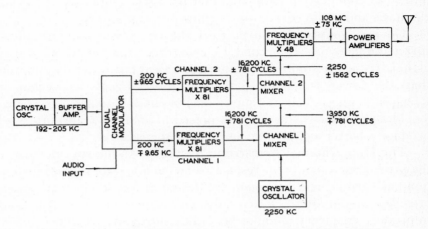

FIG. 16.11A. A block diagram of the dual channel modulator circuit.

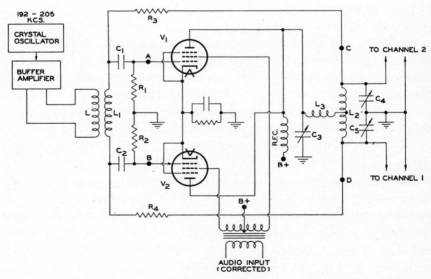

FIG. 16.11B. The modulating circuit of the dual channel F-M transmitter.
(Courtesy *Communications Magazine*.)

resistors. At the frequency used by the carrier, the reactances of C_1 and C_2 are much greater than the resistance of R_1 or R_2. Hence, the current through each branch will be practically $90°$ ahead in phase, with respect to the voltage across L_1. Since the voltages across R_1 and R_2 are in phase with the current through the resistors, we note that the voltage received by each grid will lead the carrier voltage at L_1 by $90°$. The required $90°$ phase shift has thus been acquired. Now to the production of the sidebands.

The grids of V_1 and V_2 are excited $180°$ out of phase, whereas their plates are connected across a common load. During those intervals when no audio-modulating voltage is present at the screen grids, no output is produced. Upon the application of an audio voltage, one tube draws more current than the other and sideband voltages appear. These are coupled through C_3 and L_3 to L_2 where the carrier voltage from the modulator input coil is directly applied.

To the carrier voltage arriving from L_1, points C and D appear as the terminals of a purely resistive network. L_2 in conjunction with C_4 and C_5 forms a parallel resonant circuit at the carrier frequency of 200 kc. Because of the resistive impedance between points C, D, the carrier voltage here is in phase with the voltage at L_1. Resistors R_3 and R_4 are merely inserted for the purpose of preventing undesirable interaction between the modulator and L_2, C_4, and C_5.

The ground connection between C_4 and C_5 produces equal and opposite carrier frequency voltages for the two separate channels of amplifiers. The equality exists because C_4 and C_5 are equal in value.

In the circuit, to this point, the $90°$-shifted sidebands and the direct carrier (or, at least a portion of it) are at points C and D. To understand how phase modulation is achieved it will be necessary to examine in greater detail the electrical action of L_2, C_3, L_3, C_4, and C_5. These components of Fig. 16.11B have been rearranged as shown in Fig. 16.12. In the rearrangement, L_2 has been separated into two mutually coupled coils of equal inductance, L_{2A} and L_{2B}. Their total inductance is equal to L_2.

· The carrier voltage is brought to points C, D. These two

points also lead to the two tripler channels, as can be seen from
Fig. 16.11B.   Because L_{2A} plus L_{2B} equal L_2, and $L_2C_4C_5$ is resonant to the carrier frequency, then the entire series branch shown in
Fig. 16.12, around points C, E, D, and F, is resonant to the carrier
frequency.

To the carrier voltage, this network offers maximum impedance
because it is connected as a parallel resonant circuit.   It is also to
be noted that, since both arms of the network (L_{2A} and C_4 or L_{2B}
and C_5) are equivalent, each is resonant to the carrier frequency.
This leads to the following result: Any voltage placed between
points C and D " sees " a parallel resonant circuit.   However, any

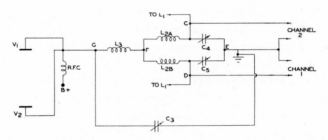

FIG. 16.12.   The electrical network wherein the sideband and carrier voltage combine.

voltage applied between F and E " sees " two series resonant circuits.   This latter fact should be kept in mind while we consider the
introduction of the sidebands between points F and E.

The sideband voltages are applied from the R.F. choke in the
plate circuit of V_1 and V_2 to L_3C_3 and the network within terminals
$CDEF$. L_3 in conjunction with C_3 resonates at the carrier frequency.   The presence of L_{2A}, L_{2B}, C_4 and C_5 in the resonant
network of L_3C_3 does not produce any interference because a voltage at the carrier frequency applied between F and E " sees " only
resistance.   Thus, whether we are considering the circuit in Fig.
16.12 from the terminals leading to points C and D or from the
terminal leading from the balanced modulator, we have a completely
resonant circuit presented to the carrier frequency.   This design is
purposely effected in order to obtain the correct phase relationships
when the sideband voltages are applied.

The sideband voltages are applied to this circuit between point G and ground. In the inductive branch of the resonant circuit (the branch containing L_3 and the network from point F to ground) the current lags the sideband voltages by 90°. This is true of all inductive branches. The inductive current flows down through L_3, and, at point F, divides evenly between $L_{2A}C_4$ and $L_{2B}C_5$. Each of these two branches appears resistive to the sideband current, since the sideband frequencies are so very close to the carrier frequency.

The sideband currents, in flowing down each branch, develop voltages across C_4 and C_5'. However, across a condenser, the voltage lags the current by 90°. Hence, the voltage that appears across C_4 and C_5 is 90° (owing to its flow through L_3) plus an additional 90° (owing to the voltage and current relationships across a condenser) out of phase with respect to the sideband voltages applied by the modulator to terminal G and ground. And, owing to the modulator input network, C_1, C_2, R_1, and R_2, another 90° shift was introduced. The overall result is this: the sideband voltages appearing across C_4 and C_5 are 180° + 90°, or 270°, out of phase with the carrier voltages at C_4 and C_5. But 270° in one direction (say, clockwise) is equal to 90° in the opposite (or counterclockwise) direction. Thus, the sideband frequencies and the carrier are combined 90° out of phase with each other. This is the desired result.

To recapitulate, we have the sideband frequencies formed at V_1 and V_2 and shifted 90° (by C_1, C_2, R_1, and R_2) from the carrier. Then, in the network composed of C_3, L_3, L_2, C_4, and C_5, the sideband frequencies are shifted an additional 180°. Since 180° + 90° is equal to 270°, and 270° clockwise is the same as 90° counterclockwise, we find that the sidebands and the carrier are combined 90° out of phase with each other. This produces phase modulation and, with it, equivalent frequency modulation.

The sideband voltages at C_4 and C_5 are equal to each other, both in amplitude and phase. We can indicate this fact in Fig. 16.13A by making their vectors equal to each other and pointing in the same direction. To add the carrier voltages to these vectors, we note that across C_4 and C_5 they are equal but *opposite* in polarity. The carrier voltages at C_4 and C_5 are opposite in polarity because C and D (from whence they are applied) are at opposite ends of the input coil, L_1 (see Fig. 16.11B). They differ, in other words, by 180°. This is shown in Fig. 16.13A. Adding the vectors for the sidebands and the carrier voltages, we obtain the result shown in Fig. 16.13B. One resultant vector, E_1, lags its carrier voltage; the other resultant vector, E_2, leads its carrier voltage. In terms of equivalent frequency variations, this means that if, in channel No. 1, the frequency swing is +9.65 cycles, then, in channel No. 2, the corresponding frequency swing is −9.65 cycles.

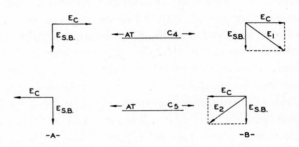

FIG. 16.13.   The vectorial addition of the sideband and carrier voltage.

When one frequency swing is positive, the other frequency swing is negative.

Each channel contains four tripler stages, multiplying each signal frequency by $3 \times 3 \times 3 \times 3$, or 81. Hence, the input 200 kc, with the associated 9.65-cycle frequency swing, becomes at each channel output 16,200 kc. Each has a frequency variation of 781 cycles. This is shown in Fig. 16.11A.

The output of each channel is fed into a separate mixer. Feeding into the first mixer is the voltage from a 2250-kc crystal oscillator and the 16,200 kc ∓ 781 cycles derived from channel No. 1. As a result of the mixing process, a difference frequency of 13,950 kc ∓ 781 cycles is produced. This is fed to a second mixer, where it meets the incoming signal from channel No. 2. We obtain a carrier output from the second mixer of 16,200–13,950 kc, or 2250 kc. For the sidebands we have ±781 − ∓781 cycles, or ±781 + ±781 cycles, or ±1562 cycles. Note what has been done here. With the negative or minus sign, we have converted ∓781 cycles to

±781 cycles. Arithmetically and electrically, this what actually occurs. Hence, we obtain a signal from the second mixer which has twice the frequency swing of either channel. From here, four doublers and a tripler (providing a multiplication of $2 \times 2 \times 2 \times 2 \times 3 = 48$) increase 2250 kc ± 1562 cycles to 108 mc ± 75 kc. One or more power amplifiers then boost the signal power to its final output value.

In the Armstrong Dual Channel Modulator, the crystal control oscillator feeding the first mixer regulates the stability (and the value) of the final carrier value. In the foregoing illustration, if we desired an output carrier of 90 mc, the crystal control oscillator would have to be lowered to 1875 kc. Any other carrier frequency in the band 88 to 108 mc can be obtained accordingly.

Frequency Stability. The stability of the carrier frequency may be seen indicated by the following example. Assume that the crystal oscillator feeding the modulator unit shifts in frequency by 1 kc, say, from 200 kc to 199 kc. In each channel the incoming 199 kc is multiplied 81 times to a final value of 16,119 kc. If the control oscillator is set at 2250 kc, then the difference frequency output from the first mixer is 13,869 kc. At the second mixer, 13,869 kc and 16,119 kc mix to produce 2250 kc, which is exactly what we wish. The shift from 200 kc to 199 kc had no effect upon the frequency modulation. Hence, no matter to what value the first crystal oscillator changes, the output frequency from the second mixer will be entirely determined by the crystal control oscillator. Actually, all that the two channels and the balanced modulator do in this system is to produce the frequency modulation. The frequency variation is increased 81 times in the channels and then transferred to the control crystal oscillator carrier.

Although it makes no difference what change occurs in the frequency of the first oscillator, too much shifting would tend only to reduce the amplitude of the signal from each channel because of attenuation in the tuned circuits. Hence, it is customary to use a crystal oscillator, although any of the other types of familiar oscillators (Hartley, Colpitts, T.G.T.P., etc.) would be satisfactory.

The phase-shift method of securing frequency modulation produces a signal with very little distortion. It is claimed that the dual-channel principle has even decreased the previously small amount of distortion present. The measured rms harmonic distortion is less than 1½ per cent for all audio frequencies between 50 and 15,000 cycles at 25 per cent, 50 per cent, and 100 per cent modulation. This is well within the standards of " Good Engineering Practice " of the F.C.C. as applied to broadcast stations.

A Commercial Unit. The arrangement of a commercial dual channel modulator is shown in Fig. 16.14. The audio channel contains both pre-emphasis and audio correction. The crystal oscillator feeding the balanced modulator 7A7 tubes is somewhere in the frequency range of 192 to 205 kc. A 7A7 serves as a buffer amplifier. Beyond the balanced modulator we find the circuit that combines the carrier and the sidebands, after which the separation into the two channels is made. Each channel consists of four triplers and a straight amplifier.

Channel No. 1 output is applied to a balanced converter where mixing with the control crystal oscillator voltage occurs. The crystal frequency is 2250 kc. From the balanced converter, the difference frequency is fed to the second mixer where the output from channel No. 2 is applied. It is here, in this mixer, that the original 2250 kc of the control crystal oscillator is formed again, with a frequency modulation of ±1562 cycles.

The final function of the modulator unit is to produce the output carrier frequency (between 88 and 108 mc) and the ±75-kc sideband variation. This is accomplished with four doublers, a tripler, and three straight amplifiers. The circuits of the power amplifiers that follow the modulator unit will depend upon the power output desired. For a 250-watt carrier, the modulator could feed into the arrangement shown in Fig. 16.15. The modulator has an output of 30 watts, which is sufficient to drive the pair of 4-125A power amplifiers to produce 250 watts of radiated energy.

If 1000 watts of output power is required, then the arrangement of Fig. 16.16 is satisfactory. Because of the additional heat dissipation at the plates of the power tubes, an air blower is necessary to carry away the heat and prevent the collapse of the tube (see Fig. 16.17). Notice that quarter-wave tuning stubs have replaced the conventional coil-and-condenser resonant circuit arrangement.

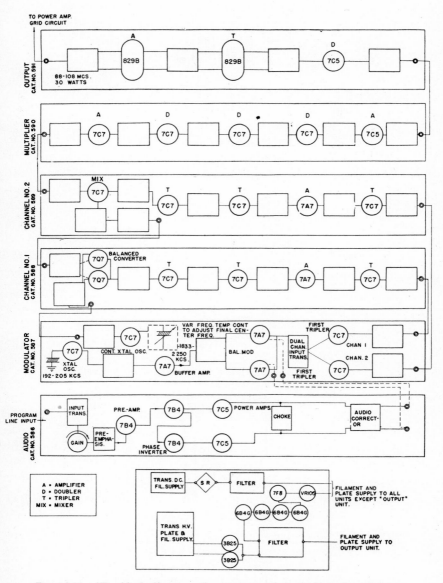

FIG. 16.14. The block diagram of a commercial dual channel modulator.

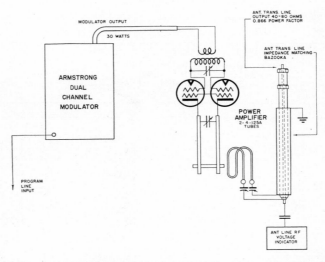

FIG. 16.15.   The arrangement of a 250-watt F-M transmitter using the dual channel modulator.   (Courtesy of R.E.L.)

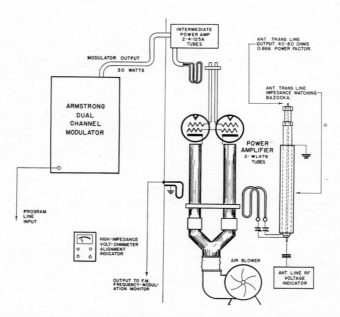

FIG. 16.16.   The same modulator driving a higher-power transmitter. (Courtesy of R.E.L.)

The air blower is plainly visible at the base of the transmitter cabinet, and the plate quarter-wave tuning stubs are located at the center of the unit. The additional output power would require the use of intermediate power amplifiers between the modulator unit and the power amplifier.

A New Tube: The Phasitron. The Armstrong phase-shift method and the Crosby reactance-tube system of producing F-M have both been known for some time. Recently, however, a new modulator for producing F-M has been devised by Dr. Robert Adler and utilized commercially by the General Electric Company. This newer system employs a specially designed tube, which produces the preliminary F-M. The tube is known as the " Phasitron," and is the modulator unit for the transmitter.

A block diagram of the exciter unit, which includes all the circuits except the power amplifiers, is shown in Fig. 16.18.

The stability of the carrier is dependent upon the 230-kc crystal oscillator. In this respect, the circuit resembles the Armstrong

FIG. 16.17. The power amplifier cabinet showing the blower needed to cool the power tubes. (Courtesy of R.E.L.)

unit. Indeed, the resemblance between the two extends even further because this system also utilizes phase shifting to obtain equivalent F-M. However, the difference lies in the fact that all of the phase shifting due to modulation occurs within one tube, the Phasitron, whereas in the Armstrong system several tubes are required to accomplish the same purpose.

The entire transmitter is designed around the Phasitron. An

internal view of the Phasitron is shown in Fig. 16.19A, with a labeled drawing in Fig. 16.19B. Although specific reference is

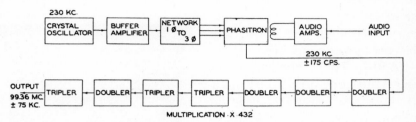

FIG. 16.18.   A block diagram of the exciter unit of an F-M transmitter utilizing the Phasitron.

made in what follows to the labeled schematic drawing, the reader will be able to gain a clearer idea of the entire functioning of the tube if he makes a continual cross-reference between both diagrams of Fig. 16.19. For every part labeled in Fig. 16.19B, stop and locate that part on the tube shown in Fig. 16.19A.

The tube is designed so that electrons emitted from the cathode reach

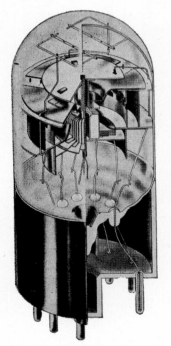

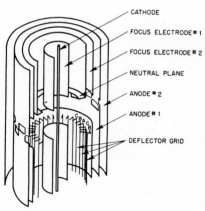

FIG. 16.19A.   Internal view of Phasitron.

FIG. 16.19B.   A labeled schematic drawing of the internal segment of the Phasitron.

the positive plates or anodes 1 and 2 in one definite plane. At all other points the electrons are prevented from reaching these anodes by shields. From Fig. 16.19A, we see that the only exposed section of the cathode is at the center. Above and below the center, two shields prevent any emitted electrons from reaching either anode 1 or 2.

Since the cathode at the center section emits electrons in all directions, or 360°, the emitted electrons will assume the appearance of a circular disk. The formation of this electron disk is shown in Fig. 16.20. In order to keep the electron disk very thin, especially at the edges, two focusing electrodes are inserted. The focus electrodes 1 and 2 are shown in Fig. 16.19B.

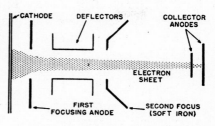

FIG. 16.20. The electron-optical arrangement in the tube for producing an electron disk.

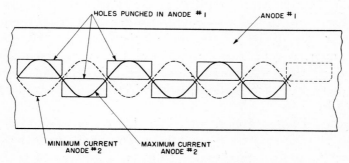

FIG. 16.21. The placement of the holes punched in anode 1.

The electron disk extends out from the cathode until it reaches the positive anode 1. When we examine this plate, we see that it has holes punched in it, each hole separated from its neighbor as shown in Fig. 16.21. The dividing line between the upper and lower holes represents the line where the edge of the electron disk impinges on anode 1. If the edge of the electron disk impinges directly on this line, no electrons will be in the plane of the punched holes and will be able to reach anode 2, which is located directly behind anode 1. Except for these holes in anode 1, no other direct path is available for the electrons to reach anode 2. This, of course, is purposely done and fits in with the action of the tube.

A specially constructed set of grid wires is situated below the level of the electron disk. The grid wires are near the outer edge of the circular electron disk, just before the electrons reach anode 1. However, because the grid wires are below the electron disk, any voltage on the grid wires will act to do only one of two things: either pull the edge of the electron disk down with a positive charge or else repel the edge of the electron disk up with a negative charge. Thus, if we connected all the grid wires together and placed an alternating voltage on them, the edge of the electron disk would rise and fall vertically (flip up and down) as the voltage changed. But whether they rose or fell, they would reach either anode 1 or, if they passed through its holes, anode 2.

The foregoing would result if all the grid wires were tied together. Actually they are not. There are 36 distinct grid wires. For the sake of explanation, every three wires have been labeled A, B, and C, successively, until all of the 36 wires have been lettered. In construction, all the wires marked A are connected together electrically, as are all the B wires and all the C wires. We obtain, in this manner, a repetition in potential for every third wire, and every third wire will possess the same polarity. In the overall view, there are three sets of grid wires, each set containing 12 grid leads.

The grid wires are arranged in this manner in order that a 3-phase voltage may be fed to them, one phase to group A, one to group B, and the third phase to group C. Fig. 16.18 indicates that the 3-phase voltage is obtained from the crystal oscillator branch. The crystal oscillator generates a single-phase voltage, which when amplified is converted to 3-phase by an appropriate network. The 3-phase voltage is then applied to the three sets of grids (Fig. 16.22A). Each phase is shown applied to a separate group of grids, with the common terminal of the 3-phase system attached to the electrode marked "neutral plane." This electrode is directly above the group of grid wires. Any voltage between the neutral plane and the set of grid wires will act directly on the electron disk passing between these two elements.

To represent the alternating 3-phase voltage, Fig. 16.22B is helpful. Each phase is shown separately, with its variations from instant to instant. The response of the edge of the electron disk to these changing grid voltages will depend upon the voltage polarity on the different sets of grid wires at any instant with respect to the neutral plane electrode.

At instant 1, Fig. 16.22B, the voltage at all the A wires is at its maximum positive value, while the voltages at the B and C set of grid wires are equally negative. Hence, above each A wire, the

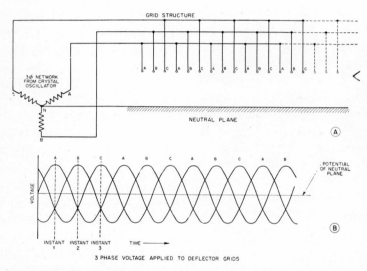

FIG. 16.22. (A) The application of the three-phase voltage to the grid structure. (B) The voltage variation of each set of grids.

electron disk is attracted downward while, above each B and C wire, the edge of the electron disk is repelled upward. The resultant shape of the disk edge possesses a ruffled appearance as shown in Fig. 16.23.

Since the grid voltage is always changing, at instant 2 we find that all the B wires are at their maximum positive value, while all the A and C wires are negative. Now those sections of the edge of the disk that were attracted downward previously to all the A wires will have gradually shifted around until they are attracted to the

B wires.   Extending the same line of reasoning, it is readily seen that, at instant 3, the edges above the *B* wires will shift to the *C* wires.   After this, the sequence occurs over again, with *A*, *B*, and *C* following in order as outlined.

If we were standing inside the tube, perched above one grid wire, it would appear to us as though the electron disk was rotating rapidly, with the ruffled edges of the disk rising and falling in step with the rise and fall of the controlling crystal oscillator frequency. Since there are 12 sets of 3 wires each, we would find 12 maxima and 12 minima in the ruffled edges of the electron disk.   This is evident from Fig. 16.23.

FIG. 16.23.   The ruffled appearance of the edge of the electron disk.

The effect of the variation in the position of the edges of the disk is to vary the amount of current that reaches anode 2, situated directly behind the hole openings in anode 1.   Anode 1 has 24 holes punched in it. Twelve are above the plane of the electron disk and 12 below. Suppose that at the instant when all the *A* grid wires are positive, the ruffled edge assumes such a position that all the electrons pass through the anode 1 openings.   This condition is indicated by the heavy, dark line in Fig. 16.21.   At this instant of time, anode 2 is receiving its maximum current.   But, as the ruffled edges of the disk rotate, anode 2 gets less and less current because fewer and fewer electrons reach the openings of anode 1.   The second anode receives its least amount of current, which is practically zero, when the ruffled edges of the disk assume the position indicated by the dotted lines in Fig. 16.21.   At this moment the electrons, at all points, are striking the solid sections of anode 1.   Between the maximum and minimum amounts of current flow to anode 2 is one-half cycle.   Thus, the current flowing to anode 2 varies sinusoidally at a frequency determined by the crystal oscillator.

It is now possible to see one reason for employing the 3-phase voltage.   Without it, we would not have any ruffled edges on the electron disk, and we could not produce the sinusoidal current variation arriving at anode 2.

Modulating the Phasitron. The foregoing represents the basic operation of the circuit with no modulation. The output from GL-2H21, the Phasitron tube, would merely consist of the 230-kc frequency due to the crystal oscillator.

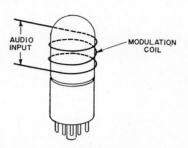

FIG. 16.24. Modulating the Phasitron tube.

Before we consider the modulation, let us note the effect of a magnetic field on the rotating ruffled edge of the electron disk. The electron disk is horizontal in position, starting at the central cathode and extending to the anodes. Suppose we wind a coil about the tube, as shown in Fig. 16.24. Then its magnetic field will extend vertically, or up and down. Hence, the electron disk and the applied magnetic field are at right angles to each other.

It can be proved, both mathematically and experimentally, that when an electron travels at right angles to a magnetic field (as it is obviously doing here) the electron will be deflected at right angles to both the direction of the magnetic field and its direction of travel. Within the Phasitron the electrons originally travel directly from cathode to anode 1 or 2. This is shown by the arrow in Fig. 16.25. Upon the application of a vertical magnetic field, the beam begins to shift at right angles to its former direction. The shift is in the direction of one of the two smaller arrows in Fig. 16.25. (Two arrows are shown, depending upon whether the magnetic flux is up or down.) These small arrows, it can be seen, are at right angles to the path of travel of the electrons and to the direction of the magnetic lines of force. How far the electrons shift either to the right or left of their original position depends upon the strength of the applied magnetic field. For a strong field, a large shift occurs; for a small field, a small shift.

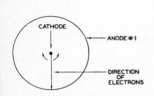

FIG. 16.25. Illustrating the effect of the modulation coil on the electron disk within the Phasitron tube.

Now let us modulate the current flowing through the coil by the audio voltages. The audio current will alternate in direction from instant to instant. In response to this periodic change in direction, the shifting of the electron disk will also be periodically to the right or left. Thus, superimposed on the regular rotation of the electron disk due to the 3-phase voltage will be this alternate shifting back and forth. Here is exactly the same type of action that occurred in the vector diagram used originally to explain phase modulation. The effect, then, of the modulation coil wound about the tube is to produce, through the fluctuating magnetic field set up by the audio currents, a back-and-forth shifting of the rotating electron disk.

Because of the shifting of the electron disk, the current reaching anode 2 will likewise vary. Since the shifting of the disk represents a phase modulation wave, the current received by anode 2 will also be phase-modulated. And from phase modulation we can obtain equivalent frequency modulation. The modulation coil is connected to a push-pull voltage amplifier tube. This, in turn, obtains its input from a 6SL7 audio amplifier. The frequency modulation produced as a result of the foregoing action is, at its maximum, equal to ±175 cycles. By means of 4 doublers and 3 triplers, it becomes possible to raise the ±175 cycles to ±75 kc. This represents a multiplicattion of 432 (2 × 2 × 2 × 2 × 3 × 3 × 3 = 432). At the same time, of course, the crystal oscillator frequency is also increased 432 times, from 230 kc to 99.36 mc. For any other frequency between 88 and 108 mc, the crystal oscillator frequency would change accordingly. To find the crystal frequency needed, merely take the assigned frequency of the carrier and divide this by 432.

A schematic diagram of the circuit from the crystal oscillator to the Phasitron is shown in Fig. 16.26. A 6SJ7 is connected to function as an electron-coupled Colpitts oscillator, operating at a frequency which, as noted before, is 1/432 of the carrier frequency. The following 6SJ7 is, in part, a buffer amplifier serving to isolate the crystal oscillator from the Phasitron. A special network in the plate circuit of this second 6SJ7 tube converts the single-phase crystal voltage to a 3-phase voltage suitable for application to the deflection grids of the Phasitron.

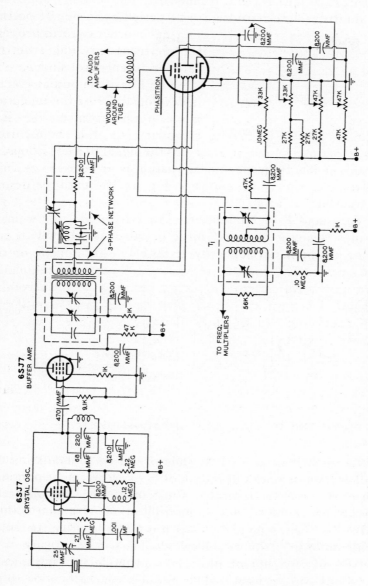

Fig. 16.26. A schematic diagram of the crystal oscillator and Phasitron circuits in the G.E. F-M transmitter.

The schematic symbol for the Phasitron is shown separately in Fig. 16.27, with each element labeled.   The voltages applied to each of the focusing electrodes can be varied by means of potentiometers in order to focus properly the electrons traveling from the cathode to anodes 1 and 2.

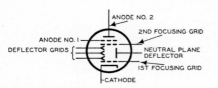

FIG. 16.27.   Schematic symbol for the G.E. Phasitron tube.

The Phasitron output voltage is developed across the tuned primary of transformer, T_1.   The secondary of this transformer feeds the signal to a 6SJ7 doubler. Beyond this point, frequency multiplication is achieved by a series of doublers and triplers (as shown in Fig. 16.18) until the desired carrier frequency is attained.

The Serrasoid F-M Modulator.   An F-M modulator which is capable of securing a relatively large initial phase shift with only four tubes has been developed by J. R. Day.   The name of this

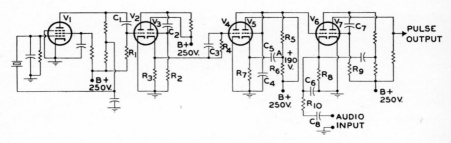

FIG. 16.28.   The Serrasoid F-M modulator.

new unit is the Serrasoid F-M Modulator.   For a modulating frequency of 50 cycles, a peak deviation of ±75 cycles can be obtained. Since an F-M carrier is permitted a maximum frequency deviation of ±75 kc, or 75,000 cycles, a multiplication of about 1000 is required.   The figure generally chosen is 972 since this represents a combination of five triplers and two doublers.

The schematic circuit of the Serrasoid modulator is shown in Fig. 16.28. V_1 is a crystal oscillator which generates a frequency having a value 1/972 of the final carrier frequency.   By placing the crystal in an oven, the frequency generated can be held within ±0.0002 per cent of its assigned value, thereby insuring that the final carrier stability is of the same order.

The oscillator circuit is so designed that the crystal current is very small, and the tube conducts for only a small fraction of time. The result is that narrow negative-going pulses are produced at the plate of the tube.   (See Fig. 16.29A.)   These pulses are applied to the grid of V_2 through a differentiating network composed of C_1 and R_1 which tend to narrow down the pulses still further.   At the grid of V_2 the pulses plunge the tube into cut-off producing positive-going pulses with flat tops at the plate.   These pulses are applied through C_2 to the grid of V_3, a cathode follower.   This tube is biased beyond cut-off by the combination of cathode and grid-leak bias, the latter being developed by the combination of C_2 and R_2 and the positive pulses which are fed to the tube by V_2.   Be-cause of its method of biasing, V_3 clips the

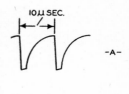

FIG. 16.29.   (A) Volt-age waveform at plate of V_1 Fig. 16.28. (B) Voltage pulses across R_3 of Fig. 16.28.

bottom of the pulses, producing a pulse across R_3 which has steep sides and is fairly square.   (See Fig. 16.29B.)

The pulses now are fed to V_4 which is a non-oscillating saw-tooth wave generator.   Here is how it operates.   The grid initially possesses no bias.   Upon the arrival of a positive-going pulse from R_3, grid current flows from V_4 into C_3, charging this condenser to essentially the peak value of the applied pulse.   During the inter-val between pulses, C_3 discharges slowly through its shunting re-sistor, R_4, but because of the high value of R_4, the voltage across C_3 is sufficiently high to keep V_4 cut-off except when the pulses are active.

A condenser, C_4, is connected across the output circuit of V_4. When the tube is cut-off, the voltage across C_4 rises because one end of this condenser is connected through R_5 and R_6 to the B+ power supply while the other end connects to ground. C_4 continues to charge until a pulse arrives at the grid of V_4, at which time V_4 is driven sharply into conduction.   The pulse reduces the internal resistance of V_4 to a low value, and, since V_4 is directly across C_4, the condenser discharges rapidly through this low resistance. At the end of the pulse, V_4 again returns to cut-off, and C_4 again starts its charging.

Now, it is most important that the voltage across C_4 rise as linearly as possible (Fig. 16.30A) because the linearity of the modulation process depends upon it. Normally, however, the charging of a condenser is not linear but exponential, as shown in Fig. 16.30B. This is so because, as the voltage across a charging condenser rises, it tends to buck or counteract the applied B+ voltage, reducing the ability of this latter voltage to keep the charging current constant. To insure that the rise will be linear, a " bootstrap " amplifier comprising V_5, C_5, and R_7 is added. The grid of V_5 is connected directly across C_4, so that whatever voltage is present across C_4 becomes the grid voltage for V_5.

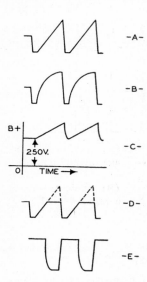

FIG. 16.30. Additional waveforms of Fig. 16.28. (See text for explanation.)

During the charging period of C_4, the grid voltage of V_5 is rising, causing the current through this tube to increase. This results in a rising voltage across R_7. Since C_5 is connected between the top of R_7 and R_5, the voltage rise across R_7 is transferred, via C_5, to the B+ voltage present at point A. Thus the B+ charging voltage for C_4 has superimposed on it the rising voltage from R_7. (See Fig. 16.30C.) This increase in B+ voltage offsets the voltage rising across C_4, keeping the current flowing into C_4 constant and producing a linear rise in voltage across this condenser.

C_4 is also connected to the grid of V_6, a cathode-biased amplifier. The bias on this tube is so adjusted that conduction begins when the saw-tooth voltage across C_4 has attained only half of its maximum value. (See Fig. 16.30D.) 0.25 microsecond after V_6 starts conducting, grid current is drawn, stopping the charging of C_4

and maintaining its voltage at this value until discharge occurs, after which the process is repeated. The voltage at the plate of V_6 drops abruptly from 250 volts to that corresponding to a fairly low value and remains there until C_4 discharges, at which time it rises steeply back to 250 volts because the tube is cut-off. The plate waveform is shown in Fig. 16.30E.

Feeding into the cathode of V_6 is the audio-modulating voltage. As this voltage varies, it changes the bias on the tube and, therefore, the time when conduction will begin. When the audio voltage is

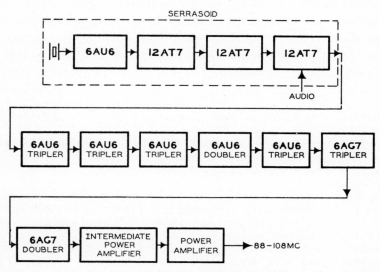

Fig. 16.31. A block diagram of a commercial F-M transmitter using the Serrasoid modulator. (Courtesy R.E.L.)

positive, the start of tube conduction is delayed because a more positive cathode is equivalent to a more negative grid. Conversely, when the audio voltage is negative, tube conduction will commence sooner. This periodic advance and delay of the start of tube conduction causes the leading edge of the plate voltage pulses at the output of V_6 to become phase-modulated. (The end of tube conductions always occurs at the same time since this is controlled by the pulses coming from V_3.)

Before the audio signal is applied to the cathode of V_6, it is passed through a correction circuit (composed of C_8 and R_{10})

which counteracts the tendency of the higher audio frequencies to produce more equivalent frequency modulation than the lower frequencies, assuming both signals are equal in strength. This circuit, it will be recalled, is required when frequency modulation is derived from phase modulation, as it is here.

The pulses at the plate of V_6 are made narrower by passage through a differentiating network consisting of C_7 and R_9 and then applied through V_7 to a string of doubler and triplers. In the resonant circuits of these multipliers, the pulses are converted to sinusoidal waves possessing the same amount of phase or frequency modulation. A block diagram of an F-M transmitter suitable for commercial broadcasting is shown in Fig. 16.31. The power output of the unit would be governed by the ratings of the final power amplifiers.

PROBLEMS

1. What is the Armstrong system of generating frequency modulation? Why is it useful?

2. What factors govern the amount of F-M produced through phase modulation? How are these factors combined in a formula?

3. Draw a block diagram of the basic Armstrong system. Explain the function of each stage.

4. What limitations must be observed when employing phase modulation to produce F-M? How does the Armstrong system observe these limitations?

5. What is a predistorter network? Draw a diagram of such a network and connect it to an amplifier.

6. Why is a predistorter network required in the Armstrong modulator?

7. When a full phase swing of 30° is utilized, how much equivalent F-M is produced when the audio signal frequency is 1000 cycles?

8. Differentiate between predistorter networks and accentuator circuits. Where is each used?

9. Why is predistorter circuit design based upon the lowest audio frequency used in the modulator?

10. How much frequency multiplication is required in the Armstrong F-M transmitter in order to obtain a fully modulated wave? How does this affect the carrier frequency and how is a final carrier value between 88–108 mc achieved?

11. How does the Armstrong Dual Channel Modulator differ from the basic circuit?

12. What stage determines the accuracy of the final carrier frequency in the Dual Channel Modulator Transmitter? Explain.

13. Explain by means of a block diagram the operation of the Dual Channel Transmitter.

14. What type of modulation actually occurs in the Phasitron tube? Why?

15. Describe briefly the operation of the Phasitron tube.

16. How is F-M produced with the Phasitron tube?

17. Would a predistorter network be required in the Phasitron circuit? Explain.

18. What advantages does the Armstrong Dual Channel Transmitter possess over the basic Armstrong circuit?

19. Discuss the differences between A-M and F-M transmitters of comparable power. Limit the discussion to audio modulating power required, carrier frequency stability, types of tubes required and overall economy.

20. What does an F-M receiver contain to counteract the effect of the predistorter and accentuator networks in the transmitter? Explain your answer in detail.

21. Explain briefly the operation of the Serrasoid F-M modulator.

INDEX

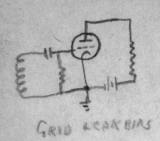

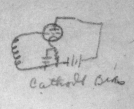

GRID &CATH BIAS

FIXED BIAS

Cathode Bias